To Chris & Audry
Weatherman —
True Champions in
the breed — a
Premier breeders.
Thank you!

.. *BJ* ..

THE WORLD OF THE AKITA

TS-256

Stephen King fans know how sincerely he praises his editor. The esteemed Mr. King I am not but my TFH editor is just as priceless, patient, and perfectly wonderful. Thank you Mr. Andrew De Prisco.

Title page: *As a growing puppy, this is one of the great dogs that opened up "The World of the Akita" to author Barbara J. Andrews and her husband and co-breeder Bill Andrews: Meet BIS Ch. The Widow-Maker O'BJ, ROMXP. Although Widow-Maker passed on in 1996, shortly before the publication of this book, his mark is still felt strongly in the Akita world, and his many progeny proudly bear his name in their pedigrees.*

Calligraphy by Hidetoshi Nakazawa, a celebrated Japanese artist. Courtesy of Richard Tomita.

© 1996 by T.F.H. Publications, Inc.

Distributed in the UNITED STATES to the Pet Trade by T.F.H. Publications, Inc., One T.F.H. Plaza, Neptune City, NJ 07753; distributed in the UNITED STATES to the Bookstore and Library Trade by National Book Network, Inc. 4720 Boston Way, Lanham MD 20706; in CANADA to the Pet Trade by H & L Pet Supplies Inc., 27 Kingston Crescent, Kitchener, Ontario N2B 2T6; Rolf C. Hagen Inc., 3225 Sartelon St. Laurent-Montreal Quebec H4R 1E8; in CANADA to the Book Trade by Vanwell Publishing Ltd., 1 Northrup Crescent, St. Catharines, Ontario L2M 6P5 ; in ENGLAND by T.F.H. Publications, PO Box 15, Waterlooville PO7 6BQ; in AUSTRALIA AND THE SOUTH PACIFIC by T.F.H. (Australia), Pty. Ltd., Box 149, Brookvale 2100 N.S.W., Australia; in NEW ZEALAND by Brooklands Aquarium Ltd. 5 McGiven Drive, New Plymouth, RD1 New Zealand; in Japan by T.F.H. Publications, Japan—Jiro Tsuda, 10-12-3 Ohjidai, Sakura, Chiba 285, Japan; in SOUTH AFRICA by Lopis (Pty) Ltd., P.O. Box 39127, Booysens, 2016, Johannesburg, South Africa. Published by T.F.H. Publications, Inc.
MANUFACTURED IN THE
UNITED STATES OF AMERICA
BY T.F.H. PUBLICATIONS, INC.

The World of the
AKITA

BARBARA J. ANDREWS

Edited by Andrew De Prisco

Acknowledgments

To the wonderful owners who so generously shared their beloved dogs with The World. My apologies for whose who did not.

To the great judges of the past who took time to understand a breed which often confounded even those who bred them. In the early days following AKC recognition, a handful of judges was as courageous in acknowledging the Akita in Group rings as they were knowledgeable in sorting them out in the breed rings.

Our gratitude to Miss Anna Katherine Nicholas (first Best in Show), Mr. Ted Wurmser (first Group I), Mrs. Virginia Hampton, Mr. Roy Ayers, Mrs. Eleanor Evers, Mrs. Michele Billings, Mr. Louis Harris, Mr. Donald J. Booxbaum, Lt. Col. Wallace H. Pede, Mr. J. Donald Jones, Mrs. Kitty Drury, Mrs. Keke Kahn, Mrs. Peggy Adamson, Mr. Mel Downing, Mr. Tom Gately, and Mr. Dale McMackin.

To my daughter Sheryl Lynn, for her invaluable help with Akita Handbooks and Akita Reference, the only existing statistical compilation of top winners and producers prior to this publication.

To Lee Ann Dorsett, without whose accurate typing and willingness to help, the continuity of ROM data might have been forsaken.

To Cathe Harvey, ROM Chair, for her unselfish dedication in maintaining the ROM System and for verifying my ROM tabulations.

To my mentor Dorothy Gooch, Skyraider Dobermans, who instilled in me a quest for excellence, along with the warning that no goal should ever get in the way of the dogs themselves.

Dedication

To my husband Bill, who gave so much of himself to this book. He unfailingly provided the right turn of phrase when I was hopelessly bogged down. His commonsense critiques saved my editor many hours of deletions. He kept my feet on the ground when my head was in the clouds. It was his encouragement, patient understanding, and total unselfishness that allowed this book to become the culmination of our joy in dogs.

But above all, he gave me the love that has always been my strength—and every woman's dream.

And, of course, I dedicate this book to our dogs. Truly an inspiration, they are the substance of every page—the ultimate cure for writer's block!

The author BJ Andrews and her husband Bill with one of their Akitas and "Daniel," one of the first Chinese Foo Dogs in their Oriental Treasures program. BJ has always been fascinated by the Orient, hence her long-time involvement with the Akita. Today this interest has spanned to China with the development and importation of the Foo Dog, a fascinating and worthy little dog that is sure to become a new American favorite.

Contents

About The Author

Barbara J. Andrews, known to friends as "BJ," is a household word in Akitas. She and Bill have owned or bred almost half of the breed's Top Ten Winners and Top Producers. Mrs. Andrews is the first to have owner-handled an Akita to multiple Best In Show wins.

Akitas O'BJ are also top winners and producers in England, Australia, Canada, and South America. In 1989 Am/Mex/International Ch. O'BJ Sachmo KoSon became the Number One All Breeds in Mexico. The Andrews have bred Champions, ranked winners, or Top Producers in Dobermans, Rottweilers, Bull Terriers, and Japanese Chins.

Mrs. Andrews has served multiple terms on the Board of the Akita Club Of America. She developed the Register Of Merit system in 1973 and created the Expanded ROM in 1984. Fittingly, in this volume, for the first time she unveils the Hall of Fame for the Akita breed fancy.

Their love of animals has not been limited to dogs or AKC events. Training and exhibition of working Quarter Horses eventually led to professional obedience training. BJ managed the Kuhwald Kennels of Paul Harris who imported top Schutzhund/Seiger-titled Rottweilers.

The Andrews were charter members of several breed clubs including the American

The author showing O'BJ Sparks A' Flyin under breed authority Eleanore Evers.

left to right, Ch. O'BJ King's Ransom, ROMXP and owner-handler Julie Hoehn, Regional Specialty judge Mrs. Maynard K. Drury, Ch. The Mad Hatter O'BJ, ROMXP (winning Brood Bitch Class) breeder-owner-handler Barbara Andrews, Ch. O'BJ Canduit Tuya and owner-handler Bill Andrews. Hatter is currently the dam of 16 AKC Chs. plus numerous Champions, Group, Specialty, and Best In Show Winners in Canada, Mexico, and So. America.

Rottweiler Club. Having imported several top Miniature Bull Terriers, including English Ch. Eleanore and that year's Junior Warrant Winner, Mrs. Andrews founded the new Miniature Bull Terrier Club Of America in 1983. She served as first President and, with the assistance of top BT breeders, started the MBTCA on the road toward AKC recognition.

A regular columnist for such popular all-breed publications as *Kennel Review, The Dog, Dog World, Working Dogs, The Canine Chronicle, and ShowSight,* BJ also does feature articles for several single breed magazines. She was Editor and Publisher of *The Akita Handbooks* (1973 through 1976) and the highly acclaimed *Akita Reference* in 1984.

Preferring to exhibit, Mrs. Andrews occasionally judges AKC specialty shows and sanctioned matches. She became the first American breeder to judge Akitas at an English Open show in 1987 when she was invited to judge Akitas, Dobermans, and Rottweilers. She was also the first American to conduct a breed seminar for the British Japanese Akita Society, England's parent club.

A popular speaker, BJ occasionally conducts breeding or canine health seminars. As Chair of the ACA Judges' Education Committee, she continues to teach Judge's Workshops. Comfortable in front of the camera, she has produced instructional videos as well as appearing on television with her beloved Akitas.

Mrs. Andrews served as Executive Secretary for the Association of Small Animal Professionals (ASAP), a national non-profit organization founded by 20 of the best known members of the dog and cat fancy.

Preface

by James P. Taylor

I first became aware of BJ Andrews while I was still in junior high school. Another of TFH's illustrious writers, Anna Katherine Nicholas, had written an article on BJ and the great Akita "Sachmo." I was immediately impressed by her obvious dedication to positively promoting this then relatively rare breed. Back then few judges were sure of themselves when it came to the mysterious bear dogs from Japan. BJ's dreams of a day when Akitas could get equal consideration in the Working Group with such breeds as Dobermans, Boxers and Great Danes would take a while, but it was obvious to all that BJ was in it for the long haul.

Yes, BJ's pace was quickened with the help of Sachmo: litter after litter this immortal dog gave of himself all that was good. His producing prowess helped the breed to capture the attention of the entire dog fancy. All across the country, countless breeders have based their entire lines on Sachmo. He helped even the best judges understand what it truly meant to be *"A-ki-ta."* To this day everyone agrees on one thing: Sachmo is the father of the breed as we know it in this country.

Where does one go after such a start on top? Well, if you're BJ Andrews, you stay there and enjoy the view!

At around this time, Akitas were starting to receive recognition on the Group level, but these wins were still far and few between. The Akita often was defeated by the flashier breeds. This, however, was about to change. Even as a puppy, "BigSon" showed the potential of being able to fill his sire's enormous pawprints, setting records in the show ring while still a youngster that had never been seen before. Rarely had anyone seen an Akita with such beautiful markings combined with soundness, showmanship, and correct Akita type. BigSon proved to the masses that, yes, this was a breed that could have it all. Breeders everywhere were inspired to breed one "just like BigSon." His contributions as a sire are legendary.

The "Widow-Maker" was next to reign, and reign he did. Beautifully presented by his breeder-owner-handler Mrs. Andrews, this unbeatable team won ten Bests in Show, more than triple the wins won by any other Akita up until that time. It was Widow-Maker who showed the "new generation" the pure essence of the Akita. Passing on the unending virtues which made him great, Widow-Maker has produced more Best in Show winners than any other Akita.

I would need my own chapter to list all the accomplishments of the O'BJ dogs. Mrs. Andrews did much more than just make a name for herself in the breed...she created a dynasty. Her dogs have served the breed as the foundation stock for breeders all over the world. No kennel anywhere has produced more top winners and producers than O'BJ Akitas.

However, BJ's claim to fame is not just with her beautiful dogs. As a writer,

BJ has few equals in her approach with style, honesty, candor and knowledge. BJ is able to put pen to paper with numerous years and accomplishments as back up. Her columns have appeared in national publications such as *Kennel Review, Canine Chronicle* and *ShowSight Magazine* for over ten years. She is a rare individual that isn't afraid to "tell it like it is." Respected the world over, BJ is one of the few that can talk the talk because she has walked the walk.

As a person, BJ is the well that gives until she is dry. On many occasions, I have waited as BJ counsels an unsure new-puppy owner only to find out the puppy was *not* bought from O'BJ but from a totally unrelated line.

In my many travels, I have been very fortunate to get to know more than my fair share of truly great people, individuals that did it their way and are a part of history...Mrs. Barbara Jean Andrews is right where she belongs, at the head of the line.

BJ and Bill Andrews with James P. Taylor enjoying a moment together at the "Red Eye Reception" before the Westminster show in 1995. This reception has become the dog fancy's most talked-about party, and it is sponsored by Mr. Taylor's monthly publication, ShowSight Magazine, the premier dog magazine in America.

The Akita-inu

MADE IN JAPAN

There's a good reason why most breed books begin with the standard qualifier, "The origin of the *(insert breed)* remains shrouded in mystery." Anthropological beginnings for most breeds can rarely be established, and it is even more uncommon when any two breed authorities are in total agreement. To add to the confusion, each researcher will proudly provide scientific data to substantiate his premise. Breed scholars, then, need not be particularly gifted, just patient, plodding, persevering; and darn good detectives. We sort through so much abstract information that "recorded" history usually comes down to a personal interpretation based on common sense. In ancient breeds which have been highly fictionalized, the task of sorting fact from fancy becomes even more tedious.

In documenting the Akita's origin, even such notable Japanese authorities as Dr. Shozaburo Watase, Dr. Hasebi, Dr. Tei Uchida, and Mr. Hiroyoshe Saito have been thwarted by many frustrating inconsistences. To further confuse us, it would seem that a few little details of the Akita's development may have been conveniently left out in the interest of cultural purity. Therefore, at the risk of sounding trite, we shall begin with that oft-used but perfectly true statement, "The origin of the Akita remains shrouded in mystery."

As a specific type of canine, the distinctively Japanese dog existed well over 3000 years ago. Skeletal remains and carbon dating demonstrate that the direct ancestors of the Akita began to be sharply defined by about 500 B.C. and as a developing breed, we can trace the Akita-inu backwards through over 300 years of written records.

As is appropriate in this first chapter, we will refer to the Japanese dogs by their cultural names. To begin with, let's do away with the confusion surrounding the suffixes "ken" and "inu." Both appendages, customarily separated from the preceding proper name by a hyphen, simply mean "dog." Thus, both Akita-ken and Akita-inu refer to an Akita dog.

Most Japanese breeds were named after the regions from which they evolved or were most commonly associated with. For instance, there were two completely different types of dogs called by the same name. The spitz-like Shikoku and the mastiff-like Tosa (the large fighting dog) were both associated with Shikoku island of the Kochi Prefecture, and they were known as the Shikoku-Kochi. As the Tosa became a distinct type, it was renamed and confusion was thus eliminated.

It's generally accepted that the modern-day Akita was developed in Akita Prefecture, in the northern part of Honshu Island, Japan. Although the breed drew genetic support from more southern regions during the restoration period, historical comment repeatedly ties the Akita-inu to a town called Odate City, which is the northernmost city in Akita Prefecture.

Odate City (called "Dog City" and "Boulevard of Dogs") lies in a basin, surrounded by towering mountain ranges. Travel from the east was cut off by the Ouu mountain range, and from the south by such severe winters that even sea routes to the area were limited. Thus there was little early outside influence on this remote area and development of the native dog followed natural evolution patterns for hundreds of years.

The Tohoku region was referred to as the "area beyond civilization" through the seventh century. The vast region, which includes Akita Prefecture, remained isolated well into the 14th century with the Hokkaido region still referred to as the Ezo-chi or "Land of the Ainus."

As an island empire, Japan itself was perfectly isolated, less affected by trade and cultural exchange than most other developing countries. The cold northern regions remained undisturbed as trade finally centered in the more accessible southern areas. This may explain why the dogs of northern Japan are among only a few "breeds" which have been preserved with so many of the physical and behavioral characteristics of the primitive canine.

It's only fitting that dogs which were later to be declared natural monuments evolved from these mountainous areas. The primitive type had been minimally influenced by other civilizations, thus they were considered pure enough to be representative of Japan and its ancient culture.

Fossil remains dating back to the Jomon culture of about 4000 years ago indicate a small to medium-sized dog which was used for hunting and protection. In 1940, an archeological discovery in northern Japan (the Tohoku region) gave evidence of another dog of considerably larger size, having a stride of

nearly 23 inches. Whether or not these larger dogs resembled Akitas is not known. We can not even be sure that they were originally from Japan but there is little doubt that they were ancestors of the present-day Akita-inu.

The Jomon Age (8000 BC to 200 BC) was followed by the Bronze Age of Yayoi or "farmers." As rice began to be cultivated between the third and eighth century, permanent cities evolved around agricultural regions. The people became less dependent on hunting as a means of survival and in the latter half of the fourth century, dominant families and powerful clans developed. It may have been during this time that variations in the domesticated canine began to develop as cultural needs shifted. Drawings on artifacts representative of the period depict dogs with no stop (brow), yet having erect ears and curled tails; features typical of many distinctly Japanese breeds such as the Shiba-inu.

Most scholars agree that the Akita evolved from native dogs crossed with Chinese imports which were then further refined, inadvertently or otherwise, by a mix-

Features of the past combine successfully with virtues of today. Ch. O'BJ A-Head of The Game (Ch. O'BJ King's Ransom, ROMXP x Ch. The Dame's On Target O'BJ, ROMXP) is a huge "American" Akita with many features of type appreciated by fans of the "Japanese" Akita.

"Akitas love snow" An 8 week old puppy (Ch. Obi-San's D'Artagnan x Ch. Inaka's Shirio Oboko) with beautiful ears and expression, bred and owned by Andrea Meloon and Tamara Warren.

ture of breeds common to Europe. That dogs from China, and Korea, were brought into Japan under the reign of Emperor Jinmu (about 660 BC) has been well established. The Chinese (Karainu) dogs may account for the introduction of the distinctly non-spitz type colors of black and black pinto. Photographs dating back to the Meiji and Taisho Period (1868–1925) depict white, black, and pinto-colored Akitas. Going back even further, scrolls from the early Kamakura Period (1185-1249) contain sketches which depict pinto-marked dogs as an incidental part of the background.

One theory holds that there was yet another type of dog native to northern Japan which was of different bone structure than the Eskimo, Chow, or Elkhound type. As there is no solid evidence of any early, large, atypical dog other than the Karainu, it seems we are stuck with having a houndy Chinese dog lurking in the background of the Akita-inu. This is notable only because the Karainu were described as having a long, narrow muzzle and long floppy ears. The tail did not curl and the bone structure was quite different from the native Japanese dogs. We may surmise that the muzzle, ears, and tail of the Karainu, when crossed with the Chinese Chow and the native dogs of Japan, would become less and less apparent, yet we see traces of these characteristics even today.

Christianity was introduced to Japan in about the 15th century and with the arrival of the Europeans, a variety of dogs were brought to the trading areas of Japan, further diluting the gene pool of the local dogs. The hound characteristics of the Karainu was intensified by the mastiff influence of many European breeds. Narrow muzzle, wrinkles, hanging flews, sickle tail, and large, soft ears still plague breeders of today.

As we shall see, Japanese breed purists recognized these "foreign" characteristics and early in the 20th century set out to eradicate them. For the most part, they have succeeded but breeders of today must realize that the hound-like features and personality traits are repressed only through continued careful selection for proper type.

When compared to the Shiba (the small Japanese dog which is rapidly gaining in popularity in the U.S.), the Akita of today bears a close resemblance to his tiny cousin. At first glance, the modern Japanese Akita-inu seems to be but a large version of the Shiba, in primitive personality subtleties as well as appearance. Both are clever and determined hunters, both show spitz-type structure, coat, and guarding instinct. While they are unquestionably related, other genetic infusions are obvious as defined by the overall size, bone-to-body proportions, wider backskull, thicker jaws, defined stops, and the color variations and patterns found in today's Akita.

THE HUNTER

The Akita is an acknowledged and skilled hunter. Not a specialist, he has been used successfully on both feather and fur. A special language called "dogwords" was used when speaking to or about the dogs. The care and training was highly ritualized such as a special manner used to tie them depending on the purpose for which they were being restrained.

The Joran tie was used for the Shogun's inspection of the dogs and the Kariba tie was used when hunting with the dogs. Dogs were given ranks according to their degree of training. Ara-inu meant a dog beginning training, the Hira-inu, meaning ordinary dog, was one that had finished the general training, and the O-hana Shi-inu or released dog was one of the highest training titles.

Different-colored leashes were also used to denote the rank, and even today one may ferret out these beautiful and highly ornate show leads in Japanese tourist centers. Ara-inu and Hira-inu wore dark blue leashes and collars, while the O-Hana Shi-inu wore a red leather collar with gold ornamentation and the Shogun's golden crest.

Many lines today retain strong hunting instincts and some Akitas might be said to be downright "varminty" in their preoccupation with hunting. There's no doubt that a pair of Akitas could (and would) do serious damage to something as fierce as a wild boar or a fully grown bear, yet I have difficulty accepting stories that the breed was used to bring large game to bay, meaning to cause the game to face a barking, yelping, bellowing, "baying" (as in hounds) pack. The Akita would be much more likely to tackle his quarry silently rather than wait for his master to arrive. This trait would make him rather ineffective as a hunting partner designed to run down and hold quarry at bay. As an aside, the human hunters must have been swift of foot and long on endurance if we're to believe they could be present when the Akita-inu would first bring the fleeing game to bay.

It's more conceivable that a smaller dog such as the Shiba chased the animal until it was exhausted, then held it at bay, barking to pinpoint location much as European hounds have been bred to do. As the hunters neared the scene, then the larger and much more aggressive Akitas were loosed on the prey to prevent its escape and to aid in the final kill.

The Matagi-inu (also known as Kari) was a mid-to-large-size red dog with a light mask. Believed to be the genetic base for the Akita-inu, it was pretty much a jack-of-all-trades. In the high rugged terrain, life was not easy and dogs had to perform a useful function in order to survive. The term "matagi," derived from the Ainu language, commonly referred to the hunting settlements which straddled the mountain ridges. It's a descriptive word for a group of people, meaning "hunter." "Matagi-inu" was not a breed name, it simply referred to a regional hunting dog which was later to emerge as Akita-inu.

As the more remote regions of Japan opened up, the Matagi-inu was subsequently crossed with the large native dogs which had developed from earlier imports and in about 1900 the Matagi-inu began to be referred to as Akita-inu. Many historians believe this dog to be the primary ancestor of today's Akita. Others disagree pointing out that, if in fact the Matagi-inu was the only ancestor, the breed would be predominantly solid red, fawn, or light brown in color. It is

Ch. Inaka's Moto-Yori No Jake at 15 months old, (Ch. O'BJ BigSon's Jake x The Shadow Knows O'BJ) bred by BJ Andrews and Ronnie Boyter, owned by Andrea Meloon and Tamara Warren.

therefore generally accepted that the Matagi-inu served as but one of the many ancestors of the Akita.

At one time, ownership of the largest Japanese breed was restricted to royalty and it was during Emperor Senka's reign that the office of dogkeeper was established. Interestingly, he is said to have trained Akitas to work with hawks, but we find this bit of information confusing. Hunting with hounds and hawks is a common sport in the desert countries, but the Akita is not a sight hound, and most of northern Japan's terrain would not lend itself to the sport of falconry as we know it. This may have been an isolated practice of nobility which grew into legend or something which at best was practiced by only a few individual Akita owners.

Japanese War. The northern island of Hokkaido is separated from the formerly Russian islands of Sakhalin, commonly called Karafuto, by the narrow La Parouse Strait. When the area became Japanese territory, travel between Hokkaido and Karafuto intensified due to the existent large-scale fishing industry.

Mutsuo Okada, a breeder and author from Tokyo, reported that a "large number of young men from the Akita and Aomori areas crossed the ocean to Karafuto..." Dogs from Hokkaido interbred with the Karafuto and Mr. Okada's observation, "the longcoat's appearance plagues breeders even today," is still true at the close of the century! He says pioneers of the breed "spent many years in strenuous efforts of purifying the breed." Well, insofar as

A most unusual sight! The Schiffs are exceptional trainers with exceptional Akitas. Steve and Abbie are avid show enthusiasts who don't limit themselves to conformation. The impressive team performs well both in and out of the ring, proving that with patience and talent Akitas can be trained to perform just about any task asked of them.

COAT, COLOR, AND CULTURE

The discussion of coat color and preferences dates back over 50 years. Coat length has recently become an issue in many countries and, therefore, should be dealt with in laying out the foundation of the breed.

There is one theory which holds that the longcoat gene was introduced as late as 1905, following the cessation of the Russo-

longcoats are concerned, they failed.

Many longcoats today display other characteristics of the Karafuto dog. They tend to be a bit more laid-back, of placid disposition, are generally more obedient and anxious to please. As these personality traits were typical of the Karafuto, it is a strong indication that interbreeding occurred.

Unfortunately, there are reportedly no pure Karafuto dogs left with which to compare the longcoated Akita. Despite the establishment of the Karafutoken Hozankai (The Karafuto Dog Preservation Society) in Hokkaido, the breed died out. A wonderful companion to children and a superb sled dog, the Karafuto exists only in the memory of those who loved him and in the gentle ways of the longcoat Akita.

The wonderful accomplishments of the Antarctic exploration team headed by Lieutenant Shirase was re-created on film. However, when Japanese film makers sought to use real Karafuto dogs they were forced to use non-Japanese dogs such as the Canadian Eskimo Dogs.

Many fanciers believe that longcoated Akitas were also used in the film, and who among us can dispute this belief? It really doesn't matter, but it is sad that one of the known ancestors of today's Akita simply faded away, another

A living monument to the Karafuto Dog, today's longcoat Akita fairly resembles this extinct ancient Japanese dog. The Karafuto Dog was larger than today's Akita and was a natural warrior. Photograph by Isabelle Francais.

casualty of 20th-century mechanization. Even more lamentable, we are told that as their usefulness declined, most Karafuto became starving strays and were killed in order to protect domestic animals and prevent the spread of disease.

In a discussion meeting of elder dog enthusiasts, there is verbal record of a dog called Moku, who was an only puppy from a litter whelped in northern Akita Prefecture in the late 1850s. He is described as being over 33 inches, with a long, goma-colored coat. It is said he could carry children on his back with ease and that as a fighting dog (which apparently he was), he could defeat two or even three opponents simultaneously! It should be noted, though, that other researchers place the introduction of the longcoat gene much further back, attributing it to the Chow Chow. Perhaps, in the interest of maintaining cultural significance, the influence of the Chow Chow has been downplayed. After all, Karafuto became Japanese territory. Yet, the evidence is there, both in coat and the distinct trademark of the Chow, the black tongue. Black spots on the tongue were considered a fault, no doubt because of the clear link with the Chow, just as hanging ears, straight tails, loose skin, and other non-spitz type faults point towards the European influence.

The "white dogs from the North," presumably the Samoyed, is mentioned by name in several Japanese works. So much variation in length, as well as texture of the guard coat and thickness of undercoat, indicates more than one longcoat gene in today's Akita. The influence of the Samoyed not only adds to the coat mystique, but should serve to abolish the silly belief that

The effect of the JKC/FCI alliance has widespread consequences. Three of these outstanding puppies will be acceptable under the proposed JKC stan2dard but the fourth, the dark faced puppy on the end, could be disallowed. Litter owner and photographer, Maurizio Moretto, Santiago, Chile, So. America.

white Akitas can not have long coats! Many excessively coated dogs have the harsh, stand-off coat with the wooly, thick undercoat of the Chow or Eskimo Dog whereas others have a softer, longer coat more like that of the Keeshond or Collie. It seems there is no pat answer to the origin of the longcoat gene. Ah, but then I told you the origin of the breed remains shrouded in mystery....

But we've solved a few inconsistencies. We have ample evidence that the "Akita-inu" was a combination of dogs native to Japan for over 2000 years. It was then influenced by early imports from China and Korea, followed by an influx of European dogs as Japan began to broaden international trade. The Karafuto was added to the gene pool after 1900 while large, mastiff-type dogs continued to be crossed with other large indigenous dogs. A half century later, European dogs continued to influence the Akita-inu both by accident and by design.

Prior to 1919, there is no documentation of an effort to preserve the native type of dog, nor is there any evidence of deliberate selection for any particular working or sporting characteristics. Even

more disconcerting for those who prefer to think of the Akita as a very ancient breed, the formal name "Akita" was not even used until September 1931, which was the year the type was established as a breed and finally proclaimed to be a natural monument. Prior to that, the Akita-type dog had been referred to as the "Odate dog," "Kazun-inu," or "Nambu" for dogs of the southern region, and "Jiinu" meaning simply regional dog. Dogs used for fighting were called "Kuwae-inu" and as we have already learned, the hunting dogs of the mountainous regions were called Matagi-inu.

And yet, we do know that this *type* of dog, one of this approximate size, existed in prehistoric Japan. Dr. Toku Uchida, in his book *Inu no Hon* (Book Of Dogs) states, "The Akita dog appears to be different from other Japanese dogs, Karafuto (Sakhalin) dogs, laika dogs and the Samoyed dogs. Instead of saying that the Akita dog is of more recent origin, one may infer that dogs with similar forms as the Akita dog existed previously in this region, as well as in other regions."

At one point, Dr. Shozaburo Watase observed in "Rigakukai, Vol. 22," "From prehistoric times the lineage of the Japanese dogs is classified into three areas: northern, middle northern, and southern lines. The dogs from the northern line entered our country from the north. These are large dogs with thick and long coats; a tail which was round and thick, short and coiled on top of the back; erect ears with rounded tips. The coat color was mostly white, but there were those with dark grey color and pintos (spots, patches, specks). These dogs of the northern line represent the Akita dog."

This may explain the "foreign" coat colors and patterns. The Samoyed dog (white, with much longer coat than is correct for the Akita) and the Eskimo Dog, which some believe may have been the Greenland Husky or Malamute, presumably infiltrated the mountain strongholds of the unspoiled Matagi-inu, thus leaving yet another footprint in the long pathway of development.

Agreeing in premise, and once more referring to the Chinese dogs, Dr. Hirokichi Saito, one of the founders of the Nihon Hozonkai (Nippo registry), states in his book *Dogs and Wolves of Japan,* that the original Akita-inu was created by crossing the medium-sized Japanese dog with the "northern dogs" and "the large dogs from the Chinese mainland" and states that this original dog "is almost extinct." He then goes on to list dogs from various regions and prefectures which he believes are of the same line. These include the Nambu, Rikuchu, Takayasu, Limaye, and Go dogs. His opinion was upheld by Dr. Taiji Kimura (of Odate City) who stated in the Akiho magazine that the Akita dog was created by crossbreeding the large dog from China with the traditional Japanese dog.

One form of the traditional Japanese dog may well be represented by the Yama-inu, a Japanese wolf, long thought to be extinct. Particularly interesting is the reference to color. Some years ago, a high school teacher captured a brindle-patterned male dog in the Ohto mountains. It was very wild, very fierce and he called it a Shima-Yama-inu. Crossbred to a female Kishu dog, the resulting litter was studied and it was

concluded by Dr. Sagara that the breeding represented the original native Japanese dog. There were more reports of the same wild wolf-dogs spotted near the Kumano River. The Yoshino Kumano mountain region was covered in virgin forest and until roadway and dam construction began, such wild dogs (wolves) may have lived not only undiscovered, but relatively uninfluenced by modern canines.

So although the exact origin of the Akita breed does indeed remain a mystery, we can safely conclude that there was once a distinct spitz-type prehistoric dog which the Japanese felt best represented their cul-

Two cheerful examples of different Akitas coats and colors. The modern-day longcoats remind us of the Akita's "northern dog" ancestors. Photograph by Isabelle Francais.

tural interests. Following establishment of the natural monument during the middle of the Taisho Era (1912-1926), a special effort was made to restore the animals to fit the description contained in the book *Nihon Tokuyu no Dobutsu* (Special Characteristics of Japanese Animals).

As to the place of origin, many areas claim that distinction and Japanese scholars still debate the issue. It's all tied to the "when" and what really began to be identifiable as the "look" the Japanese decided was appropriately a natural monument.

Dr. Yutaka Doura published a book in 1920 in which he chastised other writers for stating that the Akita dog was of recent development. He politely explained, "This is due to the confusion created by the use of the names "Odate dog" and the "Akita dog." He says that although Odate was the center for dog fighting, the name was used on Akita dogs which were raised from time immemorial in one region of the Tohoku area, thus he opposes the theory of the recent development of the breed based on its connection with dog fighting and Odate City.

Katsusuke Ishihara noted that during the early part of the Showa Era (1925), "there were few dogs that possessed what was considered the standard in each breed." He tells us "as research of the Akita breed progressed, it became evident that there was crossbreeding among the Akitas. For this reason, there were those who felt that the Akitas should not be considered the representative of the large-size Japanese breeds. However, the true Akita lovers believed that despite such crossbreedings, it will be possible to breed the original qualities back into the Akita through selective breeding. Thus, the effort to purify the breed was begun." He pointed out that although the foundation for purification began before WWII, the devastation to the dogs caused by the war undid most of that early work.

A NATURAL MONUMENT

It's important to understand the meaning of the natural monument. There was much grief and unhappiness over the decline of so many things in Japan which had existed since recorded history. Understandable. Sort of like our continued fascination with "cowboys and Indians" and the Wild West. But we must remember that American history is a blink of the eye compared to that of most eastern civilizations. Think how saddened we are today at the declining num-

bers of wild mustangs, the decimation of the wolf and the bear, the forests being stripped and the buffalo, once a symbol of the Great Plains, now only to be seen in farmed or protected herds. Multiply that sadness many times over and you may begin to understand how strongly the Japanese felt about their declining cultural symbols, one of which was their "native dog."

Think how very discouraged Dr. Watase, who pushed for and helped write the natural monument bill, must have been when he journeyed to Odate to study the Akita-inu. It is significant that the Akita was the first to be surveyed, indicating perhaps that the Japanese placed great pride in their largest breed. Saddest of all, Dr. Watase found the Akita to be in such decline that it could not be included as a natural monument at that time. How ironic that one of the monuments selected suffered from the same foreign influences as did the culture they were trying so desperately to protect!

A scientist, but also a lover of the dogs, Dr. Watase urged that a movement for the preservation (restoration!) of the Akita dog begin immediately. After all, how could an indigenous dog, which everyone wanted to hold up as an example of things past, things to be preserved, things to be revered as purely Japanese, be honored if the breed was no longer Japanese? What a heavy heart he must have had.

But, as the aftermath of WWII taught us, the Japanese are not inclined to sit around and bemoan a problem. They are doers, builders; if they see a problem, they fix it. They seem more inclined to look into the far future from a cultural viewpoint than are most Westerners. And so it was that Akiho (Akita-inu Hozankai Society) was established in Odate city in 1927 but it would be ten long years before the first Akita-inu standard was officially adopted by Akiho.

Like most true stories, this little piece of history has a not altogether happy ending. Not everyone in the Odate area understood what the breeding effort was all about. One must remember that most were still engaged in or supportive of dog fighting.

Frankly, they were less concerned with re-establishing a primitive spitz-type dog than with continuing to win in their sport! There were even those who refused to cooperate, arguing that the Tosa-mastiff-type dog in fact represented the true Akita dog.

And so, when the survey team returned in 1931, there were still very few dogs which could be considered representative of the purists' ideal of the Akita-inu. Equally disturbing, Dr. Watase had passed away in those few short years, and perhaps it was in his honor and not due to the quality of the dogs presented, that Dr. Tokio Kaburagi, leader of the survey team, declared a few of the dogs to be natural monuments. He cautioned breeders that the Akita-inu was far from finished and urged them to greater effort. Finally, in 1937 the first Akita dog standard was adopted.

As we study the history, it becomes clear that the Odate Akita never really evolved into today's Japanese Akita. Following World War II, the Ichinoseki line, the Nikki line from the southern region of Akita Prefecture, as well as the Ohira, known for white cheeks and red coat, were all used to help restore the type which had been lost to Odate City's obsession with dog fighting.

Japanese breeders are proud of the restoration of a true Oriental dog. Although there was some early criticism regarding efforts to recreate a natural breed (monument) through artificial selection, that was logically overridden, and today the efforts of over half a century have resulted in a dog which probably reflects the ideal held by Dr. Watase and many of his predecessors.

Moto-Yori's Marko No Inaka, (Ch. Obi-San's D'Artagnan x Ch. Inaka's Shirio Oboko) is an armful at 8 weeks old. Marko grew up to be a multi-Group winner, owner-handled by Andrea Meloon.

JAPANESE REGISTRIES

Unlike the registration systems of the Western world, Japan has several "pedigree" associations for native breeds. The various registration societies have caused no small amount of confusion for those who find the names and time periods difficult to sort out. In a nutshell, the Akita-inu Kyokai (commonly referred to as Akikyo) was established in 1948; in 1927, the Akita-inu Hozankai Society (Akiho) was formed to preserve and improve the Akita breed and is the most significant Akita club.

Nihonken Hozonkai (Nippo) was established in 1928 or 1923—there is some discrepancy, with supporters of Nippo insisting it is the oldest Japanese dog registry. Known as the Japanese Dog Preservation Club, Nippo is granted to be the more traditional of the early organizations. In 1948 the Japanese Kennel Club (JKC) Akita Club, operating under FCI rules, was organized.

Purification of the natural monument had begun but there was still one major obstacle to overcome. Although narrowly based, this problem was largely responsible for the previous decline in type and remained an impediment to speedy restoration of a completely "Japanese" large dog. Because of its horrific nature, this part of Akita development is always treated much like the implications of World War II—lightly. Usually only given a cursory treatment, the Akita today, particularly in America, carries much of the genes which were developed in Odate City.

THE WARRIOR

Ironically, one of the first examples of selective breeding may have been the result of that dark period of dog history which links the Matagi-inu with the mastiff-type canine. While we can be sure that villagers occasionally retained a pup from a certain female due to her courage or skills as a hunting companion, there was no particular thought about developing a dog for any purpose other than as a strictly utilitarian helpmate.

With a stronger agricultural base, less work meant more free time and so as always, man's mind turned to sport!

Dog fighting has been around since the first wolf decided to hang around a cave and

the club-wielding resident encouraged him to fight off other animals in defense of the home territory. As unpleasant as the subject is to most people, the sport is as old as time and crosses all national boundaries.

The formalized fighting of dogs evolved in Japan during the Kamakura Period (1185–1333) under the reign of Shogun Hojo Takatoki. Dog fighting was called "inua-wase" or "inukui." A passage from Volume 5 of *Taiheiki* reads, "He loved dog fighting as a form of entertainment to such an extent that he collected dogs by way of taxes..." We know that the people bred dogs in great numbers, striving to provide the regent with the best fighters. There are estimates that at one time, nearly 5,000 such fighting dogs, outfitted with elaborate tinsel and brocades, were in existence. Again quoting, " A dozen dog fights were held there monthly, which were observed from the rooftops and gardens by dignitaries with their families and friends." We are told that it was not uncommon for up to 200 dogs to be released into an arena at one time. It must have been a bloodbath fit to excite even the most bored dignitary!

This lovely American bred bitch, Kobun's Shoko-Go-No-Shukan (Ch. Nanchao's Raiko-Go-No-Sanmark x Ch. Ben's Shira Hime) was bred by Ben and Melanie Herrera. Her owners, Sharon and Jack Osborne, bred her to Kiyoshi Yamazaki's white faced Shinto, a breeding which produced a beautiful litter.

For those who enjoyed hunting games, there was a sport called "inu-ou-mono" or dog-chasing game. This was also popular during the Kamakura Period and seems to have persisted well into the Muromachi Period (1392–1573). The rules were simple. A dog was released from the center of a large circle and mounted samurai with bows attempted to kill it before it escaped from the circle. White dogs were used for more formal or important occasions. Although white was regarded as denoting purity, we surmise that white dogs made a better target; and those special occasions would be especially exciting as the wounds would show so clearly against the white coat. While this seems barbaric to us now (and it is), it is no worse than the human slaughter which was concurrent in other countries.

Furthermore, we can not shield man's inhumanities from our studies if we are to understand the development of the breed. To gloss over the unsavory side of the Akita's background would only serve to distort history and confuse the student, particularly regarding the breed's determination to be dominant.

Dog fighting became so popular and so highly developed a sport that a special breed was developed for that purpose. Enter the Tosa-inu, a large, loose-skinned, mastiff-type breed which was by then native to Shikoku island. Being only human, the Japanese were not content with a breed which had developed for over two centuries. The Tosa was a great dog but man is always certain that everything can be improved upon. Someone decided that a more agile and even more powerful dog would be better. No doubt, they looked around and noticed that they had the makings of the perfect outcross right in their backyard!

The Akita-inu had been quietly evolving into just what the Satake Clan was looking for. Already increased in size from the mid-size Matagi-inu, the "Akita Matagi-inu" had proven better for hunting in deep snow and the new variation was also much prized by the city people. The Akita Matagi-inu was brave. It would confront a bear and not back down! It was much more agile than the current fighting dog. Can't you just imagine the excitement as someone explained how the added bonus of a thicker coat and that wonderfully curled up tail which might not be so easily injured would greatly improve the thin-skinned, naked, long-tailed Tosa? Is it any wonder that fight enthusiasts ultimately turned their attention to this handsome, hairy homebred? And so it was that the Akita Matagi-inu was crossed with the Tosa-inu.

In 1899 the Tosa Fighting Dog Club went on tour, taking the Tosa with them. There are reports that the Tosa finally met the Akita in the first match of breed-to-breed fighting after the tour ended in Odate. Differences in fighting style are described and, although the outcome of that tournament is not entirely clear, the highly attended match no doubt contributed to the interbreeding trend of the time. The Akita-inu, being a hunting dog, may have lacked the killing instinct of dogs developed expressly for pit fighting, but when crossed with the Tosa-inu, the result was an awesome fighting machine.

Refinement of the Akita as a fighting dog was popularized by the Satake Clan and most activity centered around Odate City. Unfortunately, detailed records were lost during the Meiji Restoration when Odate was captured and burned, almost completely obliterating the breed's geographical history of that time. There are, however, two photographs salvaged from other areas. One dated 1898 shows two Akita dogs which were presented to Emperor Taisho as a wedding present from the school children of Odate. The other appears to have been taken about 1905 and shows an Akita named "Shiro," owned by a Mr. Kitayama of Odate City.

A slightly more civilized form of dog fighting (meaning more like one on one, rather than releasing a hundred combatants at a time) continued during the Meiji Period (1866–1912). Clubs such as the Enyukai (Garden Party Club), which was formed in Odate in 1897, were in high fashion. The various clubs hosted fighting tournaments and fans would pack lunches, prepared for a full day of entertainment!

We may extrapolate then that widespread

dilution of the primal dogs occurred as fight fans tried different combinations. Certainly, they were more concerned with prowess in the fighting arena than they were with bloodline, color, or structure. Any thought of preservation of the native breeds was completely ignored in the quest for a strong, brave, fighting dog.

In an effort to stop gambling on dog, bull, and cock fighting, laws were passed in 1907 which banned all animal fighting. Following the 1908 ordinances which required licensing of dogs, the overall fighting practice was officially outlawed.

The law notwithstanding, the sport, along with a preference for large powerful dogs, persisted until well after World War II. Giant breeds such as the European mastiff, German Shepherd, and St. Bernard continued to be deliberately crossed with the Akita up until the late 1930s.

Fortunately, there were other more acceptable breeding efforts which also had an effect on today's Akita. One such example involves a dog lover of long ago. There is some confusion as to the identity and true character of this regent, but we prefer to believe that the nobleman was a kindly fellow who was exiled to Akita Prefecture for some minor misdeed. Whatever his crime, he was forced to live his life as a provincial ruler. Being so far removed from the fast track, it may have been simple boredom which led him to such a strong interest in dog breeding and related sports. We're told only that he encouraged land owners to compete in creating a large, powerful hunting dog. That he was successful is clearly evident. The type of dog which evolved was very similar to the Akita, complete with keen hunting abilities and a fearless, alert spirit. Reasonable conjecture would lead us to accept that this popular and highly prized dog was a noteworthy ancestor of the modern-day Akita-inu.

Dog fighting is a prominent part of the Akita's heritage and although it's an aptitude which we properly downplay, we would be fools to attempt to rewrite history. The Akita is still astonishingly capable of defending himself and more to the point, he will seek to establish dominance over other animals with which he lives. Understanding why your Akita wants to be boss-dog allows you to accept his dominant attitude with other dogs. If you find that too difficult, then another breed would be a better choice. It is unfair to the animal to attempt to erase nearly a century of genetic development through "behavior modification."

RESTORATION LINES

The modern family tree of the Akita was researched as thoroughly as possible by Mr. Taiji Kimura. It was his considered opinion that the more important Akitas of today could be traced back to dogs such as Tochi-Nigo, a male owned by the first Chairman of the Akita-inu Hozankai, and an akagoma female called Babagomago, owned by Mr. Kunio Ichinoseki. He concedes that there were other very influential dogs such as Kumago, a black brindle female born in Odate City in 1934. She was owned by Mr. Watase but there are no known photos of her.

Following the establishment of the Akita-inu Hozonkai in 1927, there was much attention paid to detail in re-establishing Oriental type. This process was seriously harmed by the continued interest and breeding of fighting dogs and later, by the ruination of the war. Although the large, sloppy Akitas remained popular, not everyone liked them. According to Mr. Katsuke Ishihara, "the true form of Akitas reappeared in Goromaru-Go and Tamakumo-Go," two Akitas he felt constituted the main lines of Akitas in his country today.

Individual dogs which are credited with having helped the restoration process are descended from the famous Ichinoseki line, tracing back to Torago, who produced Toshigoro, which line continued on to Arawashigo, who produced Tamakumago, the black brindle so noted for his wonderful coat. The Ohira dogs from Akita Prefecture were also very influential as can be seen today in the white-masked red dogs.

These lines were successfully bred to the Goromaru line and breeders in the Tokyo area took advantage of Tamakumago, not specifically for his color but for his tight skin, good head development, and coat quality. Consequently, both colors became popular and greatly sought after in hopes that all the other fine qualities of these respected animals would come through too.

Probably Goromaru-Go's most persistent and serious competitor was Kongo-Go, his complete opposite in many features of type. Kongo-Go was large, throaty, long of back and short on leg with a loose tail and faulty coat color and texture. Nonetheless, due to his size and personality, he was widely used at stud and had quite a following among the show enthusiasts in the Tokyo area where he was raised. His German Shepherd Dog-Mastiff-mix type persists in many American lines today which trace back to the Dewa line of imports.

According to Mr. Hiraizumi (judge and officer of Akiho since 1949, second generation Akiho officer), there were only 16 Akitas left in Odate City following the war. Breeders were inclined to put quantity (producing numbers of "Akita-inu") ahead of quality and, although Mr. Hiraizumi produced the dogs behind Kongo-Go, he stated that the dog was typical of such desperate breeding practices. Mr. Hiraizumi faulted Kongo-Go's undesirable structure, coat quality and color

Goromaru-Go was owned by Mr. Susumu Funakoshi, born in 1948 out of Futatsui Goma-Go by Ichinoseki-Go. This favored noble sire was the major contributor to Japan's restoration lines.

(kurogoma), his loose skin and coarse head type, and his weak rear.

A definite link between coat color and type will become apparent as we study the breed, and this breed specialist makes the point that wise breeders used the akagoma-colored Goromaru line to correct shortcomings of the Kongo dogs. Again and again, we see references to correct features, such as Tamakumo's tight skin and lips, linked to a specific color. We are told that it was the correctness of type which just happened to be wrapped in a certain color that made Japanese breeders seem "faddish" about color. Mr. Hiraizume was of course correct and some features still tend to be linked to certain colors. This is not unique to the Akita breed and is a genetic restriction that experienced breeders have managed to work around.

Goromaru-Go was of the Ichinoseki line, owned by Mr. Funakoshi of Akita City. He was akagoma (red) pinto, and as he continued to compete, his tight skin and noble bearing, combined with his Samurai attitude, gained him great favor and a loyal following. Born in January 1948, he died in 1956. Goromaru-Go was also a favorite stud and so it was that his offspring competed with those of his nemesis Kongo-Go, both being of the Tokyo area.

Another prominent dog and winner of the Akiho Meiyosho (highest) was the brindle dog, Azumazakura-Go. It was this dog which set the stage for a new interest in the brindle coat color, thus a color preference based on a dog of overall remarkable character and type was initiated. His son, Azumagumo-Go, was the result of a deliberate in-breeding and represented five generations of Meiyosho award winners.

While these individual dogs are im-

Mansumaru, early Akita from 1950s' Japan. Photograph courtesy of Liz Harrell.

mensely interesting to pedigree buffs, one must be aware that dogs who were themselves not inbred or tightly linebred upon, or which appear eight to ten generations in the past, have little influence on today's Akitas.

As we move into the 1930s and estab-

lishment of the Akita dog as a natural monument, Japan was opening its doors and developing a much wider trading base. It was a fascinating place to visit. Military as well as missionary travel increased and there were a few scattered reports which indicated interest in the indigenous dogs but no public records of Akita-inu being brought to America.

The first publicized arrival of an Akita-inu was the pet of Miss Helen Keller. We are left to wonder whether Kamikaze, (who died and was replaced by his litter brother Kenzan) was an example of the unwillingness of the Japanese to part with superior dogs or whether these litter mates were reflective of the breed's development at that time. Much ado was made of Miss Keller's trip in June 1937, and the gift of a Japanese puppy by the Ministry of Education made headlines in the *New York Times.*

The puppy did not survive, but when the ministry heard of his death, they sent the litter brother to Miss Keller, this dog being obtained for the purpose by a senior official of Akita-inu Hozankai, Mr. Ichiro Ogasaware. While there is no question of the sincerity of the gesture and the respect commanded by Miss Keller, it was indisputably not a very good breed specimen, flopped ears and all! Compared to other quality specimens of the day, the dog presented to Miss Keller would be, at best, termed pet-quality. Nonetheless, she wrote of her love for the odd Japanese dogs, commenting on their high intelligence and loyalty.

THE WAR

Just as most accounts of breed history leave out details of the Akita's background as a fighting dog, most written accounts omit a major part of world history. As awful as it was, the effects of WWII upon the Akita can not be ignored.

One has only to study photos to see the German Shepherd influence on the Akita. Following the outbreak of serious hostilities, non-Japanese records suggest that large numbers of German Shepherd Dogs (GSD) were imported into Japan. Given that dogs had been used with success in World War I, it may be that leaders in Japan turned to the past to preserve the future. We shall never know as this part of the Akita's past is too painfully associated with the horrors of the war.

Not only do we see evidence of GSD characteristics in dogs such as Kongo-Go, many Akitas today retain the distinctive dark saddle marking, and the muddy tan with lighter points is not uncommon. One can not help but notice that the larger, upright ear is often found in a dog with a longer, lower

Tamukumo-Go, owned by Riyosuke Tadamoto, whelped in 1950 out of Sankatsu-Go by Arawashi Go (combining the two main Akita lines in Japan, Ichinoseki and Dewa). A handsome brindle male and Meiyosho winner who was exceedingly masculine and an important sire for the Japanese.

profile. The wolf-like skeletal frame usually has a more rounded croup, thus a lower tail set. Such dogs will often have excessive rear angulation. Referring to Mr. Hiraizumi's mention of Kongo-Go's weak rear, we note that he is more angulated than was considered proper and appears narrow in the upper thigh area, problems which still confront breeders today.

If we can look at these faults and not recognize the influence of the old German Shepherd, we can be sure of one thing: the Japanese were not blind to them! In addition to faulting anything reminiscent of the mastiff, all of the new or rewritten Japanese standards list the Shepherd-like characteristics as very faulty. Perhaps in eradicating so much of what is obviously Western influence in the Akita, Japan sought to rid itself of the cultural intrusions of the past. So it has been said.

The breed suffered near extinction following Japan's surrender. People were without food and shelter and, although Allied forces provided help, it was a time of hunger and pain. Dogs were a luxury that only the well provisioned could support. Those who thought to keep their beloved dogs were accused of wasting food, and therefore, of being enemies of the state. Consequently, many dogs were killed. Others were abandoned, not a few starved. And everywhere, those which were capable of breeding did so.

THE EXPORTS

Ultimately, the government offered to subsidize the care and feeding of a champion Akita if the owner was unable to provide these essentials. It's unlikely that this generous cultural backing was ever fraudulently requested.

Type notwithstanding, the breed experienced a steady recovery and Akitas registered in Japan grew from estimates of a thousand dogs between 1950 and 1960, to several thousand by the late 1960s. The country had already been plundered and they were obsessively protective of all things considered a natural monument or a national symbol.

Even so, with the rapid re-establishment of the breed, an overpopulation problem developed. With space being at such a premium, and cash still hard to come by, there were many cheap dogs during the 1950s and early '60s. While top-quality Akitas were seldom sold to Americans at any price, second-rate, or what we would

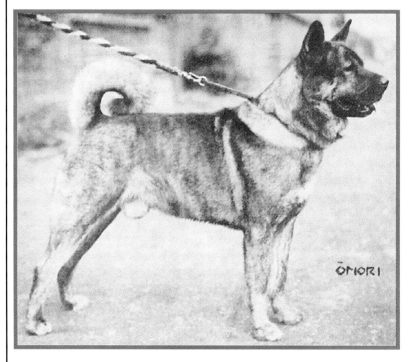

From the 1930s, Taro-Go was the grandsire of Akidate-Go who sired Dewa-Go. Photograph courtesy of Liz Harrell.

breed became rather rigidly divided between the Dewa and Ichinoseki types. The Dewa breeders aligned with the Nihonken Club and the other three clubs concentrated on the Ichinosiki line. By 1960, the firmly established Akita-inu Hozonkai Club was generally said to be responsible for the development of the "new" Akita.

It must be pointed out that Americans, as the conquerors, were tolerated and occasionally emulated, but we were not loved and were not considered friends. It is therefore understandable that Akita breeders rarely ever let their finest dogs fall into American hands. Many Japanese felt their call pets, were often sold for under a hundred dollars. Even fewer American dollars could buy pet produce, complete with "papers." Yes, there are licensed pet dealers in Japan, and many of the dogs represented to Americans as top-quality specimens were actually of questionable purity, and, in fact, considered as rejects.

So for a while, the export business was good. Good for Japan and in the long run, good for Americans who took this big exotic dog into their hearts as well as their homes. Had we been allowed (by AKC) to continue to import from Japan, the breed would not have evolved in such different directions.

As it was, Americans were left to work with a gene pool which was later to be considered untypical in the country of origin.

As registration reciprocity between the AKC and the JKC (Japanese Kennel Club) has become a reality, we still should not forget the lessons of the post-war days of "export." At the close of 1991, AKC agreed to admit the Japanese Shiba into Miscellaneous class and full "recognition" for that delightful breed was attained in June 1993.

Kinch-Go Abe. Photograph courtesy of Liz Harrell.

THE LEGENDS

Marauding bears are rarely a problem anywhere and let's face it, "game" is no longer plentiful in developed nations. Wild boar is still hunted in some areas of the States and yes, I know a couple of owners who use their Akitas for that purpose. There are still those few individuals who will probably never be content until all the wild bears are gone and they proudly report that the Akita still retains the courage and instinct to be a modern-day "bear dog."

Torn between not wishing to promote the hunting of animals for sport and yet, wanting to acquaint you with what makes an Akita an Akita-inu, I have settled on the following story. It was printed in "The Akita" circa 1962 and accurately describes the way in which the breed performed with their human partners. Obviously set in post-war time, it mentions that this is the "old way" and I feel it's entirely plausible. It was submitted by Emile C. Schurmacher:

Representing the famous Ichinoseki strain is the male Jiromaru-Go, a littermate to Goromaru-Go. Photograph courtesy of Liz Harrell.

The Legend of the Yezos Bears

Driven off their mountain by the rains, the huge bears had taken over the village. There was only one chance to survive: so they called in the Akitas.

The word had spread swiftly throughout northern Hokkaido on that day last spring: notify all owners of Akitas. Their dogs are urgently needed to drive the great killer bears out of Muju.

From Teshio and Furebetsu and from as far away as Wakkanai and Soya they soon began to gather. Determined little Japanese with bows and arrows, homemade lances and even a few ancient samurai swords. Businessmen, merchants, farmers, mechanics. Until there were more than 50 of them with their dogs.

The dogs were Akitas, an old and native Japanese breed noted, among many other things, for courage in hunting bear and wild boar. Big, sturdy fellows weighing up to 120 pounds. Some of them appeared to be almost as large as their owners, massive and muscular, with well-knit frames.

The majority of Akitas were on leads of ordinary chain or leather. Several among them had the green-colored leads of aras, companion dogs. Two of them bore red-colored leads of champions.

Men and dogs stood quietly, awaiting the orders of Kano Niyaki, captain of the Teshio police. But for the modern clothes worn by some of the men and the trucks lining up to carry them to Muju, the scene might have been enacted a thousand years ago. One thing was certain: not since long before the American occupation had the Japanese responded so picturesquely to a Yezo bear emergency.

It was Inomi, the little charcoal burner of Muju, who had fought his way down the swollen Teshio river with a plea for help after the coming of the disastrous spring rains. Two alert Japanese cops found him in the wreckage of his raft on the river shore several miles above Teshio, more dead than alive from exhaustion and starvation.

They fed him some rice and tea, his first meal in three days. They took him back to headquarters. There he told his story to Captain Niyaki.

It wasn't only that the people of his little mountain village were starving, Inomi explained. That had happened before when the Teshio was in flood and always, somehow, they had managed to survive. This time it was different. Muju was also being menaced by bears.

The great Yezos, largest and fiercest of all Old World bears, had come down from the mountains after the violence of the rains made forage scarce. They could not be driven back. They stalked through the village in hordes, raiding the storehouses of everything edible and destroying what they could not eat.

One courageous farmer, Adashi Hukura, had tried to drive a 600-pound Yezo away from his door with a pitchfork. The bear's sweeping paw brushed aside the pitchfork as if it were a straw, pulling Adashi toward him. Long fangs, almost as murderous as a tiger's, bit through Adashi's skull as if it were a ripe melon. The farmer died instantly.

Four others had been bitten to death by the terrible Yezos. One youngster had his head and neck almost torn from his body. Many others were mauled and badly clawed but managed to escape with their lives. Villagers either fled or barricaded themselves in their homes. The bears were in undisputed control of the entire community.

Captain Niyaki listened as Inomi blurted out his tale of horror. When it was finished he stared for a thoughtful moment at the ceiling. Then he summoned the town council and asked Inomi to repeat his story. The others listened, and then they too stared at the ceiling and at one another. Captain Niyaki put their perplexity into words:

'We can send supplies to Muju. But how can we rid the village of the Yezos? This requires firearms and since we turned them over to the Americans, there is not even a small rifle in Teshio. Nor a shotgun.'

'There is a way,' suggested Councilman Namura, who owned an Akita. 'We can hold a bear drive as was done in the old days. Our dogs still possess the courage.'

So it was that the captain and Namura with Akitas and their owners came to Muju and formed a long line at the edge of the village. Captain Niyaki decided upon the plan of action.

'We must drive the Yezos toward the river,' he pointed out. 'If we let them escape into the mountains they will return to spread new terror after we are gone.'

Namura paired the dogs off in teams, which is the traditional manner Akitas hunt and fight both bear and boar. When Captain Niyaki gave the order to advance, the dogs, on lead started forward at a brisk gait, heads high and alert, long tails curled over their backs.

On that first drive none of the Akitas was unleashed although they tugged eagerly on their leads. The great brown bears with the whitish crescents on their breasts gave ground immediately before the yelling hunters and their dogs.

Nine of them, weighing up to 650 pounds, were killed with hunting arrows. They died quickly with the many shafts protruding from their bodies like long porcupine quills. For many centuries the Japanese have been rated as fairly good archers, and since the ban on firearms there had been a keen revival of interest in the sport.

The remaining Yezos, eight in number, bolted hellbent toward the other end of the village, heading for the safety of the forests of Japanese cedars and the mountains beyond. They discovered that their retreat had been cut off by a curving line of men and dogs.

Two bears tried to break through that line. One of them was met by the spear of a sturdy little man from Furebetsu named Kurio. It was a six-foot spear tipped with a needle-pointed, razor-edged foot-length of scrap metal.

Kurio braced his legs and put the head of the spear adroitly into the white crescent of the rearing Yezo. Snorting and howling with pain and fury the bear came right on, impaling himself deeper as Kurio grimly held on.

Suddenly a huge paw lashed out. It caught Kurio on the shoulder, swatting him to the ground, stunned and bleeding. It was then that Namura, standing nearby, quickly slipped the lead of his dog Fuji.

The big Akita flashed forward, hurdling Kurio as he lunged. His open jaws snapped shut and his teeth found a deadly grip in the side of the Yezo's neck. Caught by surprise, the bear turned away from Kurio, trying to get at this new menace. Namura came in at a run and drove his own spear directly into the Yezo's heart.

The other bear tried to escape through the line past an archer. Before the Japanese had a chance to string his bow two Akitas sped by him. One was owned by a man from Teshio, the other came from Furebetsu. Although they had never hunted together before, the Akitas worked as a superbly coordinated team.

The first dog dashed toward the bear as though he was going to jump right for its throat. His charge became a feint and he swerved, nipping at the Yezo's left haunch.

The bear swatted out at him and missed, just as the second dog silently leaped and held onto the bear's right ear. The Yezo whirled, roaring with rage. Again the first Akita came charging, this time directly head-on. His front paws shot out, and he braced himself against the Yezo's chest as he completed his upward leap, his fangs buried in the bear's nose.

Both dogs held on as spearmen closed in on the bear and quickly killed it.

Pursued by Akitas, the other six Yezos retreated toward the Teshio river. Two of them were speedily brought to bay and killed by hunters. Three more were surrounded on the river bank and went down fighting. The last one plunged into the swollen river and, swimming rapidly with the current, was very soon lost from view.

So the savage Yezos were driven out of Muju with the help of the Akitas, much as they have been driven out of other villages of Hokkadio for the past ten centuries.

A script fitting for a Disney movie, this story is utterly believable. Oddly enough, although the Akita is a fine hunter—not only of bear and boar but also of deer—he is classed by the Japanese as a working dog. Once a protector and possession of royalty, he is so affectionately regarded as a companion and protector of the home that he came to be revered as a symbol of good health and prosperity.

There are many legends associated with the Akita and one of the most charming stories I heard when we first became interested in the breed was that female dogs are used to babysit the children in Japan. I thought it was just another one of those beguiling stories which surround most breeds but have little basis in fact. Surprisingly, it seems the legend may not only be true but may even be practiced today in the more remote areas where women still go into the fields to work.

open field stretching behind and no people save for four small children in an area which we would call the front yard. As they drew closer to the tiny houses, he commented on the absence of an adult, whereupon the guide pointed out the two dogs lying in the shade of the front stoop.

Smiling, the guide pulled over so they could have a better look. The two dogs were Akitas. As they sat on the shoulder of the dusty little roadway, the smallest child wandered over what must have been an invisible boundary line. The American guessed it was a little boy although all four were clothed in long dresses. The dog started across the yard after him. The two men watched more intently, sure that the other Akita, which they suspected was a small female, would arise from her resting place and offer challenge to the trespasser. Such was not the case, for although the small Akita did get up and was indeed a female,

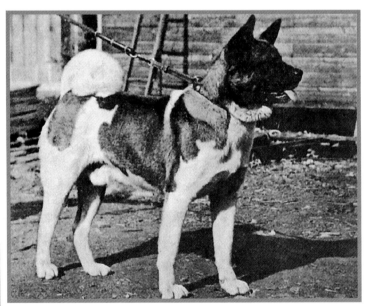

Hakko-Go, Japanese stud dog in a piebald pattern. Note the correct tail set, the long legs, and smallish head with large ears.

A successful wrestler was known to reward himself (no doubt for all the accrued bumps and bruises) with a yearly hunting expedition to Japan. On one such trip, while in the company of his guide, he was exploring a sparsely populated hunting region. They noticed two small dwellings side by side near the roadway with an expanse of

she only stood watching the other dog go about her task of herding the youngster back to join his playmates. The busy babysitter seemed careful not to make eye contact or acknowledge the presence of the other bitch.

The intrigued wrestler may have been presumptuous in his evaluation of the situation, but sincerely felt that had the one bitch trespassed into the other one's territory under other circumstances, there would have been a serious altercation between the two dogs. He was a dog owner and due to his detailed observations, we tend to agree with him. Not unlike the Japanese people, the Akita seems to have a finely tuned understanding of duty and honor.

While we would never suggest leaving small children to be watched over by a dog, we have nonetheless heard of several similar incidents in which the family Akita showed an uncanny understanding of territorial

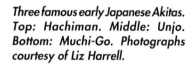

Three famous early Japanese Akitas. Top: Hachiman. Middle: Unjo. Bottom: Muchi-Go. Photographs courtesy of Liz Harrell.

bounds and the limits to which small children might be permitted to roam. The mother dog allows her nestling pups only so much freedom and wild dogs have been filmed reprimanding their young for wandering out of the prescribed safe limits. Many domesticated dogs have lost their primitive instincts and could care less where their pups are off to. Akita moms are usually very watchful with their litter. As many Akitas, both male and female, consider the family's children part of their "pack," this aptitude is not surprising.

For example, I know of a family who lived in a subdivision in a quiet Georgia town. Many of the neighborhood children would gather in their front yard to play under the watchful supervision of the family's female

In the United States in 1960, Mr. Patee with Major (on left) and Cindy (on right), two early Akita imports. Photograph courtesy of Liz Harrell.

Akita. They swore to us that on more than one occasion, she had prevented the kids from chasing a ball or other toy into the road, allowing them to retrieve it only when she accompanied them, turning her head from side to side to watch for oncoming cars. This bitch was extremely dominant and no neighborhood dog dared trespass on her property, but when she was "on duty" with the children, she only acknowledged strays with a warning glance.

The respect accorded to the Akita in Japan is still evident in our modern fast-paced world. It is one of only a few breeds to appear on postage stamps and official documents in its country of origin. Tachibana-Go was the model Akita prominently displayed on a Japanese stamp, circa 1952, and the breed continues to be symbolized in other official ways.

The new-old Akita has become more than a natural monument to the people of Japan, indeed it seems to have an almost religious significance. When one is ill, instead of receiving flowers or get-well cards as would be customary in the States, one might receive a small statue of an Akita as an expression of the giver's solicitous wishes. A small statue is frequently given upon the birth of a baby, signifying that the giver wishes the baby to have a long, healthy, and prosperous life.

Important Akitas were skinned, their pelts were preserved and prominently displayed by proud owners. This was just one way in which very special dogs were honored, and the high esteem with which they were regarded could be forever remembered. Al-

Around 1961, Hazel Shaffer with two imported Akitas, Gyokushu and Kotohamahime. Photograph courtesy of Liz Harrell.

though these customs may seem strange to us, they have great meaning to the Japanese.

Museums in this country contain artifacts which are of historical significance but which do not denote any particular reverence or love for dinosaurs or prehistoric man. Conversely, the Akita museum located at Akiho headquarters is a strong statement of the love the Japanese people feel for the Akita breed.

a particular breed, much less an individual dog.

HACHI-KO

He was not a particularly handsome dog, but the beauty of his soul transcends the common definition of "show quality."

He was the pet of Professor Ueno, who taught a course in agriculture at Tokyo University. Like most suburbanites, the professor was a commuter. Unlike his

Akitas on American soil, this family belongs to Marge Rutherford in California (circa 1960).

The headquarters building was constructed in 1978, the 50th anniversary of the breed's official recognition by Akiho. There one will find many interesting artifacts such as hunting gear which was used in connection with the breed, carefully preserved dog skeletons, and, somewhat shocking to American visitors, the pelts or skins of famous Akitas.

This is but an extension of the personal reverence with which many dogs were regarded by their individual owners. The story of Hachi-ko still enchants the American fancy and has captured the hearts and imagination of school children all over the world. Even though we have grown up on Lassie, Lad, and other such fictional dogs, many Westerners consider it strange that a country would immortalize

fellow travelers, the teacher was escorted daily to the train station by a big fawn Akita dog! In the evening, Hachi-ko would return and, ignoring friendly advances from passersby, he could be seen patiently waiting for his friend at the busy Shibuya train station.

They became a common sight, and it wasn't unusual to see them strolling around the Shibuya area, enjoying snacks from nearby food vendors.

For over a year, the pattern continued. People took it for granted that the dog would be there, morning and evening. On May 21, 1925, the professor was late. We can only imagine the dog's confusion as he waited and waited. There was none who could explain to him that his friend had died of a stroke before leaving the university.

Professor Ueno had a cousin who agreed to care for Hachi-ko. But this was not enough for the distraught dog. Food, a warm bed, and the like were of little interest to him. He continued to make the long trip across Tokyo alone. Sure that his master would arrive, the big dog waited every afternoon for the four o'clock train. He could be seen watching the passengers as they exited, his head lifting expectantly as he spotted someone who resembled Professor Ueno. People talked.

The professor's cousin retrieved the dog several times and then found someone else who was willing to care for the somber Akita. Professor Ueno's former gardener lived near Shibuya station, and he had known Hachi-ko as a puppy. The gardener saw to it that the dog had a place to live, but it was obviously not a place Hachi-ko called home.

Once again, commuters took for granted that the big dog would be there at the station. Always alone. The station master took pity on him and provided a bed, and others brought him choice morsels of food. The few times the dog seemed physically ill, an old friend of the professor who was also a veterinarian saw to him. Dr. Itagaki came to the station, probably at four o'clock when he could be sure Hachi-ko would be there....

By 1932, Hachi-ko's loyalty was made much of by the press. A fund was organized to erect a bronze statue

Litter from Marge Rutherford in February 1961which contained Kemuri and Little Sumi.

commemorating the dog. The Society for the Preservation of Japanese Dogs was eagerly assisted by station personnel and on April 21, 1934, the statue was unveiled. The old dog watched, but he was not impressed. One year later, he died. Hachi-ko was 11 years old and had been lonely for too many years.

When war broke out and munitions were in short supply, the statue was melted down for weapons, and not long afterwards, the area where it had stood was leveled by bombs.

With so much rebuilding to be done, it would seem that one small bare place would have gone unnoticed in the rubble. With all the hurtful memories, recollection of a devoted dog who loved his master might surely have been forgotten. But no, when the reconstruction began, Hachi-ko was not forgotten. Money was raised for a second statue, with school children saving their coins and the older people wanting to remember. Loyalty. Unswerving. It represented a lot to the people of Japan, and indeed, the world took note.

And so it was that the son of the original sculptor was commissioned to erect a new statue of the famous dog. Once more, commuters passed the faithful dog. Some must have been reassured. Hachi-ko was home.

There is a spring festival there every April. Remembering the devotion of an Akita dog and hoping for a comparable amount of human devotion, people leave food offerings at the foot of the statue. Shibuya Square is a favorite meeting place, especially for lovers and students. Hachi-ko would've liked that.

A seven-week-old Taikatsu owned by Marge Rutherford.

In 1983, students at Tokyo University decided that 50 years of waiting was too long. They carried a bust of Professor Ueno from the school and placed it by the statue of Hachi-ko. And so, finally, the story of faithful Hachi-ko is ended. Man and dog were symbolically reunited. From somewhere, the two of them must have smiled as they looked on.

Should we find it odd that the intense loyalty so highly valued by the Japanese people is immortalized in a statue of a dog? What better creature to symbolize undying devotion? That this was a real dog and not a work of fiction makes it all the more intriguing. That these cultural values were so wonderfully exemplified by a breed that had already been declared a national art treasure must have pleased them greatly. That it was a breed famed for nobility and bravery was even more significant.

Understanding how all the pieces fit together, one can readily see that glorification of Hachi-ko not only was a quite natural thing to do, it was also a statement of values. This in no way diminishes the wonderful story of a dog's utter devotion to his master, but it may help us to understand why even in modern times, Hachi-ko and his statue have so much meaning for the Japanese people.

Japan is an old country and like most, it has tradition. In order to understand the Akita, it's helpful to understand how he came to be and what an important part of tradition he is in his country. Although we may feel that skinning a dog and preserving his pelt or having his body restored by a taxidermist is not to our liking, we must understand that this was the highest token of respect in Japan. And if giving a statue of an Akita is only a superstitious tradition still carried on today, think how foolish we Americans must appear with no thirteenth floor in our hotels!

I hope you now understand that the mystique which surrounds the Akita is not dependent on the image of an ancient, pure, and "untainted" breed. You know the old saying, "it's what's inside that counts." The beauty of the breed is the stuff that works of art are made of but there's a lot more to the Akita-inu than the length of his ears or the color of his coat.

To say that the Akita is not a pure breed is no insult to this great dog. Actually, it's the influence of opposing types which adds to his mystique. It's to his credit that he is a dog developed of different breeds. Isn't that why he's so good at so many tasks? He's a hunter which can be used on fur and feather. A courageous fighter, a loyal and capable guardian, yet he is at the same time, a tender, gentle, and innately sensitive companion. There are few breeds so skilled at serving man in so many varied and useful roles.

The Akita-inu was molded by necessity—and then carefully restored to completely reflect the values of an entire nation. The Akita-inu is indeed a gift from The Land of the Rising Sun, graciously accepted and deeply loved by America.

Today's Akita fancier owes much to the efforts of early breeders and importers who worked to restore and establish the breed for future generations. Puppies owned by Marge Rutherford.

The Early Years

IMPORTS

In post-war Japan, diligent efforts were underway to refine the breed, but dogs of European influence (including the St. Bernard and German Shepherd Dog) were occasionally bred from. Consequently, most early imports reflected the variation in type common to 1950's Japan.

Anxious to recapture the look of the indigenous dog and to quickly eradicate the foreign look, many Japanese breeders resorted to extreme measures. Although not revealed in written works, it's very likely one emergency method was interbreeding with the small native breeds. After all, what faster way to go backwards? There were several breeds, which being smaller to begin with, had not been used for dog fighting, and were therefore much less tainted with mastiff type. Additionally, those of the isolated mountain areas had been less affected by the influx of dogs during and immediately following the war.

The Shikoku (from southwestern Japan), the brindle Kai (from the mountains of Honshu), and the predominantly white Kishu, (from the mountains of Mie Prefecture) were all of a very natural occurring spitz-type. You may remember mention of a Kishu bitch used to mate with the brindle wolf. Such old, mostly pure native types surely were not overlooked in the restoration of the Akita-inu!

Even as the Dewa and Ichinoseki lines became dominant, other sub-types were common. Mr. Hiraizumi admitted that size was sacrificed for type and purity. As an example, he describes a strain about 25 inches tall, with prick ears, tightly curled tail, immense thick coat, full cheeks, and a very "Oriental" look, often to the point of appearing foxy. As luck would have it, he said many of this type were faulted for being frail and timid, not at all what breeders were hoping for in the courageous Akita-inu. What

would you guess happened to those dogs which exhibited good type but poor temperament? Right. Many were either destroyed or conveniently sold to unsuspecting foreigners. Traces of these shy but typy dogs persisted well into the 1970s in the U.S.

Struggling with a damaged economy and scarcity of food, Japanese owners seemed just as eager to part with Akitas of the large "foreign" type. Many are described as measuring 28 inches or more, with the loose skin, soft ears, and rather coarse appearance of the old Odate dog.

In the confusion of much rebuilding, all Japanese breeders did not yet have a clear mental picture of the finished product. Most Japanese began to agree that the largest native dog should look like the other relatively "unspoiled" dogs—the problem was how to get there. In the States, breeders were not as aware of or as concerned with restoring type; they just loved the Japanese treasures they had made off with, and they wanted everyone else to appreciate them!

Many present-day breeders take pride in tracing the origins of their line back to Japan, but it's usually a wasted exercise. Somewhere along the way, almost every dog or every kennel name which appeared on a Japanese pedigree has been referred to as "outstanding" by American pedigree buffs. The sad truth is that there was seldom any verification for such claims.

For example, one may hear of a female called Kumago, a black brindle owned by Mr. Watanabe, a prominent figure in the Akita breed. Sired by Ichinoseki out of a bitch called Aka, Kumago (or Kuma-Go) was presumed to be a good bitch and is behind some early imports, but there is no photographic evidence of her quality. What is one man's cup of tea may be another man's bitter brew. We must remember Mr. Hiraizumi's accounts of the depleted numbers of dogs which truly represented the pre-war national monument, and his admission that dogs which lacked in quality were of necessity, mated in an effort to replenish the breeding-base population.

This is not to say that there were not some very good dogs imported during those early years but for those who wonder why the Akita in Japan looks so different today, the answer becomes embarrassingly clear. The majority of early imports were brought back by returning servicemen who had no idea what the Akita was supposed to look like. To be really honest, even the average Japanese owner wasn't aware of the lofty goals of Akiho, Akikyo, or Nippo! As breeders in Japan became better directed, the dogs offered to Americans were mostly of a type breeders in Japan considered unsuitable and which they successfully bred away from.

To make matters worse, we were severely limited by a narrow genetic pool obtained over a 20-year span compared to the Japanese, who had many options available, and used them over a 40-year period. Further hampering efforts of the 1950s and '60s, most American owners were not breeders, and those who bred

Edita van der Lyn, Akita Tani's Kosho (by Shoyo Go x Haiire Kitsune) and Toto represent a fascinating bit of Akita history. Liz Harrell, who supplied the photo, tells us that Edita trained for the RAF in World War II, and she had Kosho already performing in her acts at less than a year old. Notice his friend, Toto, just one of several Dachshund Edita used in her act. The famous Kosho also appeared in a movie with Faye Dunaway and Anthony Quinn.

their beloved dogs did so with little understanding or regard for genetic principles or that elusive quality called "type." Conversely, Japanese breeders concentrated efforts in a direction which was increasingly clear to them, but which remained obscure to most Westerners, hence the noticeable differences today.

While the physical results differed, perhaps our direction was just as noble. Americans went to great lengths to bring the big dogs back simply because they loved them as dogs! Many had become adoptive masters while stationed in Japan, and they just couldn't bear to part with their buddies. And in truth, what better reason could a breed have had for its development?

The first Akita to be registered in the States is said to have been a large male named Taro, brought in by a military officer. He was placed with a family in Mountain Home, Arkansas, but due to his inconvenient location, he never produced pups which were registered. Leigh Simons brought back three bitches and a dog and the Hulls settled in Tucson with another pair which produced several litters. Ted Brinks, Director of the San Diego Humane Society, also owned a pair. On the east

Ichiban Shanpan (Tochifuji x Jimer's Hikari of Maru) owned by Nancy Hoeltje. She was the top winning bitch in 1964 and 1965 and the top winning Akita 1965 and 1966 under the Akita Club of America point system. Of lovely champagne color, she was renowned as an outstanding show dog. Feminine, yet she produced some of the biggest boned pups when bred to Koyamo's Kotaishi, as evidenced by her most famous son, the 28", 130 pound Ch. Kuma Ryoshi.

coast, Dr. Greenlees settled in New York state with a white female, but records of any progeny from most of these early animals have been obscured by time.

Most early importers are no longer active but some whose names will be familiar to pedigree buffs are the Shaffers from Nebraska and the O'Sheas from Pennsylvania. Ben Kam's son Walter is credited with having brought four puppies, three females and a male, to San Gabriel, California, said to have been purchased from a pet shop in Tokyo.

So it happened that in the U.S. the breed evolved more or less haphazardly and with the continued influence of other breeds or mongrels. This resulted in even more dilution of a type already adulterated by outcross stock in pre-war Japan. Denial doesn't fit logic. Just as we do not downplay the utilitarian beginnings of the breed, the dog fighting era, nor the significance of the war, we can not exclude the random genetic combinations which were the basis of the breed's development in America. Like it or not, we must accept that the result of this 25-year span of history was finally accepted into the official AKC stud book as purebred.

If this seems shocking, it shouldn't be. The Akita is not unique in his mixed-up past. The fact is, this sort of crossbreed mingling occurred at some point in many AKC-registered breeds. How each breed continues to develop has been largely dependent upon the direction set in the country of origin. Due

to international politics and the rather intolerant position of the American Kennel Club, such was not the case with the Akita-inu.

As you will learn, in order to achieve AKC recognition, Akita breeders gave up the right to import from the country of origin. Having closed the stud book, AKC remained steadfast in its refusal to recognize Akitas imported from Japan. Moreover, even those dogs which listed Japanese Kennel Club (JKC) registration numbers in a four-generation pedigree issued by a recognized registry were not eligible for AKC registration. Knowing these things, we can begin to understand how the Akita developed as two such different types within the same breed. Not until 1993 did AKC begin to accept imported JKC Akitas into its stud book.

Even more confusing for those trying to sort out the domestic past and how it relates to the appearance of the breed today, up until the late 1970s, Akitas were usually referred to as "east coast" and "west coast." These terms were used not only to reference the area of the country the dog or the line came from but to distinguish noticeable differences in type.

We must remember that the ordinary problems of being a "rare breed" were compounded by an entirely different transportation system of the 1950s. Dog owners were pretty much limited to motor-car travel; consequently, many unsuitable matings were made out of necessity. Ironically, American breeders found themselves in much the same limited situation as post-war Japanese breeders, but for different reasons. What is nothing more than a day's drive to us now, involved a week of un-air-conditioned auto travel over single-lane roads, often across great expanses of nothingness! Motor homes were practically unheard of. There were no giant motels at every interstate interchange—indeed, there were no interstates! Some determined owners traveled by train, but only the most wealthy and venturesome considered flying with their dogs in order to accomplish a breeding or to exhibit away from home.

Therefore, many breeding programs suffered due to unalterable limitations. While most breeders claimed to be engaged in efforts to "preserve the breed," much of what went on can be called nothing more than convenience breeding. Many litters were the result of inbred matings; i.e., the breeding together of closely related pairs. In some cases, the results were good but as could be expected, many such accidental or convenient matings proved disastrous. Worse yet, the progeny was usually sold as "breeding stock," which practice caused many unsatisfactory genetic combinations to prove unfailingly dominant in pedigrees of the 1960s and '70s.

It's best left to individual interpretation and AKC achievement records to sort out which of those early matings passed on a legacy of type, health, and soundness, and which genetic mishaps became the progenitors of problems that still haunt breeders of the 1990s.

Even though the Mid-west and the South began to be noted for exceptional quality, it was as though these parts of the country didn't exist when speaking about type. Right on into the early 1970s, it was common to hear people speak of the "big" west-coast dogs and the "small" east-coast dogs. Even closely related dogs which wound up on opposite coasts, produced type and size more common to their respective areas as they were mated with local stock. Gradually, the east-coast/west-coast differences became less apparent as air shipping came

Akita Tani's Kuromaya, whelped 2/68, a fifteen-month old youngster shown with a very young Pete Lagus.

Ch. Aitochi's Stinger of Sugar Run, whelped 11/75. Co-bred by Pat Flynn and Jean Fein, sired by Ch. Kazoku's Riki Maru of Okii Yubi, a half brother to Sachmo. Stinger's dam is Ch. Yubi No Okii Yubi, a littermate to Yukan No Okii Yubi, the sire of Ch. Okii Yubi's Dragon House Ko-Go, ROMXP. Stinger was rescued and briefly owned by the Andrews before being resold to the Tuckers.

within the financial grasp of most serious breeders, and families shifted from one coast to the other, bringing their beloved Akitas with them. After AKC recognition, Akitas traveled to more distant shows with professional handlers and some opportune matings were accomplished in this way.

By the close of the 1970s, one seldom heard a line referred to by its region. Truly, we had grown apart from the many odd similarities shared with our Japanese counterparts. We began to see and use dogs from thousands of miles away rather than limit ourselves to local dogs. The breed was becoming more uniform and lines were less likely to be considered "regional." It had taken Japan many decades and many generations to recognize the Odate Dog, the Matagi-inu, and other regional types as Akita-inu. It had taken the United States only 30 years to establish its own Akita and to recognize type irrespective of region.

Fortunately, there were some good dog people at the time who traveled to Japan and were aware of that which was considered truly representative of the national dog of Japan. Those people, many of whom were AKC-licensed judges, worked hard to preserve the type as represented in a few outstanding imports. Thankfully, the influence of these remarkable people and their dogs was not completely lost in American breeding programs. They deserve our gratitude for a Herculean effort, which received no support from the American Kennel Club.

The early differences of size and features of type were often linked to individual imports which settled in the respective areas. To enable us to sort out how those differences became established, it will be helpful to mention some of the Japanese dogs that were the basis for a few of the prominent foundation lines still to be found in pedigrees of the '90s.

EAST-COAST LINES

Some of the influential Japanese dogs behind east-coast lines were Jap. Gr. Ch. Tochihibiki-Go and Nisikigi-Go (which produced Shiroi O-Sama-Go) and Kita No O-Go and Kuroyuri-Go (which produced Aka-Goma-Joo-Go). These two pairs were the grandparents of Issei Riki Oji Go, a dominant sire for the O'Sheas of Hatboro, Pennsylvania.

Issei Riki Oji-Go was bred to Kuma's Akai Kosho-Go (by Krug's Santo ex Kogi-ko), a foundation bitch for Sam and Barbara Mullen. This mating produced Ch. Mitsu Kuma's O Kashihime-go, Mitsu Kuma's Splashdown (Sachmo's granddam) and the breed's first Group winner, Ch. Mitsu Kuma's Tora Oji-Go.

Issei Riki Oji-Go is a first generation Japanese-American breeding for Lillian O'Shea (Koehler). He won consistently in the Miscellaneous Class prior to AKC recognition.

The Mullens' New Jersey-based Mitsu Kuma kennels became well known for Akai's contributions. Another bitch from the Shiroi O-Sana-Go (alias White King-Go) ex Aka Goma Joo-Go breeding was Issei Yoko Hime Go, the dam of Ch. Mer Prince Suna Go, CD.

Another line which strongly represented the restoration movement in Japan was the Oshio line, which is still found only four generations back in a few pedigrees. Jap. Gr. Ch. Kumazakura-Go is the grandsire of the red Oshio's Mako-Go who sired the red pinto Ch. Oshio's Taisho-Go. Traces of Oshio (from Long Beach, CA) type are still to be found in a few old dogs such as Ch. Tschumi's Flash. Descending in yet another direction, Kumazakura-Go sired the west-coast Cripple Creek's Thor, grandsire of Ch. Kin Hozan's Toklat, CD and ROM.

Ch. Chaguma's Yokozuna Tenshu (Teddy Bear of Toyohashi-Seiko x Tochihanahime of Meyers) owned by Ben Nakagawa. He was a top winner of the Seventies but is best known as the sire of Ch. Kenjiko Royal Tenji, ROMPX.

A dog which was dominant for "Ichinoseiki type" when crossed with Oshio's Saiko Hime-Go (daughter of Oshio's Taisho and Oshio's Hoshi-Go) was Ch. Clar-Chid's Romio Fug Yama. His grandparents were the Akiho dogs, Dai-Un-O-Go and Banyome-Go. Fug Yama is behind the Tetsu Hito kennel of Phil Gray and perhaps best known as the grandsire of Phil's flashy Ch. To No Koichi, who in turn was the sire of the brindle ROM dam Ch. Alii's Storm Warning. Making an odd connection but one substantiated by type, Fug Yama is also the maternal great-grandsire of Ch. Tschumi's Flash.

The famous top producer, Am/Can/Ber. Ch. Kenjiko Royal Tenji is the grandson of Jap. Gr. Ch. Teddy Bear Of Toyohashi Seiko. Although Royal Tenji was an east-coast dog, his sire was Ch. Chaguma's Yokozuna Tenshu, a west-coast dog out of Tochihanahime of Myers. In fact, many of the old Frerose dogs are actually linebred on Teddy Bear.

The imports, Kusumaru Go and Takara-Hime Go, produced Miyamori's Kiyome Of Kin Hozan who, bred to Royal Tenji, produced Suzi Of Frerose.

For a brief time, the Azuma dogs were influential in several eastern and mid-western breeding programs. Azuma Muni Hiro was by Jap. Gr. Ch. Ko-Shann out of Jap.

Ch. Meiun-Hime. When bred to Mare Tenshi (by Jap. Gr. Ch. Kumo-Maru ex Jap. Ch. Kumo-Giku) Muni Hiro produced Kazoku's Koka No Hoseki. Mare Tenshi's full-brother Azuma Taro Maru was bred to a few early bitches and one notable descendent was Oshio's Miko Go.

The Kensha kennel name of the Shaffers was firmly established by their import Gyokushu Of Tojo Kensha, a fawn male called Taiho. Hazel Shaffer's big dog became the grandsire of Krug's Sotto and also of the great producing bitch, Michiko of Kensha, a foundation bitch for Okii Yubi kennels.

Bettye and Francis Krug were very prominent on the East Coast. Krug's Santo (by Gyokushu Of Tojo Kensha out of a bitch named Sheba) was behind many eastern lines, including the dominant Sakura dogs. Bettye made an inspired breeding with Krug's Michiko to Ch. Sakura's Bushi. From that litter emerged two excellent bitches, Ch. Krug's Koko and Ch. Krug's Ichiban Akemi-Go. Ichiban became the top winning Akita bitch preceding AKC recognition.

Barbara Miller's foundation sire for the Maryland-based Sakura kennels was Prince Jo, CD, sired by Krug's Santo. Bobbi's foundation bitch was Michiko of Kensha,

Sakura's Chujitsu, owned by Robert Campbell. Chujitsu is prominent in many old Okii Yubi pedigrees.

CD, bred by Renee and Hazel Shaffer. Before her death in October 1971, Michiko produced three litters. The first was sired by Prince Jo and contained two outstanding males, Sakura's Banjaku and Sakura's Bushi, who was number two Akita for 1970 and second in Miscellaneous Group ratings. Her second litter was by Krug's Santo, Prince Jo's sire, and a linebreeding as Santo's sire was Michiko's grandsire. The second litter produced two outstanding females: Sakura's Chujitsu (foundation female for Robert Campbell) and Sakura's Chie, top-placing bitch in 1969. Her third litter was also by Santo and contained Sakura's Dangan and Sakura's Donsu, who became dominant in west-coast lines.

By 1971, Barbara also held the distinction of having three generations of obedience-titled dogs! Although obedience was the only "class" in which Akitas could compete with AKC-registered breeds and many owners enjoyed showing off their "miscellaneous dogs" in this way, it was still a remarkable accomplishment. The first was Prince Jo, CD, followed by his son, Ch. Sakura's Bushi, CD, and his son,

Oyen's Muy Macho, a Krug-bred dog of the early seventies, owned by Rosemary Aigner of Long Island.

Rowdy San, (Jap. Gr. Ch. Teddy Bear x Jap. Gr. Ch. Haru Hime) a litter brother to Tom Cat, Kabuki, etc. Bred by Don and Barbara Confer, Rowdy was owned by Terry Arndt, Jade-Shogun Akitas.

Krug's Sachi, CD, owned by the Aigners in Long Island.

Although considered "west coast," Jap. Gr. Ch. Haru Hime is behind many east-coast pedigrees, including the Dawsonville, Georgia kennels of Robert Campbell. Haru Hime was bred to Sakusaku's Tanuki-Go, producing the red bitch Toyo-No Namesu-Joo, a foundation bitch for Okii Yubi. Bob shipped Namasu back to the West Coast to be bred to the mighty Ashibaya Kuma, and that mating produced Yukan No Okii Yubi, who sired Ch. Okii Yubi's Dragon House Ko-Go, an all-time top producing dam.

WEST-COAST LINES

On the West Coast, Goronishiki-Go and Fukuchiyo-Go produced Mex. Ch. Triple K Hayai Taka. He was bred to the daughter of Jap. Gr. Ch. Kinsho-Go, producing Triple K Miko, dam of the famous Ch. Fukumoto's Ashibaya Kuma.

Mex. Ch. and Jap. Reserve Ch. Sakurahime was not particularly influential but she did produce Nakkusu's Yukihikari, the granddam of Tomo Kuma No Kin Hozan, who in turn was the granddam of the legendary Ch. Okii Yubi's Sachmo Of Makoto.

The Confers' famous litter by Jap. Gr.

Ch. Teddy Bear Of Toyohashi Seiko, out of well-known Japanese import, Jap. Gr. Ch. Haru Hime, contained such notable Akitas as Ch. Sakusaku's Tom Cat-Go (sire of Ch. Gin Gin Haiyaku Go Of Sakusaku), Sakusaku's Tiger Lily (dam of Sakusaku's Lady Lil), Rowdy San (sire of Ch. Gaylee's O'Kaminaga), and Tusko's Star (dam of Ch. Wanchan's Akaguma).

Haru Hime was both the dam and granddam of Ch. Toyo-No Charlie Brown, a brindle male owned by Carol Foti. A popular winner, Charlie Brown sired several litters, but Haru Hime's influence was not greatly noted through that particular dog.

Walter and Camille Kam brought back several Akitas from Japan, thus founding the Triple K kennels, responsible for so many great Akitas. Camille's magnificent Mex. Ch. Triple K Hayai Taka was out of Goronishiki-Go and Fukuchiyo-Go. Hayai Taka's beautiful coat and overall balance came through strongly when he was bred to the lovely Mex. Ch. Triple K Shina Ningyo. Shina Ningyo was herself a daughter of Jap. Gr. Ch. Kinsho-Go, a son of Jap. Gr.

Ch. Imperial Fuji Hime (Kinsei Suna Nihon-No Taishi x Triple K Kiyomi) the first top winning female, owned by Ben Nakagawa.

Akita Tani's Shoyo-Go, (Jap. Ch. Kinsho Go x Akarui Kokoro) born in 1961, owned and bred by Liz Harrell. Shown in 1964 taking his first big win, he defeated thirty in the Miscellaneous Class under the famous judge (now deceased) Major Godsol, handled by Wade Chandler.

Ch. Kincho-Go Abe. When mated to Hayai Taka, Shina Ningyo produced Triple K Miko, the mother of Ashibaya Kuma.

Camille also produced the handsome brindle Ch. Triple K Shoyu-Go. He was sired by her Kanpuzan dog who was bred to Ch. Triple K Chiyo, a granddaughter of both Jap. Gr. Ch. Sakurahime and Hayai Taka.

It's interesting that the Akita Tani kennel's most famous sire, Akita Tani's Shoyo-Go, was also sired by Jap. Gr. Ch. Kinsho-Go, the sire of Shina Ningyo. Shoyo-Go was bred to two of his half-sisters by Kinsho Go: Akarui Kokoro and Haiiro Kitsume, both girls out of Gin Joo Go Of Triple K. Liz Harrell did several early foundation breedings such as Shoyo-Go bred back to his dam, Kokoro. As he was already the product of a father-daughter breeding, their litter produced the very inbred dog, Akita Tani's Tatsumaki, ROM.

This is but one example of how closely related many lines are which today have totally different "looks." The owners may have taken different routes to the city of their dreams but they all started out from the same neighborhood!

The top winning Akita, Ch. Fukumoto's Ashibaya Kuma, was empowered from both sides of his pedigree and he quite naturally went on to become a top producing sire. His sire was Mex. Ch. Kinsei Suna Nihon No Taishi, CD. This big dog was a grandson of Tochifuji (Jap. Gr. Ch. Tochihibiki ex Tamafuji) and Mex. Ch. Triple K. Shina Ningyo. Ashibaya Kuma's mother was Triple K Miko, daughter of Shina Ningyo.

Barbara and Mac McDougle, Gin Gin Akitas, produced a dog in their Los Angeles-area home which was destined to become famous on both coasts, Am/Can/Mex. CACIB Ch. Gin Gin Haiyaku-Go of Sakusaku, ROM. Sired by Tom Cat (Teddy Bear ex Haru Hime), the brindle dog (known to all as "Chester") enjoyed an outstanding show career, but became sterile at an early age. He was originally owned by Joan Linderman, who showed him for a while, then sold him, and amazingly, this great young dog was soon resold again to New York State, where he was brilliantly campaigned by Stephanie Rubenfeld (House Of Treasures) and Sara Kletter, most often handled by Fran Wasserman, Date Tensha kennels.

EIGHTEEN MISCELLANEOUS YEARS

The breed was admitted into the AKC Miscellaneous class on July 13, 1955 and was eligible to compete the following January. This spiked wider interest in the strange dog from a country many people knew little about and which some still thought of as the enemy.

At any given time prior to official AKC recognition in 1972, the right to represent and protect the Akita was likely to be claimed by several opposing clubs.

Beginning in the 1950s, there were strong organizational attempts by American Akita fanciers. The Akita Dog Association Of America was established in 1952 but was limited in scope and membership. Based in southern California, it was preempted by the more nationally oriented Akita Kennel Club, which was founded June 1956, as presided over by Janet L. Fisher.

The Akita Kennel Club Of America started with only 11 members and 30 dogs on its rolls—a small beginning, but one which was to ultimately serve the breed from coast to coast. The club had high ideals and, despite the normal bickering and arguing, Akita fanciers of

Ch. Kin Hozan's Tuff-Enuff of Kinouk (Ch. Fukumoto's Ashibaya Kuma, ROMXP x Kin Hozan's Shokin) one of the first all white champions, bred by Bea Hunt, owned by Joan Harper Young.

the early '50s were strongly united in their love for a breed which drew something akin to worship from true dog lovers.

The Akita Club Of America (ACA) was an outgrowth of the Akita Kennel Club Of America. In 1959 the word "Kennel" was dropped, along with some troublesome members and a few old-fashioned ideas, and The Akita Club Of America was born.

What is reported to be the first request to move the Akita into the Working Group was made in June of 1964, but the request was denied. We were told that there were too many clubs, too many differing opinions, and not nearly enough cooperation and cohesiveness between Akita breeders. A top AKC judge was widely quoted as having said, "Akita people are as feisty as their dogs." There are those who remember, shake their heads and re-quote that comment in the 1990s. It is a given that the breed attracts strong-willed people who are inclined to want to be dominant!

Nonetheless, these early clubs lent unity to breeding efforts and served as a communications vehicle. In 1972, The Akita Club Of America was finally named as the official AKC national breed club.

From the first Akita Specialty shows in South California in the early 1960s. AKC judge Rick Chashoudian inspects and awards his class winners. Photographs courtesy of Frank Thomas.

The early days of the Southern California Akita fancy. Some of the exhibitors are Marge Rutherford, Richard Beauchamp, Phil Padia, Ed Straighter and Bob Judd. Photographs courtesy of Frank Thomas.

Membership has fluctuated dramatically from a small nucleus of dedicated fanciers who "stuck it out," to nearly 600 members in the late 1970s, dropping to little more than 100 active members during tumultuous periods of the '80s, and as we embark into the '90s, ACA membership stands at about 300.

California was heavily influenced by people of Oriental descent and so it was only natural that many Japanese families gravitated to a dog so closely associated with their homeland. Many became actively involved in the breeding and exhibition of the Akita and naturally, they leaned towards the more exotic and Oriental-appearing dogs. Clubs sprang up which reflected the preferences of those who advocated the Japanese-style dog and they sponsored and promoted many educational projects.

One such promotion was the Nisei Week Akita Show. In August 1970, an evaluation meeting was held, complete with comments on the show, the state of the breed in the U.S., and a wonderful presentation of slides from the 58th Annual Headquarters Show in Japan. Dr. Hiraizumi provided comments and analysis of the Japanese winners, and after having the opportunity to judge our show, he also offered comments on the American dogs.

Mr. Hiraizumi was a very personable speaker, one whose knowledge of the Akita began in his early childhood. He was one of two active members of Akiho who had intimate knowledge of the Akita before World War II. His father was chairman of Akiho for 17 years, and Mr. Hiraizumi was a judge and an officer of Akiho for many years during the post-war period. In 1966, he had become the Head Judge of Akiho. Even with these impressive credentials, he informed the audience that had the slides been presented in Japan, he would not have been allowed to make a critical comment on the quality of the dogs!

As had been alluded to by Dr. Ogasawara, Mr. Hiraizumi declared Akitas in this country to be 20 years behind their relatives in Japan. He said that the winners of the Akita Show here displayed the basic type, but he intimated that they would not win at the big Headquarters Show. He pointed out that the Kongo line was strong in our dogs, mentioning again the generally sloppy facial traits of loose jowls, wrinkles, and round eyes. He said our coats lacked brilliance, clear, distinct color, and fullness. He wasn't overly impressed with the long, swayed backs and weak hindquarters either! He finished his assessment of our dogs by stating we had some serious tail problems. Hard-put to find something nice to say about American dogs, he settled for compliments about the size and bone but again mentioned that for proper balance, sturdy bone structure must be accompanied by a rich

Kuma Ryoshi at 5 months, weighing 70 pounds. Owner Terry Arndt called him "Snoopy."

Two legendary dogs from the late 60's and early 70's, Ch. Kuma Ryoshi and Rowdy San, owned by Terry Caudill-Arndt. Terry says, "I took this photo around 1970, never dreaming they would soon be enemies. No one then told buyers that males would eventually fight. It is one of my treasured pictures, at the time they were just friends."

coat of proper length. He explained that our coats were too short, especially the hair on the tail.

Regarding color, he felt there were not enough white Akitas but was happy to see the large number of red and brindle-colored dogs and relieved that there were not too many kurogoma-colored ones. He felt that the really rich and brilliant red color was lacking in our dogs and referred the disappointed owners to the slides of winners from the Headquarters Show. He advised breeders to work for better facial traits, stronger joints and hindquarters, and tighter tails, emphasizing that a tail which is not tightly wound denotes a dog lacking in strength and masculinity.

Mr. Hiraizumi said he judged by first impressions; that just as we judge people by their dress, speech, and general carriage, so a judge makes his decision on that first impression which is color and condition of coat. He said that is the first thing taken into consideration, and if those features are right, he would then continue with overall structure, followed by the finer details, such as the shape of eyes, ears, nose, and mouth. Even as he emphasized that color and coat are traits which are the most eye-catching and he admitted it was a major factor in selecting top winners, he reminded the audience that it was only one item in a long list of quality traits.

In closing, he reiterated that the three major faults in our dogs were coat (too short and lacking in color and condition), general weakness in bone structure (especially in joints and rear quarters), and poor tails. As an aside, he chastised owners for the poor muscle tone resulting from a lack of exercise.

During a question-and-answer session, Mr. Hiraizumi made many valuable statements. Because much of that session is still applicable, we will reprint some of his responses.

Asked about color breeding, i.e., breeding red with red to get excellent red, he said, "The concept of color breeding is good in theory, but is not so in practice. For some unknown reason, it was found that breeding two dogs of the same color did not produce the desired color. For example, breeding white with white did not produce a pure white."

Still curious about coat, someone asked, "What is the proper length?" to which he replied, "There is no specific length in terms of centimeters or inches. The overall appearance of the coat is of more importance than actual length. The coat of an Akita-inu comes in three layers. There is a wooly undercoat, a medium-length middle coat, and a coarse outer coat. If the coat is in proper condition there should be a general appearance of a bristled, yet soft quality or fluffiness. It is this fluffy quality which gives the coat its look of fullness and is not only desirable but also sought after. If, on the other hand, the wooly coat was not dense

Parnassus Meiyo of Akita Tani, bred and owned by Akita Tani Kennels. Pictured at seven years of age, going First at the Chicago International Show handled by Rusty Cunningham Short. Meiyo, a daughter of Japanese Ch. Teruhide, was the top Akita bitch for four years and was BOS at several specialties.

enough, then the outer coat would not stand nor bristle in the desired manner."

Responding to a question about size, Mr. Hiraizumi said, "As in the length of coat, actual size in terms of measurement is not considered, for measurement will reveal little differences in size. The important point to be taken into consideration lies in bone structure. A small-boned dog will give an impression of being weaker and smaller compared to a large boned dog." On the same subject, he also stated, "In the beginning (dog fighting era), the Akitas were large, and size was sacrificed in order to improve its quality. The small size detracts from the basic qualities which have been refined and emphasis is now being placed towards producing a sturdier dog. In answer to your question, yes, the trend will probably swing not so much towards a larger dog, but towards a sturdier one."

Due to so many references to the shortcomings of Kongo and the kurogoma coloring being undesirable, Mr. Hiraizumi once again explained, "Dogs of the kurogoma coloring which began with Kongo are generally found to display the undesirable traits of loose skin, wrinkles, and poor coat condition as depicted in Kongo. In contrast, dogs with the brindle coloring generally have tighter skin, a good coat condition, and a better overall structure."

When asked about the effect of climate on coat length, he pointed out that many parts of Japan are much hotter than in the States and reminded them that many of the good-coated dogs he had shown slides of were from those areas. He explained that one reason some dogs appear to have a short coat is that it lies flat on the body and he felt this was tied in with too rich a diet. For those who were still uptight about coat length, probably due to the longcoats, which were just as common back then, he elaborated with the following: "When speaking of the length of coat, appearance rather than the measured length is taken into consideration. A coat that has a bristled, full or fluffy, and hence 'long' appearance being desirable."

As could be expected, some people wanted him to obtain dogs for them but they were told that in his position as Head Judge of Akiho, he could not do that. Indeed, upon the death of his own dog, Mr. Hiraizumi was unable to obtain another dog for fear of being thought to endorse a particular dog or line. He did offer to help devise a method for importing dogs for he was anxious to see American breeders make progress.

The show was judged the following year by Mr. Zenzo Watanabe, considered one of the three most qualified judges in Japan at the time, and the Assistant Head Judge of Akiho.

He too brought slides of Meiyosho award winners and discussed the relative merits of the dogs. For those new to the post-show meeting, he explained that the Meiyosho award is the highest award which can be attained by an Akita in Japan. Under their system of Branch, Regional (both with entries of 70–250), and Headquarters Shows (with 100 entries), the Meiyosho award could only be given at Headquarters-sponsored shows. Some shows gave out none, for it was not an automatic win. From among the Tokuyu or Superior dogs, "the Akita is judged according to an absolute standard" and therefore, the Meiyosho winner may be considered the Grand Champions of Akiho Shows.

Discussing the phases of the Akita, he said the winners of 1970 were built more slightly than those of 1960, but, although they were smaller in stature, they were more tightly built and better balanced. He explained that in the first 20 years, the dogs were huge because that's what was wanted. He said that they became increasingly sloppy and so it was that after the first 20 years, the pendulum swung in the other direction.

He said those small dogs were very typy and very balanced and that this trend continued for about five years, but that the trend had again reversed itself and currently the dogs were once again increasing in size and substance. But, said Mr. Watanabe, breeders were guarding against regressing

"Tad," a brother of Kuma Ryoshi, pictured with breeder Laura Brown. Photo taken by Terry Arndt at the Japanese Cherry Blossom Festival in San Francisco circa 1972.

to the old type of Akita while at the same time, they were remaining "very aware of the necessity to produce large, good quality Akitas. It is easy to produce a small Akita with the qualities. However, to produce an Akita in the largest size and to maintain the quality that the smaller dogs have is not easy."

It is indeed much easier to produce a smaller sound dog in any of the large breeds. Mr. Watanabe knew and took for granted that his listeners knew certain things as well. What is equally interesting is that not once does he seem to have made much ado about what we call soundness. He repeatedly mentions balance, and he praises certain dogs for their muscular development, but soundness, as we know it in the American show ring, was not considered. We should state that in Japan, the dogs are not gaited and judged on movement as is the practice here.

The audience must have thought he was joking when he told them that there was only one type in Japan! He said, "They do not breed to perpetuate a single type. Therefore, they are more or less a uniform breed today." In a country which was yet to develop so much as an identifiable "line," Japan's accomplishment must have sounded miraculous!

Mr. Watanabe reiterated Mr. Hiraizumi's comments regarding the links between coat color and certain features of type but said, "However, as a practice, we do not try to perpetuate a single color or qualities and breed for that purpose." Pressed more on the subject, he responded, "The brindle-colored Akita in Japan is one of the oldest colors. I am at a loss to explain why brindle dogs produce better structural qualities. But somehow they have produced better structured and well-balanced Akitas." He ended the subject by stating that of the 37 Meiyosho winners listed in the book, eight were brindles.

Made aware that many people were not showing their larger sized dogs, Mr. Watanabe warned against losing the Akita standard by having two distinct types of Akitas, the large-sized local type and the more slender or trimmer import type. Little did he know that the AKC would take steps to ensure this did not happen.

He mentioned that ears were not properly shaped and facial features were not desirable; that the quality and condition of the coat had improved but the color of the brindles and whites was only fair. It was felt that Tani-rei of Oshio kennels had the best red tones.

He added that overall our dogs lacked the spirit needed for the show ring. He explained, "An Akita of good character should not be aggressive towards other dogs in the ring. Yet, if challenged, he should have the courage to meet or face his opponent. In the ring, he should stand erect with his tail tightly wound giving an impression of alertness and pride." He insisted, "To sit or to look from left to right is to display disinterest and a lack of pride." It is worth noting, however, that American dogs are carefully trained not to challenge in the ring and shifting the gaze may have been a way of avoiding a confrontation which they knew their owners would not want. As sitting does demonstrate submissiveness, this may have been deliberate on the part of dogs who wanted to be "good dogs" under the American system of judging.

Making allowances for the different styles of exhibition does not mean we should forgive the lack of character to which Mr. Watanabe referred. There have always been those who would forgive a hanging tail and in fact, there are people today who should know better and yet they insist that "as long as the tail goes up when the dog moves, it's O.K." Mr. Watanabe would be shocked by such a statement made in his presence!

Before closing this pertinent part of history, we would like to share Mr. Watanabe's description of the eight factors which are necessary requirements under the standard. He said the first and foremost is proper height. Then, size or weight in relation to that height, followed by structure and balance. Next is the quality of structure (looseness or tightness of skin), followed by color, quality of coat, spirit or character, and finally, health.

History can be better viewed from a distance and there is much to be gained from the foregoing talks. I've presented the information in the appropriate time frame of the breed's development because so much of what the Japanese judges said is no less applicable today. Even so, we must not let Mr. Hiraizumi, Mr. Watanabe, or any of the Japanese scholars become our gurus. We are entitled to independent thought and to have developed our own "fads" and concepts.

THE WAR CONTINUED

Demonstrating loyalty to Japanese type as evidenced by scattered groups, many owners continued to import and breed from imported stock. Most clubs were actively seeking AKC acceptance for the breed but by the close of 1971, two things had become very clear: The American Kennel Club was adamantly opposed to the continued importation of Japanese Akitas and to the use of import type in breeding programs!

In a letter dated November 8, 1971, Bobbi Miller wrote to Joe Vogl, then president of ACA. In this letter, Bobbi related a conversation between Mr. and Mrs. Jones, AKC judges and owners of an Akita, and John Brownell of AKC. Bobbi said the conversation indicated that "AKC does not like the trend to smaller, lighter boned Akitas and the AKC would prefer that U.S. fanciers not breed to or from Japanese imports as the Japanese themselves have told the AKC that Japanese pedigrees leave much to be desired."

Ch. Shogun's Keiko Kuma of Jade, (Ch. Kuma Ryoshi x Keiko) bred by Margaret Hannigan, owned by Jade-Shogun Akitas.

(While the Japanese may have admitted that the breed was not exactly "pure," once again history affords us a better overall perspective and casts suspicion on the reasoning of the American Kennel Club. The Akita, among many others, had been refined long enough to have been considered pure, especially when compared to many other breeds eagerly accepted some 20 years later!)

Ms. Miller writes, "Mr. Brownell wondered if there was enough American bloodlines available to stop all breedings to and from imports. *They will not recognize us while we continue to breed to and from imports."* Bobbi says that Mrs. Jones asked whether or not the ACA knew of the American Kennel Club's position on this matter.

This information was cause for much discussion and debate. You can imagine the soul-searching which went on among breed purists who wanted to preserve and develop the "Japanese Akita," the name then used by everyone. Another thorn in AKC's touchy side. No one thought any more about the name than calling an English Springer Spaniel or Portuguese Water Dog by their right name. Obviously, AKC thought about it. A lot.

People continued to import but by January of 1972 there was an across-the-board admission that what breeders were getting from Japan was not "show quality" and in many cases was not at all typical of dogs which were winning in Japan. Breeders in the States felt caught in a squeeze. We were told that our Akitas were not nearly as good as those in Japan, yet we seemed unable to get those "good ones" to the States. We were told to breed better ones but the best we had was often frowned upon by AKC judges when presented to them in rare breed shows and fun matches. Most fanciers wanted to be able to compete in AKC shows and have "AKC-registered" litters. People muttered that we were just spinning our wheels, getting nowhere with AKC, and being ripped off by Japan. Others disagreed and supporters of the breed became split as "the battle" heated up.

In an open letter, Gus Bell, Matsu Kaze Akitas and also Chairman of the Standards Committee, made the following observations: "If you receive the ACA newsletter you probably have noted in the past two issues that the proponents of the imports appear to have taken over that publication and I now feel that it is time to take issue with them and take the question to the general membership and to the membership of the various chapters. Let's face it, we all have or should have one aim in common and that is to get the Akita recognized by the American Kennel Club."

Gus relates a conversation he had with three AKC-licensed judges in which they agreed that the only possible way they see to get the Akita recognized is to "perhaps change the name of the breed to *American*

do it now before the Akita is relegated to another 16 years in the Miscellaneous class."

Sam Mullen of New Jersey hit the nail on the head when he said that Mr. Brownell (of AKC) felt that in light of AKC's refusal to recognize any registering agency in Asia, the chances of the Akita's gaining AKC recognition were reduced. They should have left it at that, but Mr. Brownell confused the issue even more by indicating that the AKC might consider accepting a Japanese registry such as Akiho, if that registry could meet AKC's requirements. Of course, we know that AKC did not recognized Akiho, Akikyo, Nippo, or even the Japanese Kennel

Ashibaya Kuma son, Ch. Kin Hozan's Tuff-Enuff of Kinouk. This exceptional dog was an early sire for the Kinouk Akitas of Joan Harper Young.

Akita." Gus says he had heard this from other judges and suggested one solution might be a tightened breed standard. Gus was losing patience as indicated by his comment, "We will be open to all suggestions from all parties who wish to submit their ideas to us but we will not be railroaded into accepting the Japanese standard as some wish us to do. I feel that we have to do something about the import question and

Club until 1993! One has to wonder if Mr. Brownell actually believed AKC would someday recognize the Japanese registry or if he was just throwing Sam another red herring.

As Gus had done, Mr. Mullen stressed AKC's concern about the size and type of imports from Japan. He indicated that officers and board members of AKC preferred the larger, heavier boned Akitas which were

Ch. Okii Yubi's Dragon House Ko-Go, ROMXP. (Yukan No Okii Yubi x Ko-Tori No Okii Yubi) #2 Bitch, #3 Akita 1979, brought out of retirement for eleven shows, handled by Ed Finnegan, for owner Barbara Andrews.

might have eliminated some of the obvious mongrels, but for some reason, it was not done.

Mr. Brownell inquired again whether there was enough foundation breeding stock in the States to allow continued development of the Akita if the AKC were to accept the breed and cut off any more imports. He was assured that there would be enough breeding stock. Mr. Brownell suggested that an immediate step toward recognition would be to write a new breed standard and submit that to AKC. He said the present standard was vague and that AKC was trying to have all standards made more concise and follow certain formulas.

By the spring of 1972, Mr. Brownell was still trying to clarify AKC's position on imports and whether or not closing the stud

common when the breed was first admitted to the Miscellaneous class. He reports that Joe Vogl, "president of the Akita Club Of America, stated that we are very aware of this problem and are trying to reduce it by now only accepting imports with Akiho or Akikyo registrations." He went on to say that this meant accepting some smaller size Akitas but felt that in so doing, breeders were giving proper attention to ear set, tail length and other problems.

He reports that Mr. Brownell suggested AKC might require two ILP (Indefinite Listing Privilege)-type photographs to be submitted in order to eliminate some of the really bad import types. He said the photographs could then be screened by an impartial body and registration could be denied on an individual basis if the reviewing body felt that the animal should not be included as foundation breeding stock. This

Ch. Kinouk's Flower Child (Ch. Okii Yubi's Sachmo of Makoto, ROMXP x Ch. Kinouk's Kori, ROM) bred by Pat Mucher and Joan Harper Young, owned by Joan Young. "Flower" is pictured winning from puppy class.

books to further imports was in reality a condition for breed acceptance into the AKC stud book. We can be sure his position was a difficult one! He had to get the parent club (ACA) to convince its members to agree to something which, on the surface, AKC couldn't or wouldn't require! The undercurrent of animosity between the AKC and the Japanese registries (country?) was not something which could be overtly discussed.

Mutterings of a rift in the club over the continued use and importation of Japanese Akitas grew louder. It was pointed out that the timing would be disastrous and any more in-fighting would have devastating effects on the ACA's status with AKC. After so many tumultuous years, the ACA had become an acceptable commodity for AKC and those in the know were quite worried that something would upset the delicate balance of the tenuous relationship. It was acknowledged that the Eastern Akita Club and the Midwest Akita Club would have to be dissolved in order to achieve AKC recognition. As with any "new" breed, there had been a long-standing struggle between various clubs, all of them wanting to be *the* national parent club. AKC wanted Akita people and their clubs to demonstrate harmony; 18 years of fighting and bickering had to end.

So, Akita people were given a recipe for recognition and to their credit, they followed the instructions of AKC. Whether giving up the right to import and other such concessions were ultimately beneficial is a question which will be long debated among the old-timers in the breed.

In June 1972, the Akita community felt that they had lost a good friend when it was reported that Mr. Brownell had retired from AKC. He was replaced by Mr. James Noland, Administrative Assistant. In a complete about-face, Mr. Noland suggested that area clubs would be most beneficial to the breed and would be looked at by AKC as a positive for eventual breed acceptance. Based on this information it was decided not to dissolve the strong regional clubs as had previously been discussed with the idea of leaving the Akita Club Of America as the single parent breed club.

June 1972 also heralded the announcement that imported dogs which had not been registered with Akiho or Akikyo before leaving Japan should be registered with one of those associations before September 1st so that they could subsequently be registered by the Akita Club Of America. Those who heard the advice thought about it and some people went to a lot of trouble to follow it. Unfortunately, not everyone heard and not everyone heeded the pronouncement. Many people didn't understand the significance and most had no idea of what was about to happen....

By August, many of the obstacles to AKC recognition had been resolved. Two which remained were the height disqualification in the proposed standard and the matter of continuing to import or breed import-type Akitas.

The height disqualification as it was proposed to the membership was $25\frac{1}{2}$ inches for males, $23\frac{1}{2}$ inches for bitches. Many members opposed these requirements, insisting on a lower height. Conversely, others felt that a higher minimum requirement would weed out Akitas which, in a quote attributed to AKC's Mr. Brownell, were "too small, fine-boned, or foxy-faced." Those with the bigger, old-style Akita enthusiastically agreed with Mr. Brownell.

Not so pleased were those who subscribed to the more recent changes in Japan and who consequently had smaller, more refined dogs. They were outraged. They loudly protested that $25\frac{1}{2}$ inches was too tall and it would be a shame to have to disqualify an otherwise beautiful dog who did not measure to the wicket. The war heated up again.

The other major problem was, of course, where breeders stood on the matter of importing. In a letter to Mr. William Stifel, Executive Secretary of the American Kennel Club, dated August 10, 1972, Joe Vogl, president of the Akita Club Of America said in part:

Sabaku Kaze's Dragon House Kami (Ch. Krug's Daiyusei x Fukumoto's Sanko Hinata) taking her first points at ten months of age under beloved "all-rounder" Mr. Phil Marsh. Bred by Betty and Walter Yelverton, Kami was the author's first Akita. Although competitive for her time, she was never used in the O'BJ breeding program.

"However, Mr. Brownell indicated to us during his visit that a change in ACA policy on imports would not affect recognition. He pointed out that the AKC would make a decision on imports at the time of recognition. To say that despite their differences, our members would support such a decision, they voted 244 to 33 in favor of the following resolution in our annual election in June.

The ACA will accept the AKC's offer to decide the import question."

Well! That removed one obstacle and the breed took another giant step toward recognition. The problems with the height disqualification remained, with a large number of respondents to the proposed standard suggesting heights of 26 inches to 28 inches for dogs, 24 inches to 26 inches for bitches and others standing by the 25½ inch; 23½ inches disqualification mark.

A referendum had been mailed to the membership, and 266 responses were received. The revised and refined standard had then been once again mailed to the membership on July 1 for a final vote. Out of 550 ballots mailed, 299 were cast with 181 voting to accept the standard and 100 votes rejecting it. Sixty-one members wrote on their ballot that they objected to the 25½

inch height disqualification. Some wanted it lowered to 25 inches, some suggested eliminating it altogether. In spite of the continued disagreements about size, hopes were still high that AKC would choose in favor of the ACA at their September meeting.

With bated breath, the fancy waited. Finally, the word came down from Mr. Stifel that there were only "procedural problems" still standing in the way. So, once again, hopes were raised that the Akita would be recognized in 1973.

In the meantime, owners stepped up the competition in Miscellaneous class. Support for this class had been mixed. Entry fees were steep and people felt cheated that they should pay so much but win no points towards a championship title. Others argued that it was the best way to acquaint the public with the breed. Others said "not so," just walking one's dog down the street was the best way for one would surely attract a crowd of interested and curious admirers.

Off the record, word was passed that if AKC was ever going to grant recognition, it would only be to a breed which was shown in big numbers in the AKC class, not non-sanctioned matches and rare breed shows. Everyone was encouraged to participate in the Miscellaneous class.

And what the heck, it was fun. Competition was great and Akita owners were becoming pretty accomplished in the ring and finding they loved the challenge. They also loved the ratings systems—and there were plenty of those!

The first formal Akita match had been held in 1960 in Van Nuys, California. Match show judges are not always competent. They were usually drawn from people aspiring to judge or friends of the local club officer, especially at a time when transportation costs were often prohibitive. Such was *not* the case at the first Akita match. The judge was the famous terrier man Rick Chashoudian, who drew a huge entry of 23 Akitas. Rick had become familiar with the breed while on duty in Japan and although he went on to become a world-famous breeder and professional handler specializ-

Ch. Kin Hozan Joi of Shijo (Ch. Fukumoto's Ashibaya Kuma x Ch. Cripple Creek's Kotei Shinju) bred by Bea Hunt and owned by Janice Scheibe. Joi went Best of Breed at the Chicago International Show, March 1975, defeating thirty seven Akitas, including ten Champions and two Group placers under esteemed Judge Peter Knoop. The puppy was handled by Barbara Andrews as a last minute favor to the owners whose handler didn't show up!

Juho Mariko No Kin Hozan, ROMP (Miyamoto Mushashi No Kin Hozan x Tomo Kuma No Kin Hozan) pictured at 8 years, handled by Ed Finnegan for a new owner who made a valiant attempt to finish her Championship. Alas, she had been poorly used by previous owners and fell short of her title by three points. She is the dam of Ch. Okii Yubi's Sachmo of Makoto, ROMXP.

ing in Fox Terriers (and is now an AKC-licensed judge), he never lost his appreciation and keen eye for the Akita.

By 1972, match-show entries had grown to nearly 90 in California and eastern and mid-west entries weren't far behind. Overall, the best dogs usually won, but as has always been so, judges unfamiliar with the breed—most fit that category back then—relied on basic principles of soundness. Thus there continued to be a great variety of "type" awarded and everyone remained a bit confused about the whole issue of what a proper Akita should look like.

Still, it's interesting to see who was doing what in those years just prior to AKC acceptance. *Popular Dogs Magazine* published a

Miscellaneous Group rating system in 1970. The list ranks Akitas against the other breeds shown in Miscellaneous, as well as the top standings for Akitas only. The Miscellaneous Group ratings were led by the Akita, with Fukumoto's Ashibaya Kuma in first place, followed by Sakura's Bushi and Krug's KoKo, a female. Fourth was a Soft Coated Wheaten Terrier and then fifth, sixth, seventh and eighth place rankings were held by Akitas, with Tibetan Terriers filling out ninth and tenth place in the national rankings.

Akita breed standings for 1970, based on wins in the Miscellaneous class under the Popular Dogs Rothman System, picked up with fifth place, Yoki Na Tora (female), Krug's Sachi, Akita Tani's Kamikaze, Triple K Tomo Go, Imperial Fuji Hime (female), and in the tenth spot, Krug's Atari.

By the next year, west-coast stars Triple K Tomo Go, Fukumoto's Ashibaya Kuma, and Imperial Ginzan were competing with bitches such as Imperial Fuji Hime in specialty matches and still holding their own in Miscellaneous. East-coast classes saw dogs such as the Sakura boys, Banjaku and Bushi, as well as Akita Tani's Yoro Kobi No Moto, and Krug's Sachi competing with the Tibetan Terrier and Soft Coated Wheaten but finding real tough going against Akita bitches such as Krug's KoKo.

One will occasionally see confusing terms after the names of Akitas being shown during the early '70s. The "Dan" titles originated from a program that began in January 1969 and patterned after the Japanese system. To be eligible, membership was required in the Akita Club Of America. There were elaborate trophies presented for each step of accomplishment, beginning with three first place wins in a competition of seven or more Akitas of the same sex at any AKC-licensed show.

Winning three firsts obtained the title of Sho-Dan, six first-place wins earned the title Ni-Dan. Nine firsts advanced the dog to San-Dan, 12 to Yon-Dan, and 15 first-place wins earned the dog the rank and title of Go-Dan. The beautiful Takuetsu trophies were designed and built by Pete Lagus and the

Ch. Akita Tani's Mitsu going Best of Winners under Judge Robert Wills in January, 1975. The Kuro Chikara daughter is handled by Stephanie Gimble, who passed away in 1990. Stephanie was one of the founders of Akita Rescue Society of America.

prestigious title and trophies inspired many owners to get their dogs out to AKC shows where they could be admired by the general public.

The final standings for 1971, as compiled by Barbara Miller, saw a lead change and the following order: Triple K Tomo Go (owner, De Polo), Fukumoto's Ashibaya Kuma (Hunt), Krug's Sachi (Aigner), Akita Tani's Kuro Chikara (Harrell), Akita Tani's Yoro Kobi No Moto, CD (Hansen), Imperial Fuji Hime (Nakagawa), Akita Tani's Shokin (Steeves), Tsuna's Momo Kaikwaki (Roper) tied with Tusko's Star (Lagus), Akita Tani's Kokishen (Steeves) tied with Tomo Kuma No Kin Hozan (Dunn), Mitsu Kuma's Splashdown (Hunt) tied with Triple K Cho Cho (Hoskins & Kam).

The 1971 Akita Club Of America high-point winners were Triple K Tomo Go, Krug's Ichiban Akemi-Go (Krug), Mex. Ch. Fukumoto's Ashibaya Kuma, Akita Tani's Akai (Cunningham), Akita Tani's Kuro Chikara, Krug's Sachi, Tusko's Kabuki (Lagus), Issei Yoko Hime Go (Merschen),

Mer Prince Suna Go (Fallon) and Yuko Of Brenrick (McKenzie).

Out West, Ch. Triple K Tomo Go, owned and shown by Ted DePolo of Toshiro Akitas, was having great success. Following his BOB win at the ACA fall specialty show in October 1971, he received his Ni-dan ranking. Ashibaya Kuma was seven times BIS at Akita specialties between 1968 and 1971 and, still holding fast as one of the top Akitas in the country, he was the highest ranking Akita in the United States as of mid-1972 and was then the only Akita to have achieved the Go-Dan award.

Like all systems, there were some discrepancies in the final tallies, depending on the method used. Nonetheless, these lists provide a pretty accurate look at the top dogs of pre-recognition time. Most of them went on to easily attain their champion titles after recognition.

There were several active clubs by 1970. The Midwest Akita Club located in Illinois; Akitas of San Diego based in Chula Vista, California; and the Royal Akita Club, also in California.

The most notable east-coast club of the early 1970s was the Eastern Akita Club with Bettye Krug as president, followed by Sam Mullen and Lou Fallon. The club was often at odds with other clubs and although there was much discussion about continuing on after the Akita Club Of America was decreed to be the only national breed club, the regional club was wisely disbanded.

It's amazing when one stops now to

Ch. Akita Tani's Nishiki Ryu, a son of Akita Tani's Chikara x a Shoyo-Go daughter going Best of Winners (BOW) under Judge Edward Bracy.

consider that as late as 1971 many clubs published lists of people desperate to purchase an Akita! The ACA actually mailed out names and addresses of people who were having problems finding a breeder. Although the ACA still maintains a breeder referral service, it's to advertise breeders, not the other way around. Most buyers can find a dozen litters within easy driving distance. Sadly, the ACA and most regional clubs must now also list the addresses of Akita rescue services!

With the near-certainty of AKC recognition just around the bend, new Akita clubs were springing up like mushrooms. By then the list had grown to include the New England Connecticut Valley Akita Club, the Raritan River Akita Club, Great Lakes Akita Club, Missouri Valley Akita Club, Royal Akita Club, Squakheag Akita Club, Akita Club of the Delaware Valley; and Akita Club of Greater Los Angeles.

Yes indeed, the Akita breed was off and running!

THE STUD BOOK

On October 16, 1972, a letter was received by the Akita Club Of America, signed by William F. Stifel, Executive Secretary, the American Kennel Club. The letter advised ACA President Dr. Vogl, "at its meeting last week, our Board of Directors accepted the following recommendation: that the AKC Stud Book be opened to the Akita effective November 1, 1972 and that the breed be removed from the Miscellaneous class and be given show classification in the Working Group as of April 4, 1973."

The letter went on to state that the AKC Board "agreed to approve the breed standard as submitted by ACA" but stipulated one obvious change. It said that under "Size," the disqualification would read: "dogs under 25 inches; bitches under 23 inches." Thus the half inch controversy was taken out of the hands of the parent club and the breeders. No one really cared about that half inch by then— we were "recognized"!

Mr. Stifel's letter also addressed the question of imports by succinctly stating, "AKC does not register any dogs on the basis of Japanese pedigrees at this time, but our Board would be willing to authorize us to register Akitas imported from Japan under policies that conform to your club's present policies—that is, that we recognize pedigrees from Akiho and Akikyo—but only as long as the American Kennel

Akita Tani's Kuro Chikara, ROM (Akita Tani's Toyo Koshaku x Shinju) otherwise known as "Black Power", at two years. Owned and bred by Liz Harrell, he was the first Best of Breed winner at Westminster Kennel Club.

Club stud book is open for the registration of foundation stock. Thereafter, the only imports that would be eligible for AKC registration would be those that met regular American Kennel Club policies applying to imported dogs whelped outside the U.S.A."

And so it was that the Akita was offered a place on the list of AKC-registered purebred dogs. The stipulation made by Bill Stifel was pretty clear, especially when viewed with that famous 20-20 hindsight. What he said was that the AKC would accept those dogs deemed purebred and registered by the parent club (ACA) but not for long, folks.... and that furthermore, once the stud book was closed, it would remain closed to any dogs registered and brought over from Japan for indeed that was "regular American Kennel Club policy" at the time.

Dogs brought over from European countries could be easily registered when accompanied by their proper certificate of pedigree, so some breeders just assumed all would carry on as usual with the Akita, meaning Japanese imports could still continue to be registerable if first registered in another country. A sad assumption for many heedless breeders.

An open letter to Akita owners dated November 1, 1972 was sent out by Joseph L. Vogl, ACA president. He advised owners that the breed had been recognized by the AKC and outlined the procedure for registering individual dogs. In a very generous move, members were told that the Akita Club Of America would pay for each dog's registration fee with the AKC.

Mr. Vogl also pointed out, "as one of its recognition terms, the AKC has placed the responsibility on the ACA of tracking down all owners of registerable Akitas. Thus, if you know an Akita owner who is not a member of the ACA or one of its chapters, ask them to request registration applications using a standard postcard."

Okii Yubi's Jitsu (Yukan No Okii Yubi, ROMP x Ko-Tori of Okii Yubi) was full litter sister to Ch. Okii Yubi's Dragon House Ko-Go, #1 Akita Dam. Bred by Robert Campbell.

Given this unorthodox approach, it's no wonder that some dogs that were distinctly not purebred managed to be registered with ACA, and subsequently by the AKC. Conversely, there were dogs which were Japanese champions, duly registered with JKC or Akiho, which were never registered with the Akita Club, thus were ineligible for AKC enrollment.

Some owners swore that they sent in applications to register their Japanese dogs. Assuming all was well, it was not until after the stud book closed and they failed to receive the eagerly awaited AKC registration certificate that they learned their applications had been lost. Since their dogs had never been registered with the Akita Club Of America, they were therefore forever ineligible for registration with the American Kennel Club. It was devastating for owners who had trusted a shaky system, only to lose out in the end. There was no recourse.

Thus it was that the process of registering foundation stock in this country was accomplished. Kay Greisen, ACA Registration Committee chairperson, worked eight hours a day, seven days a week, to straighten out the ACA stud book and handle the flood of paperwork. In November 1972, she and Eric processed a total of 616 applications, accepting 440, returning 144 for correction and rejecting 32.

Competition in the regular classes was scheduled to begin on April 4, 1973. The final word on imported stock was contained in the President's message, which warned, "registration of imports from Akiho and Akikyo to continue only as long as the stud book is open for registration of foundation stock." Those few short months were hardly long enough to satisfy many breed purists!

A lot of ups and downs, some people felt left out, some pretty poor examples of the breed were recorded in the stud book; but when it was all said and done, Joe Vogl and the many hard-working people of the Akita fancy had much to celebrate. An 18-year struggle for recognition had been achieved and the future was bright indeed!

AKC—AT LAST!

The Akita had become eligible for competition in the regular classes and was assigned to the Working Group classification. Believe it or not, there were those who feared the breed would be forced to compete in the Non-Sporting Group, sort of a catch-all classification for breeds which don't fit neatly into any of the other established groups. These fears were well founded for in some countries, the Akita does compete in the same ring as the Poodle and the Bulldog!

The first show held following AKC recognition of the Akita was Silver State Kennel Club, Las Vegas, Nevada, April 8, 1973. The judge was Mrs. Winifred Heckman, who judged 39 Akitas ranging from backyard pets brought to swell the entry, to some of the most outstanding dogs of that time.

With 18 dogs competing, Winners Dog (WD) for a five point major was none other than Triple K Tomo Go owned by Ted DePolo. Reserve Winners Dog (RWD) was Hozan of Matsu Kaze owned by Dewitt and Bell. Gin Gin Haiyaku Go of Sakusaku, then owned by Joan Linderman, won the novice class, defeating Chaguma's Yokozuna Tenshu, owned by Ben Nakagawa.

Another name familiar to Akita fanciers is Wanchan's Akagumo, the listed owner is Goldsby. He placed fourth in American-bred, the class being won by Triple K Sake, owned by Kam and Jung. Fukumoto's Ashibaya Kuma owned by Bea Hunt was third in open with Kanpuzan Go, owned by Kam and Linderman placing fourth.

Ch. Katagi No Ayame Go, "Sweetie" was owned by Barbara Andrews, who bred her to Ch. Sachmo (her paternal Grandsire) which produced Ch. O'BJ Dame of the Game, who bred to Orca, produced Ch. The Same Dame O'BJ, ROMP - dam of Ch. The Widow-Maker O'BJ, ROMXP

Kuma Ryoshi as a huge adult. Terry Arndt says, "He was known as 'The Dancing Bear' as he greeted one and all this way. Except other male dogs!"

There were 21 bitches in competition with Gin Gin's Bijutshuhin, bred and owned by Barb and Mack McDougle, going Reserve Winners Bitch (RWB) to Imperial Fuji Hime, owned by Ben Nakagawa. The lovely Fuji Hime went on to be named Best of Breed (BOB) at this historic event.

Interestingly, Bijushuhin was entered in novice class where she defeated Akita Tani's Mitsu, owned by Liz Harrel. The lovely Triple K Chiyo, owned and bred by Camille Kam, was first in American-bred, with Don D's Dietka of the HOT, owned by Kletter and Rubenfeld placing second. Second in open was Triple K Cho Cho, CD, owned by Ciel Hoskins. Third went to Jamel's Oso Cute, owned by the formidable team of Towbin, Patten, and Rivkin, with fourth going to Junikita's Kuro Shinju, owned by the Wrights.

These placements might not have been so prophetic had that first show been judged by a lesser judge. Obviously, they were indicative of great things to come and obviously, the placements were a lasting tribute to Winnie Heckman's well-deserved reputation for "finding a great dog." She was a great dog lady and a strong supporter of this breed, so it's only fitting that she had the honor of awarding some of the future greats of the breed.

The first Akita Club Of America supported entry was held on Sunday, May 27, 1973 at the Plainfield Kennel Club in New Jersey. It was hosted by the Raritan River Akita Club, presided over by Mr. Louis Fallon. Little did anyone suspect that Lou would soon file suit against the Akita Club Of America and the American Kennel Club in what turned out to be a very long and costly battle for ACA. Back then, the well-respected Lou and his wife Simone were devoted workers for the Akita and responsible for much good breed publicity and some terrifically supported shows.

The breed judge was Gerhardt Plaga, one of the best all-around judges. Unfortunately, the entry was small compared to the whopping turnout in Las Vegas. There were only three class dogs in competition due to the disqualification of one puppy dog,

Dragon House Nikki-No Kenicia (Yukan No Okii Yubi x Nikki No Okii Yubi) photo at 8 months. Bred by Robert Campbell, owned by Barbara Andrews. Her most famous get are Ch. O'BJ Nikki No Nikki, ROMP and Ch. Raiden of Jo-Uba, ROMX.

oddly enough, owned by Lou Fallon. Winners Dog was Sakura's Bushi, with RWD going to Sakusaku's Tom Cat Go.

With seven bitches competing, Best of Winners was Sakura's Ensho, owned and bred by Bobbi Miller. RWB went to Mitsu Kuma's Okashihime Go, owned by Morris and Mullen.

Best Of Breed honors went to new champion, Mitsu Kuma's Tora Oji Go, owned by Art and Terry Wright. Working Group judge Henry Stoecker did not place the Akita.

The arrival of the July 1973 AKC *Gazette* was one of the most exciting pieces of mail ever received by Akita owners and exhibitors for it contained the listings of the first long-awaited, duly recorded, Akita champions. They were Ch. Imperial Fuji-Hime owned by Ben Nakagawa, Ch. SakuSaku's Diamond Lil owned by Joan Linderman and Ann Diener, both residing on the West Coast. The east-coast brigade was represented by Ch. Kin-Go of Sham-R and Ch. Krug's Ichiban Akemi-Go, both owned by Bettye Krug. And of course, Ch. Mitsu Kuma's Tora-Oji-Go. All three of these east-coast dogs lived in Maryland and the sixth Akita published in that issue, Ch. Sukoshi Kuma, CDX, also lived on the East Coast with owner Dr. G. Roth.

You will note the Companion Dog Excellent title following Kuma's name and in September 1973 yet another obedience title holder added the magical letters "Ch." before his name. Ch. Akita Tani's Yoro Kobi No Moto, CDX, owned by G. and F. Hansen.

Only one dog was published in the August *Gazette,* that being Ch. Triple K Tomo Go, owned by Ted DePolo. With but a few exceptions, the remainder of the dogs published as champions in 1973 read like a who's who of foundation sires and dams.

By the time the breed was admitted into the regular classes, size had become a problem in certain lines, at least partially due to inbreeding on some of the smaller-sized imports. You will remember the all-important half-inch which sparked so many hot debates prior to getting a breed standard approved? Well, lowering the requirements to 25 and 23 inches hadn't solved the problem. The AKC *Gazette* discloses many early Akitas were disqualified for failing to meet the height requirements.

This is confusing to breed enthusiasts who argue that many original imports were of great size, their faults being those associated with the Mastiff or St. Bernard. This is true but we must remember that there were also some very tiny imports, particularly in the late 1960s. Then too, exhibitors were less well schooled in the early years and so they innocently entered their dogs without first measuring them. Today, most first-time exhibitors have been made aware of the height requirements and it's rare to have a dog measured out in the ring.

Although not a big dog, the young male owned by Terry and Art Wright became the first Akita to win the Working Group. Wasting no time, in April 1973, Ch. Mitsu-Kuma's Tora Oji-go had placed second in the Group at Mason and Dixon Kennel Club in Hagerstown, Maryland under judge R. Gilliland.

On October 13, 1973, Tora defeated three dogs and two bitches to take Best Of Breed under the highly respected Phil Marsh. By Group time, the Atlanta sun was warming what had started out as a chilly fall morning. The Working Group assembled and several top-ranked dogs paraded into the ring with their expectant handlers. No one paid much attention to the "new breed," the Akita. That was a mistake for the exceptional dog was handled by the very talented, very professional George Alston.

Tora had beautiful side gait and George showed him to perfection. The dog was in marvelous condition, said to have been walked at least three miles daily. George told us that walking him instead of jogging served to really tighten his frame and build more muscle. Whatever they did, it worked and Tora looked great. As the judging progressed, the brindle dog stayed "up" and George worked him just enough to keep him interested.

From the famous "double Japanese Grand Ch. litter" (Jap. Gr. Ch. Teddy Bear of Toyo Hashi Seiko x Jap. Gr. Ch. Haru Hime), Ch. Tusko's Kabuki was bred by Don and Barbara Confer. Kabuki had a stunning headpiece and was a very masculine appearing dog. He's described for us by his owner Dr. Pete Lagus,
"Ch. Tusko's Kabuki came to symbolize 'type' in the early 70's just at the time of Akita recognition by the AKC. He was a massive animal who commanded instant respect and admiration from all who saw him. In fact at one time, there were more than 25 Akitas being shown in the U.S. named with some variant or derivative of "Kabuki." Most of them were NOT related to Kabuki, but so majestic was his presence that people hoped to imbue their own animals with at least some of his qualities by incorporating his name. Kabuki was the top winning Akita in America in 1972 and is the sire of the first Winners Dog at a National Akita Specialty."

This was long before the Working Group was split into today's Working and Herding Groups and it took quite a while to sort through so many dogs. George and Tora never let down as Mr. Wurmser went about the business of gaiting and examining each contestant.

When Ted Wurmser turned and pointed to the Akita, there was a moment of stunned silence, followed by enthusiastic applause even though very few people realized his-

Ch. Matsu-Kaze's Kayala of Kinouk, a daughter of Ch. Hozan of Matsu Kaze, is also the granddam of Ch. Kinouk's Flower Child. Breeder and owner Joan Harper Young, Kinouk's Akitas.

tory had just been made. Owners of the five Akitas shown earlier in the day had long since departed the show grounds. Tora, however, seemed to know he had done something very special as he stood proudly on tiptoe to receive the blue ribbon.

George Alston's face was flushed with pride, he knew his name had just gone into someone's book as the handler of the first Group winner. Ted Wurmser? He probably didn't think about such extraneous things, he had simply awarded a great dog of a breed which he had long supported.

We cheered and clapped until I thought my hands would fall off, but Best in Show judge Glen Fancy did not see fit to write one more line of history on that sunny Georgia afternoon.

By the close of the first year, the list of Group winners was all too short. Ch. Mitsu Kuma's Tora-Oji Go and Ch. Gin Gin Haiyakugo Of Sakusaku both placed twice, Ch. Shuso's Saki Tumi Of Okii Yubi, placed once and set a record as the youngest Group placer, nine months of age, which held until the early '80s, and Azuma Rikki Maru placed once.

Rather embarrassing, but there were more dogs excused or disqualified than were acknowledged in Group at this early stage. The following dogs were excused or disqualified: Echol's Amai Reiko; Don D's Kiku; Daimyo (not Akita Tani's Daimyo); Fallonway No Tanashii Gamara; Ket Ket's Tiger Bear; Krug's Kiowa of Indian Hy (first place withheld); Lijo's Zono No Neuchi Go; N Bar J's Cho Cho; Sakura's Hagane; Sakura's Fubatsu Marsu Tu.

Many judges were noticeably uncertain about the strange new breed and their apprehension about approaching such a large, imposing dog was somewhat understandable. Other judges were as delighted with the opportunity to award the Akita as the owners were to receive those first "real" awards! Those judges who felt good about Akitas and were confident enough to take the plunge by awarding the Akita at Group level were: Mrs. M. Drury, Mr. R. Gilliland, Mr. C. Hamilton, Mrs. V. Hampton, Mr. R. Ward, and Mr. T. Wurmser.

Breed standings for the first year of AKC competition, as published in *The Akita Handbook,* included some new additions to the previous top winners of non-AKC show competition, but for the most part the top dogs were still the top dogs.

The breed also had its first white champion. Dick Woods proudly displayed his handsome Ch. Kita Maru at the prestigious Chicago International, held in the old Amphitheater. The crowds which milled up and down the Akita benching sections were appropriately awed by the big white dog. The west coast soon produced its own white champion, Tiare Caudill Arndt's massive Ch. Kuma Ryoshi.

Through the first six months of 1974, the high-point standings as tabulated in *The Akita Handbook* listed dogs and bitches separately. The system included 100 extra points for a Group first, 75 pts for Group second, 50 pts for Group third and 25 bonus points for a Group fourth placement and the standard one point per Akita defeated. Dogs which won or placed in Group usually defeated several hundred dogs and many top winning champions of the other breeds and so it was determined that a system of Group bonus points was in order. The leaders were: Ch. Gin Gin Haiyakugo Of Sakusaku with a total of 205 points, followed by Ch. Imperial Ginzan, Ch. Mitsu Kuma's Tora Oji-Go, Ch. Akita Tani's Yorokobi No Moto, and Ch. Sasaki Konjiro Taro (60 pts). The females were led by Ch. Jamel's Oso Cute (with 75 pts), Ch. Akita Tani's Yoru Bara, Ch. Imperial Fuji Hime, Ch. Sakusaku's Diamond Lil, and Ch. Kosho Ki's Natsu Kaze (with 36 total points).

The Handbook editorial (by this author) pointed to the rise in popularity, stressing that Akitas would soon be available from commercial outlets unless breeders took strong measures to protect their breeding stock and carefully qualify prospective buyers. Show puppies were selling for three to five hundred dollars.

One year later, the ratings listed a few new names in the top ten: Ch. Matsu Kaze's Kuro Tenno was number one, with Ch. Kazoku's Riki Maru Of Okii Yubi, Ch. Konjiki's Banacek, Taki's Aite, and Sakusaku's Hinode following in that order. Bitches were still led by Oso Cute, with Kin Hozan Joi Of Shijo (a puppy bitch handled by the author to a huge BOB win at the Chicago International KC show) in second place and Sakusaku's Perfect Pearl, Ch. Fio Princess Kira Of Kirabran, and Gin Gin Ursa Minor in third through fifth place.

The list of Group placers had grown to include: Brenrick's Gemini, Sakusaku's Hinode, Taki's Aite, Ch. Jamel's Oso Cute, Ch. Gin Gin Blaize Of Morlite, and Ch. Akita Tani's Yoru Bara.

By early 1976, new names among the top-five rankings for dogs included: Ch. Taki's Akaguma Sakura, Ch. Gaylee's O'Kaminaga, Ch. Wanchan's Akagumo (later to become the first Best in Show Akita), Ch. Toyo No Charlie Brown, and Ch. Okii Yubi's Sachmo Of Makoto (to become the number one sire of all dogs competing in the Working Group). Girls were led by Ch. Cho Jo's Michiko Hime, with new names such as Ch. Matus Kaze's Nobara Of Chereed, Ch. Mitizi No Okii Yubi, and Ch. Indian Hy's Red Feather, appearing in the top five.

The Akita Handbook carried a strong editorial that year entitled "Tattle Tale Tails" and indeed, lazy tails, even sickle tails, were still being given ribbons by careless judges.

Ch. Okii Yubi's Sachmo of Makoto, ROMXP (Mikado No Kin Hozan, ROMP x Juho Mariko No Kin Hozan, ROMP) owner handled to B.O.B. at Philadelphia KC December 1977. The record-breaking Supported Entry was judged by Mrs. Virginia Hampton, a lady whose opinion was always respected in the Akita ring and who is today an All Breed Judge. Owned by the author.

Vi-Brook Tonya, BigSon's dam. She was sired by Ch. Dragon House Wri of Sandhill (Yukan x Sabaku Kaze's Dragon House Kami) and her dam was Dragon House Nikki No Kenicia (Yukan x Nikki No Okii Yubi) co-bred by BJ Andrews and Brooks Smith. Smith bred under the kennel name Vi-Brook prior to Jo-Uba, and Andrews previously used the Dragon House prefix.

Actually, there seemed to be more problems with things like ears and tails even though the breed was improving in soundness and balance. Those dedicated to the standard, even with its little omissions and changes from the Japanese versions, were muttering and complaining about "type" and "disqualifications." While that was not new, they now had an official written standard to which they could refer those they considered educable.

Ch. Okii Yubi's Southern Bell (Yukan No Okii Yubi, ROMP x Nikki No Okii Yubi) bred and owned by Robert Campbell.

A guest editorial by Carol Foti bemoaned the lack of consideration given to white Akitas and the difficulty they faced in the show ring. For the first time, fanciers had a national publication, one which presented ratings, new champions, top producers, and a forum for discussion which was no longer automatically self-censured out of fear for jeopardizing the breed's chances at recognition. *The Akita Handbooks* were non-political and non-aligned; just good factual information which was eagerly soaked up by both novice and experienced owners.

The breed was gaining popularity from coast to coast and the Akita Club Of America announced the first National Specialty to be held Sunday, October 17, 1976 at the San Fernando Kennel Club in Los Angeles. The judge was to have been Dale McMackin, with Sweepstakes assignment going to Mr. C. L. Savage, who had been so instrumental in helping the breed to become recognized. As it turned out, J. Council Parker judged the regular classes and Mr. McMackin did not judge a National until two years later.

Gus Bell had ascended to become ACA president and in relating a conversation he had with Mr. John Lafore, Jr., then president of the AKC, Gus made the comment that Mr. Lafore was impressed with the premium list and the indications that the bickering and disagreements of Akita people were simmering down. As Gus said, "even as late as one year ago, we were still bickering, and the AKC knew it, but now we've begun to stabilize and they have recognized the fact. Let's keep it up and don't drop the ball now..."

The then most prestigious all-breed publication, *Kennel Review Magazine,* published ratings systems for both breed and Group accomplishments. These ratings more accurately reflected a full calendar year as they were compiled from the November through the October *Gazettes,* thus covering shows from January through December.

Between 1977 and 1980, there were many new names on the top-ten lists. A California bitch, Ch. Golden Sun's Tanhea, bred and owned by Merry Wicker, was consistently defeating the males, and, in fact, was holding the top spot until Ch. Wanchan's Akagumo took his BIS near the close of the year. Ch. Okii Yubi's Sachmo Of Makoto was appearing every year in the top ten and Ch. Gin Gin Haiyaku Go Of Sakusaku was still right at the top until 1978 when he began to concede his place in the top five to younger dogs.

By 1978, Ch. Tobe's Peking Jumbo had crashed the charts, suddenly appearing in the number-three spot. Royal Tenji was holding onto the number-one spot and Bill Byers' Ch. Nan Chaos Samurai No Chenko was moving up in the ratings. The year 1979 saw a female ranked as number one in the Kennel Review System, Ch. Tamarlane's Silver Star, owned by Dean and Bonnie Hermann. She was followed by Gaylee's O'Kaminaga, who had been quiet the previous year, and Samurai was pressing in third place with Jumbo in fourth.

By summer of 1979, Ch. Okii Yubi's Sachmo Of Makoto, bred by Robert Campbell, owned by Bill and Barbara Andrews, had become the number-one Akita sire of all time and he caught the attention of the entire dog world when *Kennel Review* listed him as the number-one sire of all dogs competing in the Working Group classification. While many top sires served over a hundred bitches a year, Sachmo had sired only 29 litters, his oldest litter being less than three years old! Breeders and judges talked about the incredibly prepotent dog; it just so happened he was an Akita, a breed many people who judged or owned other breeds would never have given a second thought to. Now they were noticing and marvelling. The Andrews continued to

show Sachmo and his name just kept coming up in ratings system both as a sire and as a show dog.

Oddly, many judges today fondly remember judging "the great Sachmo dog" even though in truth, they never actually did so. But admire him they did and so the Akita breed became more than just an interesting show dog. Those judges who did have an opportunity to go over him are proud to have awarded a dog who was to become the top sire of all Working dogs of all time.

In 1980 came the emergence of yet another top winning bitch, Ch. Matsu Kaze's Holly Go Lightly, bred by Gus Bell and shown by his estate and Bea Hunt. Sachmo and his son Jumbo were right behind her in the ratings race and yet another great bitch, Ch. Big A's Stormy Of Jobe, owned by Gary and Janet Voss, appeared on the top lists as a Best In Show, Westminster KC, and

Mikado No Kin Hozan, ROMP (Am/Mx, Ch. Fukumoto's Ashibaya Kuma, ROMXP x Mitsu Kuma's Splashdown) bred by Robert Campbell, is pictured at about 18 months of age. He sired 10 AKC Champions, including Ch. Okii Yubi's Sachmo of Makoto, ROMXP.

Am/Can. Ch. Kebo's Jazie Masumi of Hikari is a multi-BOB winner owned by Pat Schwarz, Yvette Foreman, and Sylvia and Frank Thomas.

As the 1970s drew to a close, new records were being established in all areas of competition. The German Schutzhund sport had gained a following in America and the first Schutzhund-titled Akita became Ch. Charisma's Miko Go No K Mikado. This handsome pinto, a half-brother to Sachmo through their sire Mikado No Kin Hozan, also attained his AKC titles of CDX and UD. He was bred by Pat Flynn and Linda Lanting out of Kazoku's Koi Shojo. His owner-trainers, Steve and Janice Mitchell, may still hold the record for the most-titled Akita and it should be noted that this dog was just as well respected in the breed ring.

National Specialty winner. O'Kaminaga was still doing well as was Chandra Sargent's bitch, Ch. Forall's Party Doll.

With the virtual cessation of an official club publication, due to the lawsuit filed by Louis Fallon, *The Akita Journal* became the chronicle of the breed. Published by Ed and Marlene Sutton and Don and Twyla Lusk, the west-coast friends broke apart and the *Journal* became *The Akita Review* in the spring of 1982, which year also saw the first issue of *Akita World.*

Ch. Toshira's, ROM handled by Sylvia Thomas winning under Mrs. Virginia Hampton. Owners, Wally and Betty Yelverton.

Register of Merit lists were expanding as new lines became noticeably dominant. New people were coming into the breed and many of them brought much more experience in areas of breeding and exhibiting top dogs. Especially drawn to the Akita were Rottweiler and Malamute owners. The aesthetic beauty of the breed, combined with the stable, no-nonsense guarding instinct, seemed to attract fans of both guard breeds and those looking for physical beauty. The Akita had both and his popularity increased.

The breed was being seriously considered in the Group and even in the Best In Show ring as judges became more familiar with the breed and more dogs were well presented.

But most of all, the public was impressed! A dog which was quiet, gentle, yet fiercely loyal and protective of his family? A big handsome dog guaranteed to draw admiration from people on the street? An innately sensitive, highly intelligent animal who looked like a bear but acted like a socially acceptable snob? What more could anyone want? The public had found the "Yuppie Dog"; the status symbol of the '80s had just arrived!

Upper left: Am/Can. Ch. Asahi Yama No Hanashi winning at 11 years of age. (Am/Can. Ch. Kin Hozan's Toklat, CD x Aitochi's Yuki Tori). "Nashi" won the 1984 National and was undefeated as a veteran. Owners, Sylvia, Aric and Frank Thomas. Breeders, Werner and Vel Oetmann.

Upper right: Ch. Tori's Yoi-Toy of Chiheisen, ROM (Am/Can. Ch. Kin Hozan's Toklat, CD x Ch. Amai Shiroi Takara). She became an ROM producer based on a five-champion litter. Owned and bred by Sylvia and Frank Thomas and Warren Byrd.

Right: Ch. Tamarlane's Silver Star, ROM (Ch. Akita Tani's Daimyo, ROM x Ch. Frerose's Sarah Lei, ROM). Perhaps the best known of the 15 champions produced by Sarah and Daimyo, "Star" was the number one Akita in 1979. Not only was she a top winner but she also was a wonderful producer whose legacy lives on in virtually all of the Tamarlane dogs. Bred by Dr. Sophia Kaluzniacki and owned by Dean and Bonnie Herrmann, she was shown by Rusty Short.

Four of a litter of eight males. These puppies show radiant good health, the result of a well nourished and cared for dam, and caring owners. They are by Ch. Jamel-Rojan's Oso Grande x Rojan's Princess Pooh Bear, breeders are Roger and Jan Kaplan and James and Carla Forte.

Ch. Storm Trooper O'BJ (photo at 15 weeks) went on to become 1982's National Specialty Best Junior Sweeps Winner.

Kobun Toshin-Go No Katana (Shinto of Shimoda Fuji x Kobun Shoko-Go No Shukan) poses for his ten week old photo! Proud owners are Beth and Steve Sims and Mleanie Hererra. He is bred by Sharon Osborne and is a fine example of Japanese type.

Precocious Puppies

HOMEWORK AGAIN!

As an Akita owner, you'll agree that most of the unbelievable stories about them are the simple truth, and the only embellishment is the love and pride so evident in the telling. If you are a non-owner, some of the incidents described in this book will test my credibility. That's OK. If you become an owner, you'll look back and laugh as you yourself share Akita stories with other non-believers!

Most people want a family companion, a burglar alarm with teeth, a forgiving friend who loves, listens, understands... and never borrows money! Breeders want a solid foundation for the living expression of their creativity. For all of us, there's a dog somewhere of the right breed, size, color, price, and personality. The trick, of course, is in finding the right one.

Unlike buying a new stereo, acquiring a dog is usually an impulsive action. The age-

Eudora puppies bred by Mark Nisbet.

But sometimes, in our fervor to brag a bit about our breed, we forget how important it is for potential owners to also know the drawbacks. It would be better if a family selected another pet than to have such a noble creature wind up abandoned to an animal shelter because of a hasty decision. The fact is all puppies are cute but Akita babies are like teddy bears and the urge to cuddle and own one is almost irresistible. As long as you realize that they will grow up .... into beasts approximating a hundred hairy pounds, then read on.

old bonding instinct between man and dog takes hold and, lo, man buys dog with little thought as to the breed or suitability. We hope you'll balance emotion with logic when it comes to choosing your "best friend."

Pet or show? Purchasing a dog isn't really all that complicated, but done intelligently, it can be time consuming. One of the first decisions you should make is whether or not you are interested in showing. If you don't have the time or interest necessary to successfully compete in the show ring, then of course you won't breed the dog, so you

Ch. The Widow-Maker O'BJ, ROMXP (Ch. The Real McCoy O'BJ x Ch. The Same Dame O'BJ, ROMP) at seven months of age.

will be quite happy with what is termed a pet or companion puppy.

Pet puppies are sold with spay (hysterectomy) and neuter (castration) contracts. Reputable breeders abide by my amendment to the Akita Club Of America Code Of Ethics which forbids issuance of AKC registrations on pet puppies until proof of surgical sterilization by a licensed veterinarian has been provided to the seller. No sensible breeder will accept a buyer's declaration that it won't be bred for they know that the dog may later be sold to someone else. Even the original owners may weaken to the temptation to make a few bucks and, ergo, good intentions melt away.

Neutering of pets is not a snobbish attitude. It's not just the breeding worth of the average dog which must be considered, it's the simple fact that very few owners are really qualified to go into breeding. Most people don't have the time to acquire the knowledge of genetics, breed-specific problems, and to see and evaluate enough dogs to choose the proper mate for their female. Even fewer individuals have the patience and the wherewithal to properly rear the litters, advertise, and ensure good homes for each and every puppy. And the indisputable fact is that there are already too many unwanted puppies and kittens in today's world. To cause more puppies to be born without the complete confidence they will be of such exceptional quality and in such demand that each one is assured a loving and permanent home is morally irresponsible.

While there may be enough friends and neighbors to take the first litter off one's hands, there may not be. Obviously that is why so many purebreds wind up in shelters. Neighbors move, friends go on vacation, and one by one, all those good homes the breeder counted on just disappear. As the litter owner becomes desperate, surplus puppies wind up in the pound, other institution, or "free to good homes" column in the paper.

It's far kinder to all concerned to prevent "backyard breedings" by withholding registration papers until proof of sterilization has been received. By giving breeding papers only on the best quality animals, responsible breeders do their part to reduce the incidence of health and temperament problems. This also protects the innocent buyer for it can be an emotionally and financially devastating experience for families who unwittingly buy an indiscriminately bred puppy or kitten.

Another option made available is the AKC Limited Registration whereby a puppy may be registered by its breeder as "not for breeding" and no progeny from that dog will be registerable unless and until the breeder lifts the restriction on the original dog.

These are simply logical and moral obligations. It in no way implies that pet puppies are defective anymore than it suggests that buyers should settle for second best just because they don't plan to show or breed the dog.

Faults which separate "pet" from "show" should be relatively minor. The pet puppy is

"Joe" (Willodeen O'PR Akari No Inochi x Great Tigers Piney Mtn Mist) a fourteen week old puppy bred by Gloria Ketcher, Ann Cody, and Donna Green.

as smart, healthy, and as carefully reared as his show-quality litter mate, but his destiny is to love and protect his family, rather than to wow 'em in the show ring. The difference between pet and show is analogous to a pleasant, attractive, successful person who is loved by all but not expected to become a movie star or an Olympic gold medalist.

A quality companion will come from the same well-bred, carefully raised litters as show-quality pups. After all, parents who have excelled in the tough competition of the ring where temperament, health and response to stress are severely tested are most likely to produce strong and healthy puppies! Dogs which have that extra something, call it star quality; dogs which exemplify breed type; dogs whose ancestors have been carefully screened for genetic defects: these are the only dogs which should be producing puppies in today's overpopulated world. To select a companion whose parents were less is to invite disappointment or emotional disaster.

There are currently new "genetic titles" which may appear after the dog's AKC registration number. This is a step in the right direction but overall not as important as knowing that the dog was displayed in public and competed successfully in the show ring. Veterinary examinations can be falsified. For example, dogs known to be free of hip or eye problems can easily be substituted in order to obtain an OFA or CERF certification number on a dog which would otherwise not pass examination. Dogs can be switched in the show ring too, but the difference is that, with dozens of informed Akita fanciers watching, it's much more difficult to perpetuate a fraud. The innocent veterinarian can hardly be expected to know one Akita from another even though colors and marking variations may be easily distinguished by show-ring observers.

Seawoods Kuma Taro shown at two and a half weeks. He's by Am./Can. Ch. Seawoods U.S.S. Buckwheat x Seawoods Tina Bear Trap, breeders Kelle and Alyce Clinton, owners Debby and Shigeki Shoemaker and Kelle Clinton. Photos courtesy of Kelle Clinton.

Another major problem acknowledged by geneticists is that those dogs that have themselves been certified free of a suspected hereditary problem can not be certified not to produce it! This means that a dog certified as clear of a particular defect may still produce it in his offspring.

A buyer should take all these things into consideration. He should request photos or video of the dam and the surroundings in which the litter is kept. If the breeder has kennel runs, the prospective owner should ask for photos of the entire kennel setup. He should evaluate the surroundings, trying to gauge what those conditions are on a day-to-day basis, not just when cleaned up for a photo. Are the dogs on dirt or a sanitary surface? Do they have good shelter or just a lean-to or shade tree? Are the kennels chain link or just cheap wire? There are breeders who swear their puppies are "house raised" but who actually condemn them to deplorable squalor. You will want to be sure how and where your puppy was raised.

Each species imprints on its kind during a brief window of time. Birds imprint immediately upon hatching, which accounts for the old story of a chicken hatching with a clutch of duck eggs, following the family to the water—and drowning. Puppies imprint from the 21st through the 28th day and if special care isn't taken by at least the 35th day, the canine can never become totally bonded to the human species. Baby dogs which are allowed to reach six weeks of age without lots of human contact, (hugging, baby-talking, stroking, picking up, and other such bonding actions) can never be properly socialized.

Having ascertained the beginnings of your puppy and how it was raised, you should still give careful consideration to future plans. Many families start out with a pet puppy, then become interested in conformation shows and decide to buy another dog which they can show. They then have two Akitas, which if they are of the same sex, will eventually have to be separated. For many owners, this is manageable but if they become really interested in the breed ring, they soon acquire another show-quality Akita. Little by little, perhaps not until they have bred that first litter, but sooner or later ... most owners reach a point where they're compelled to address the question of what to do with the original pet.

If it can't be shown, it can't be bred. It has to share house time now with the

Ch. The Target Rose O'BJ (Sea Breeze Gold Digger O'BJ x Ch. The Dame's on Target O'BJ, ROMXP) at two months with owner Mario Moretto, Sr. in Santiago, Chile.

show dog(s) and be kenneled or crated, at least part of the day. It mopes and is hurt because after all, it was once the only dog, number-one dog, a house dog. The owner feels like a traitor when forced to think of placing the dog. So what does one do? Give up on show and breeding? Build kennels? It's a tough decision, but usually the pet dog is much happier being with another family where it's truly a pet and is number-one dog again. These

questions are best considered before purchasing.

Before you decide, go to a few shows and try to determine if this is something you might become interested in. Most families are quite happy to enjoy the company of their pet and leave the showing to those with more time and more determination. It's expensive to campaign a dog, and there's no denying it's stressful. Show schedules get in the way of holidays, family vacations, and school events.

On the other hand, many owners find that show weekends provide a wonderful social outlet and a time for the whole family to share a common interest. Weekend jaunts become mini-vacations filled with new sights and new attractions. The children may become involved in Junior Showmanship and will make friends which last a lifetime. So will you.

So if you think there's the slightest chance you may become involved in exhibiting, start out with a show-quality puppy. This affords a choice which you otherwise will not have. Show puppies don't have to be shown or bred, but pet puppies can't be.

If you purchase a show puppy, it does not automatically follow that you will breed it. Many owners show their dog to an AKC championship for the same reasons they might sponsor a race car, own a competition horse, or excel in golf or tennis. More and more discriminating owners delight in seeing their dog in the winner's circle but wisely elect not to breed it.

You need not limit your search to local breeders. Air shipment of puppies is quite safe, inexpensive, and, in the long run, easier on the youngster than a drive of several hours.

Although you've already discarded those old wives' tales about purebreds' being high-strung and show dogs' being somehow less fit than "regular" dogs, let me explain something which you may not have considered. The stress of constant traveling, changes in climate and water, being poked and prodded by hundreds of strangers, missing his family, and feeling the tension and frustrations of his handler all severely test a dog's mental and physical health to the limits. A dog which excels under these conditions is almost always far superior, physically and mentally, than the average or "regular" dog! Therefore, show records are important even if you're not

As early as three months, Kudos For Kolor owned by Terry and Patty Naulty, displays a perfect ear set and size and a lovely crested neck. Her head is very dry, meaning no undesirable wrinkles or loose skin. Nose pigment has not yet filled in, not unusual in youngsters with white muzzle markings and not a cause for concern prior to six months of age.

interested in showing or breeding your own puppy. In addition, a successful record in the conformation ring indicates the breeder has invested tremendous amounts of time, money, study, and effort. He or she didn't just buy a female and go into the puppy-manufacturing business!

If you feel this is all rather stuffy and not really important, it will help if you understand that dog shows evolved as a means of evaluating which dogs were fit to reproduce. The first formal dog show predates the Kentucky Derby as America's premier sporting event! According to the American Kennel Club, that is still the sole reason for conformation competitions today. So whether or not you plan to show, you'll want assurance that your puppy comes from above-average stock and that he was created by dedicated people concerned with sound, healthy specimens which look and act like Akitas. Isn't that what you hope to own? OK, then you do understand how important it is that at least half of the first 14 dogs on the pedigree have achieved their AKC champion title!

Every person who breeds a litter should love their dogs and so you'll quickly discover that everyone you talk to has "the best" puppies. But remember, that's why serious breeders prove their dogs are of above-average quality. If the litter owner hasn't been willing to publicly test his breeding stock, buy your puppy elsewhere. Do not be taken in by any of the standard excuses offered by irresponsible breeders.

Those excuses range from "He doesn't

like the show ring" to "We don't have time to show right now." Some breeders claim to have shown and found it to be "too political," "expensive," or "time consuming." "Politics" is the cop-out of those who show inferior animals but I agree that exhibiting is expensive. So is paying a stud fee and getting the brood bitch to the most compatible stud, even if he lives a thousand miles away. So is providing basic veterinary health care and raw beef and premium dog food for the litter. And loving and properly nurturing puppies is about as time-consuming as it gets! Yes, I agree. Rearing quality animals is time consuming and it's expensive. That's why the time, money, and effort which that irresponsible breeder saved will be spent by you a thousand times over if you buy from him! Look elsewhere for your puppy. Exercise your right to ask questions and get clear, concise, and verifiable answers. The breeder should be happy to prove that licensed judges agree that the sire and dam (and preferably all four grandparents) are soundly built, mentally stable, healthy, free of visible genetic defects, well socialized, and lastly, of recognizable breed temperament, type, and structure. Good breeders will jump at the opportunity to drag out photo albums or tell you about the champions they've bred. Study the pedigrees. If a pedigree shows two or more generations of that person's kennel name, and most of those dogs are champions, that's a very good indication that the breeder has worked diligently to produce exactly what you want!

Don't be misled by famous dogs or champions further back than the third generation. Ninety percent of the genetic influence represented by the pedigree will be in the first three generations. You should expect at least half of the first three columns to the left to be all champions.

Avoid puppies represented as "breeder quality." There is a simple fact about this oft-used sales term. A dog is only breeder-quality if you have the right dog to breed it to! There will always be someone anxious to

Champion Crown Royal's Candy Contessa at fifteen months, owned by Kerry Much, Larch Mt. Akitas and breeder Ingrid Linerud, Crown Royal Akitas.

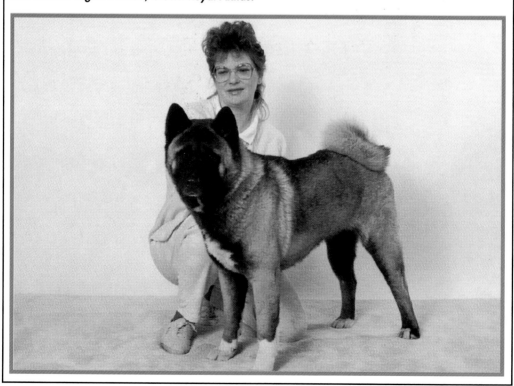

tell you about this perfectly awful pet-quality bitch that produced many champions. If it's true, it's a powerful testament to the wisdom of the person who owned her and knew exactly how to utilize a very predictable genetic combination or it was like dropping a quarter in a slot machine and winning the million-dollar jackpot. To hope that you will have either the same luck or skill is foolhardy and costly. The fact is that registration tables indicate the odds are more than 3000 to one against this happening.

So steer clear of ambiguous terms such as "breeder" or "possible show" quality. It almost always means the dog would be unfit for the show ring (or breeding), but the seller figures you'll become attached to it before you discover the sad truth. You must also remember that such terminology is a clever way some folks have of getting around the ethics code which forbids the selling of pet puppies for breeding purposes. Beware of such unscrupulous practices.

As you become more involved in your quest, you'll probably encounter breeders who don't even own a champion but who claim to have "top show-quality" litters! By now you have learned a lot not only about Akitas but also about people.

If you're still having trouble sorting out the breeder's answers, you might ask if the untitled dog has won its majors. A "major" is a win of three or more points at a single show. The number of points is calculated for each show according to the number of dogs in competition. A dog must have won two or more majors in order to become a champion. If your question leaves the breeder at a loss for words, you'll know that they know less than you do about the show ring. You will then have to judge the puppies as they are, without the assurance that licensed judges have agreed on the quality of the parents.

If you encounter a breeder who has several "older puppies," you may want to know why they have so many unsold puppies before making a decision. What's the track record of the breeder-seller? Do they seem knowledgeable enough to help with problem solving? Are you confident that should

anything go wrong, they'll still be around to help you out? Can they back up promises and do they have the ability to live up to their guarantee? If you buy a show puppy which doesn't turn out, would you want it replaced with one of the same quality? From the same

Brother and sister Am/Can. Ch. Seawood's U.S.S. Buckwheat grew up to be #2 Akita in Canada in 1985. Both future winners, photographed at five and a half weeks by their breeder, Kelle Clinton, are sired by Ch. Akita Tani's Daimyo, ROM x Ch. Golden Sun Seawood Wa Wa L'Wilac, ROM. Owners are Alyce and Kelle Clinton. Am/Can. Kaipo Gabo became #3 Akita bitch in Canada in 1986 by going B.O.B. each of four shows. Kaipo is owned by Leslie and Art Gabo and Kelle Clinton.

parents? Does the litter owner seem more concerned about you and the puppy or about making the sale?

OK, finally, you have a list of conscientious breeders who are expecting puppies, and you must narrow your choices. You've talked or exchanged letters, received pedigrees, printed material, photos or video. You have probably discovered that you're going to have to get on a waiting list, especially if you plan to show. Well-bred puppies are always in demand so you might as well be patient. Easier said than done, eh?

Most responsible breeders will keep the babies until they are at least eight to ten weeks old. This allows time for complete worming, first shots, and for most congenital problems to become evident. It enables the astute breeder to determine which pups are more likely to succeed in the show ring and which may be sold as family pets. Good breeders may keep certain pups even longer to evaluate them more accurately, but they will be conscientious about socializing them and giving them house time and love so that the buyer receives a well-started puppy.

You should never, ever remove a puppy less than seven weeks old from its mother and siblings. Most states forbid interstate transportation of puppies under eight weeks of age. One of the most important reasons, to you as the future owner, is that the puppy must be properly socialized as a canine. The first eight weeks are critical to a baby dog for it is during this time that puppies learn the social rules taught by mama dog. If you take him away from his mom and siblings too soon, he may never really know he's a dog and you are quite likely to encounter serious behavioral problems as he matures.

Ownership of a fine animal should be a pleasure, not a burden. You should receive complete health records and a schedule for booster shots and wormings. The puppy should be healthy and bouncy at time of purchase. Care and feeding instructions should come with him, and a really conscientious breeder may provide you with other printed material to assist you in training and rearing your puppy.

If done properly, you've invested time and you've learned a lot about dogs while you were getting ready for a big step in your life. You have carefully selected a new friend who will bring many years of comfort and pleasure to you and your family.

Seawoods Kuma Taro at three and a half weeks.

THE FIRST WEEK

Whether your puppy was shipped or you drove to pick him up, chances are good he hasn't been fed for several hours. He'll be hungry when you get home but may be too excited to eat right away. If you don't have the same brand of puppy food he was raised on, or you intend to change brands, offer him

Seawoods Kuma Taro at eight and a half weeks.

any of the following: raw or lightly cooked hamburger with cooked rice or oatmeal, a boiled egg, or a half cup of room temperature cottage cheese. Hopefully his breeder has been feeding him such foods and he will dive right in with no resulting digestive upset. Whether he's accustomed to such natural food or not, it rarely upsets the tummy for it is, indeed, natural food.

Be sure he has fresh water and don't bother with distilled or spring water; it's very unlikely he's been drinking that. He'll have to get used to your tap water sooner or later so it's better to do it now and not put him through two changes. You may help him through the first day or so by adding a tiny bit of lemon juice to the water. This eases the transition in taste and smell but most pups could care less and will suffer no ill effects from the change in water.

If he was shipped, he may have been bumped around and startled by a lot of strange noises so he may be a bit jumpy for the next 24 hours. Although few people consider it, his ears may ache from the noise and air pressure. Reassure him on the way home, give him a little time to "find" himself, then let him take a quiet nap after he eats.

Hopefully you've considered proper nutrition before the arrival of your puppy. If you haven't, let me remind you of the importance of vitamin C, fresh foods, and a premium brand of puppy food. Beginning now, don't overfeed him. Overly rapid growth and excess fat will put too much strain on those tree-trunk legs and that roly-poly back. Pet or show, he must grow up big and strong with straight bones and no joint problems. Follow the breeder's instruction regarding calcium supplementation. We don't use it but our pups get plenty of dairy products along with their meat. If in doubt or if feeding more than 25 percent meat, then the pup may be safely supplemented with a small amount of bonemeal.

It's not unusual for a new puppy to be somewhat disinterested in food. A long trip or stomach upsets due to changes in water and environment may also reduce appetite for the first couple of days. But there is one other common and usually overlooked problem which is easily corrected if understood. The puppy has been used to eating with litter mates, and possibly with his mom or other adults. When there is a group of dogs, excitement builds as they await a meal. They know food is being prepared and watchful anticipation replaces the pre-hunt gathering. The release of certain hormones and blood chemicals, which would normally occur during the chase, are released as the domestic dog eagerly listens to the arousing sounds of can opener or refrigerator door, dry food being poured into the bowl, and the enticing sounds of stirring and mixing which translate to conclusion of the hunt. By the time his bowl is placed before him, your dog should resemble one of Pavlov's. He is salivating and eager for his share of the food. Now, re-read the last phrase. His share of the food.

A perfect example of the Collie-ear stage. This 10-week old male is owned by Gerd and Graziella Hippler. The ears are erect at the base but tipped forward on the ends, a common stage of ear development. He is also east-west in front, another normal growth stage of large-breed puppies.

A group or kennel situation closely approximates the conditions which stimulate appetite. Social bonding and establishment of position, perhaps a scuffle or two over the best location at the rim of the bowl; in every way, "feeding time" in a group situation is sure to arouse the canine appetite. Meal time in a one-dog household is quite likely to lack the same excitement.

Therefore, the best time to feed a puppy is when the family eats. Not only does food preparation for the family increase the anticipation time, the culmination of that domestic hunt through the refrigerator and kitchen cabinets is, you guessed it, the pack feast. Dogs are pack animals—social eaters. Unlike the cat family (with the exception of lions), dogs enjoy the social sit-down dinner.

Contrary to what most people think, when the dog begs food from the table or your late night snack, it isn't because he's starving or even because he's unable to resist your peanut butter sandwich, it's because it's the socially correct thing to do! Instinct prompts him to beg a turn at the "table" from his pack leader. So go ahead, show him you understand. If you're only having a snack, don't hand him part of your food, but do feel free to get up and put a morsel of food *in his food bowl.*

Twice a day feedings for at least the first year are recommended. You may want to give him a mid-day snack until he's three or four months old. After that, he will begin to skip the snack or to eat less in the evening and you'll know lunch is no longer necessary.

The exception is the true chow-hound. The garbage-disposal. The glutton. If by four months, you can't see a "waist" on your pup, either from above or in profile; if you can't feel his ribs; if he looks sort of like a sausage with legs, he's got a serious problem which you have unwittingly created.

Large breeds are quite different than medium- to small-sized dogs. They have a slower metabolism so twice-daily feeding is quite sufficient for his needs and for your need to nurture him. Actually, nature enabled the larger canines to get along quite well on one meal a day. Unlike the small carnivores (fox, coyote, jackal) which hunt or scavenge many small meals during a 24-hour period, the wolf descendant is programmed for one large meal per day. On days when no large kill is made and the previously stored larder is empty, the wolf cub may go hungry. If still nursing, his mom may feel the pinch but the pup will be fine. If weaned, (ergo, the wolf-pup that lives with you now) he will suffer no ill effects and, left to his own devices, he would eat certain grasses, roots and other vegetation, thus

why. Do not allow him to use newspapers. You will only prolong the process and by ten weeks, you'll need the Sunday edition for one piddle! Take him directly to the spot you'd like him to use, even if it means carrying him there for the first couple of days. If he's an apartment dog who needs to use an elevator or go down a long flight of steps, carry him, being careful not to squeeze his bladder area. Place your hand over his or her "faucet" and apply a little pressure there as you lift the puppy. This should stop any leaks until you get to the potty area. Puppy will soon have enough bladder con-

Goshen's Samurai of Mariah (Ch. King's Ransom x Ch. Tar Baby) and Tahoe at five and six months.

allowing the intestinal track to be cleansed. We feed the domesticated dog twice a day because of the possibility of gastric torsion (bloat), which is virtually unknown in the wild dog. But then wild canines don't eat from bags.

The questions most asked at this stage are relative to housebreaking. If done right to begin with, it's so simple with the Akita puppy that it will be over within a week to ten days. For the first few days, resist the temptation to allow him the run of the house. Keep him in the crate except for short inside play periods. Remember to take him straight outside as soon as he awakens. You know

trol to enable it to wait out the elevator ride or make it all the way down the steps and across the parking area to the proper place.

No food after 7 p.m. and limited water after 8 p.m. will help him to be clean overnight... If you take him out the last thing before retiring, after he's been in his crate long enough for his bladder to have become full, he will promptly relieve himself and should remain comfortable overnight. If he awakens you with real distress sounds, he can be forgiven for finding it hard to wait, especially after a hard day complicated by the change in water, food, altitude, and climate. Take him out, praise him quietly when he goes, and with no further fuss or play, put him back into his crate and prepare yourself for his protests. No sense getting angry. Don't give in either. Ignore him. Read a book or watch TV until he realizes it is not time to get up.

When to take him out? One, after every meal; two, after playtime, which stimulates bladder and bowel; three, upon waking after every nap; and four, always, first thing in the morning and the last thing before going to bed. When you take him out to "go potty," avoid distractions as you allow him to eliminate. Don't talk to him until he's begun his little chore, then softly praise him. Use the same words each time as he performs. You'll be a-mazed at how quickly he learns and how the prompt-word can hurry him along when it's rainy, cold, or you're in a rush. Later on, you'll be glad you taught him to eliminate on command.

This lovely two months old female has perfect ear size and set, and a "butterfly nose." The pigment will continue to fill in but were it to remain this way, she would be ineligible to show. Kudos is owned by Patty Naulty, bred by BJ Andrews.

This is especially true with bitch puppies, prone to hold urine when at their first couple of shows. Males will want to mark the new territory so are never a problem, but getting either sex to have a bowel movement in a strange area can be a bit trying if not voice trained.

Keep him crated when you can't supervise him and until you're sure he's mastered bladder control. If for some reason you don't have a crate, build a temporary blockade with wire or a baby gate. Put down plastic sheeting over the living room carpet or block off a corner of the kitchen.

This allows him to see you but will keep him in about a 2 x 3 foot area. For now, keep his den area very small. He won't soil his eating and sleeping quarters unless he's positively ignored or has diarrhea. Actually, he will come to appreciate having a private den. Many youngsters will go into their crates of their own accord when tired or wanting to den with a favorite toy.

Do not shut him away in a bathroom or laundry room. He wants to be with you and to be part of the daily activities, not shut away in solitary confinement! If he can see that the house is where you live, if he understands that is your den, he won't soil it. If he's shut away in another room, he may think your living room is the toilet area....

You must understand that at this age you have what amounts to a human toddler. He'll be into everything. You must safeguard this "baby" just as you would a small child. Protect him from electrical cords and things he can pull over on top of himself or get tangled in. Be sure to secure poisons and household chemicals in a safe place.

Don't leave him loose in the house (as a puppy) and then get upset when you come home and find he's been into the garbage or chewed your best shoe. Would you leave a three- or four-year-old child alone? Especially with a candy bar? How can you possibly expect this baby to resist those tantalizing smells in your kitchen garbage? First you praise him for eating plain old puppy food; then you scold him for eating wondrous goodies. No wonder he's confused! That pitiful, shamed look isn't guilt. It's a broken heart. He doesn't understand why you suddenly hate him for something you just praised him for a few hours ago.....

Fortunately, puppies mature quicker than children so it won't be long before he's caught on to your household rules. He'll learn which are his "toys" and what is forbidden. By six months or so, he will have acquired such good manners that he will be a welcome guest wherever you go. Left untrained, he can just as easily form undesirable habits which are difficult to correct and unpleasant to live with.

You'll have new situations arise, whether you've been in the sport for ages, or this is your first dog. Call your breeder. No one has a greater interest in your puppy than you and the person who created him. The vet really doesn't care whether he grows up sound, handsome, typy, well mannered, etc. He has hundreds of clients and, re-gardless of his bedside manner and interest in the well being of his patients, he hasn't one dime invested in your puppy. Let's be honest here: his hopes for the future are not pinned on whether your puppy's bones are strong and his feet are tight!

If you bought from a successful kennel, the breeder knows more about raising a healthy puppy than does the average veterinarian. Unless you're lucky enough to have found a breeder-vet, it's doubtful that your vet has ever reared large-breed pups to maturity. Depend on him for medical treatment and advice. Depend on the successful breeder for everything else which has to do with the puppy he created. If your breeder doesn't have the answer, he'll say so because his first interest is the welfare of one of his "kids."

Throughout the life of your puppy, the breeder should be your counsel in all matters relating to the dog. He or she may be busy and you must remember, breeders have a family and a life other than dogs, but he'll always be there in a crisis. He'll join with you in a good laugh or a good cry. Hopefully, when a decade has gone by, you will still be able to reach your breeders when you'll need them the most. Losing your best friend isn't easy. It helps to know you have an old friend who truly understands your loss....

Give your puppy something to chew on. He's cutting teeth and just like any youngster, he knows that gnawing on something helps ease the gum irritation. Chewing also exercises jaw and skull muscles which in turn will help ears to stand. Chewing aids in keeping the teeth clean, but, most of all, it's an instinctive de-stressor for the carnivore! For goodness sake, think of it as healthy recreation for your pet, not as something he does just to aggravate you.

Understanding the importance of chewing, you have only to ensure that your puppy has the right objects. Never give him squeaky toys or soft rubber toys. They are dangerous to large breeds, too soft to last, and guaranteed to quickly give up their squeaker to be swallowed by a puppy. The hard English rubber balls and solid rubber toys are fine.

Acceptable puppy possessions (yes, he needs his very own things) are: Nylabones®, American-made rawhide chews, knots are the best, big and just right to carry around to all those important places puppies are on their way to. And OK, those disgusting cow's hooves are guaranteed to cause guests to cast inquiring glances at each other when your back is turned but, go ahead, your puppy will love them.

One of the best chew-toys is a chilled raw carrot. He will probably shove it around with his nose and sniff it and then look at you as though to say, "What am I supposed to do with this?" If he doesn't catch on right away, pick the carrot up and play-tease him with it so that he grasps it. You may find that adding a small amount of grated carrot on top of his food will clue him in to the interesting fact that carrots are edible. Just as human infants discover that a cool object is more soothing to sore gums, your puppy will quickly catch on. Just warn the rest of the family that you're keeping the puppy's "popsicles" in the freezer too.

I cautioned you against chocolate-flavored chew toys because chocolate

can become a dominance-aggression contest. Furthermore, too much sustained pulling can cause the teeth to become misaligned, and many authorities also believe it places an unnatural strain on the neck vertebrae, especially in large, heavy puppies.

The best toy is cheap, and will be found at your local meat market if you're lucky enough to have a butcher who buys hanging beef. Most supermarkets purchase beef already cut and packaged so try the specialty butcher

The safest and longest lasting dog chews available come from Nylabone®, as this lucky puppy well knows. Composed of tough nylon or more pliable polyurethane, the Nylabones® and Gumabones® solve a number of puppy dilemmas at once: emerging teeth and tender gums, jaw development, relief from puppy stress and boredom, and more.

can be deadly to dogs, particularly young puppies. Never give him sweet treats which might someday encourage him to empty the candy box left sitting within his reach.

There are many tug-of-war toys on the market. Some are supposed to help clean the teeth. In spite of that, I must caution you against tug-of-war games. An occasional contest will do no harm but, if it becomes a frequent pastime, it

shop or a local processing plant. Request beef shank bone or what is commonly called a knuckle bone. Buy several, they keep for months in your freezer. Your puppy will love it and you will hate it—it is definitely an outside treat!

Don't be disappointed if he doesn't appear to be thrilled the first time you give him a raw beef bone. From his point of view, it isn't ripe yet. It needs to

Besamé mucho! *Akitas are not known to be demonstrative, so don't tell Am/So Am. Ch. The Target Rose O'BJ or her frequently kissed owner Maurizio Moretto, Akitas Ace of Santiago, Chile.*

be properly aged, which is why he buries it. So play fair. Don't give it to him in the house! Frustrated, he'll probably spend a few moments shoving the floor around with his nose and then, having performed the age-old ritual of burying the bone, he'll walk away, instinctively confident that his treasure is safe and will be edible when he returns. You may misread him and think he rejected your thoughtful treat. Worse yet, you may think "the book" was wrong!

Unless he helps to convince you by hiding his prize behind the recliner, under the sofa, or in the corner behind the dresser!

You may not find it until it's well on the way to being properly aged. *Then* you'll remember this page! Retrieve the smelly thing and give it to him outside. Yes, it's perfectly safe. His digestive system can handle it although it would have been better preserved had he properly buried it to start with.

Avoid the baked white "sterilized" bones. They're a bit brittle for a dog with as much jaw power as an Akita, even a puppy. Personally, I consider them to be a fitting comment on the sterile society in which we live! Isn't it a shame that so many animals are deprived of that which is natural, healthy and immensely satisfying?

"C.J." (Sea Breeze Gold Digger O'BJ x Ch. O'BJ A-Head of The Game) a four months old male owned by Renwick and Leslie Thompson, shows exceptional head development, especially the triangle-on-triangle effect of the ears, eyes, cheeks and forehead.

If your new kid tries to bury his puppy possessions in your flower bed, you must help him to find a better place. He's not stupid. Actually, he selected your garden space because the ground is softer and he figures that's why *you* dig there. No doubt he's impressed by your ability to find such nice soft earth.... And knowing you buried your own treasures there, he's

Champion Crown Royal's Candy Contessa is a beautiful bitch at six weeks of age.

confident it must be a *really* safe place. It will take you only a few moments with spade and shovel to build him a storage chest of his own.

Select an area as far away from his bathroom as can be managed. If you prepare him a digging spot close to the area you've asked him to defecate in, he'll refuse to use your designated vault. By now you will have caught on that a little common sense goes a long way. On the other hand, if all of this seems silly, perhaps you should skip the rest of this book and settle for an aquarium. *(The Publisher will happily recommend a hundred great T.F.H. books to get you started too.)*

Maybe you'll just decide it's too much trouble to provide him with nature's perfect chew toy. Fair enough, that's why rawhide and synthetic bones were created. Maybe your Akita will never know what he's missing.

One comment about rawhide before leaving the subject of toys. If you give a young puppy rawhide chews (leather!), he may see no difference between his toy and your leather shoes. Despite the oft-told tale of puppy chewing best pair of shoes, it's usually the old, favorite pair that succumbs to the puppy's budding teeth. Why? Because just as important as his innocent need to chew, is his love and fascination for the scent he treasures most: Yours. So, be prepared if you decide to give your puppy leather chew toys. Older dogs usually understand which is which and, of course, they already have your scent down pat.

If all this seems a bit much, remember that providing him with acceptable chewables not only saves your valuables, but it's much less trouble and far safer than having him undergo general anesthesia to have his teeth cleaned a few years from now.

Among the most frequent queries from new owners are those having to do with the first few nights. "Will he cry?" Yes, probably. "Should I pick him up?" You can't resist! He won't want to be held long though, your body heat will make him uncomfortable. "Should he be crated?" Absolutely, read on. "Can he sleep in the bed with us?" Gads, no! Unless you don't mind sleeping with a hundred-pound bear a year from now.

Predictably, these questions are often followed by another call a few days later. "He hates his crate!" I'll bet he does. "He yells when I put him in the crate." Well, wouldn't you? Now is the time to train him to the crate. Let's talk about it because, even if you never use a crate after he's learned house manners, you will still want to begin to establish basic rules of behavior, otherwise known as mastery, control: Making sure he knows who's "boss." Looking at that little teddy bear now, you can't imagine him being anything but snugly, but, just like our children, he can grow up into a pretty unruly, anti-social adult unless we set limits and help him to find his place within the "pack" hierarchy.

So, you should begin his training promptly, while he's still small enough to fit into the crate he came in. If you picked him up from the breeder, you really should purchase an adult-sized crate. As a last resort, fabricate a facsimile for the purpose of training and housebreaking, then discard your makeshift "crate."

He'll probably resent being shoveled into his crate when he has so much to do. After all, he's only just arrived and he needs to check out his new surroundings, establish his territory, and, most of all, enjoy the company of his new friends. He will usually take a nap while you are busy. That means he's ready to wake up and play just as you're ready to settle down for a quiet evening of television or a good night's sleep.

If he was shipped, he'll be partially resigned to being crated anyway. If you have an older dog you can crate and take along with puppy for a ride across town, that will help. He will observe that the other dog enjoys being crated and going for a ride and like all youngsters, he'll mimic the adult's behavior. In fact, re-read that sentence. Remember it. It can work for you and against you. If your older dog is undisciplined, it will be hard to get the new puppy to obey rules which the older dog ignores. Conversely, the older dog can be a tremendous help in explaining the basics to the new arrival.

Before you begin the following lesson, prepare yourself by assembling a couple of missiles, a good book or other distraction

Shukan's Aka Kuro Shogun (Shinto of Shimoda Fuji x Kobun's Shoko-Go-No-Shukan) at four months. Breeder-Owner is Sharon Osborne.

(for you, not the puppy), and all of your patience and self control. The missiles, should it become necessary, will be hurled at the noisy puppy.

You will have taken him outside to relieve himself before you shovel him into the crate. You gave him a safe and proper chew toy in his crate. The crate is located in the same room that you are going to remain in to perform this teaching exercise. It should be situated in a convenient location. You'll defeat the purpose of training if you set this up when he's already worn out, tired and sleepy. Better that he's calm and a bit worn down but not exhausted. Hopefully, he'll resent being closed in his crate at the time you've set aside for the training session so that this can be done at your convenience, not at 2 a.m.

At his first verbal protest, immediately bark "No!" He should cease crying in order to see what his new parent is barking about. Do not praise him. Continue across the room to your seat or if you were so lucky as to have made it that far before he complained, resume reading or whatever you were doing when he first yelped. It won't be long before he'll whine

Ch. Hasu Nikko winning BOS at the first Region IV Specialty at a year and a half old. Although totally out of coat, she defeated 56 bitches, handled by teenager Pete Lopez, Judge Lawson Williams. Nikko took Pete to a Best Junior in Show Award and in 1988 she was the #2 ranked bitch.

Asa Taiyo's Lone Star Lawman (Ch. The Widow-Maker O'BJ, ROMXP x Ch. Classic's Sugar And Spice) owner-breeder-handled by Russell and Jill Drennan, co-bred by Dave and Lee Ana Dorsett. Finishing with BB wins from Bred-By Class, he became a Group winner at ten months.

or bark at you again. Once more, give him a sharp, loud, authoritative "NO!" This time, he will test you by saucily responding with a comment of his own. Try not to laugh. Go back to his crate, grumbly growling on the way, give it a good side to side shake as you exclaim "NO! Shut up" or "NO! Quiet" or whatever command you're comfortable with. With no further comment, return to your chair, pick up your magazine, and ignore him.

He will probably remain puzzled (and quiet) for a moment or two and then, tentatively, he will risk yelping again just to see what happens. Your response must be immediate. Pick up the ammunition you've stored within easy reach (an assortment of pot lids is

Ch. Jamel-Rojan's Oso Grande (Ch. Bar BJ's Brown Bomber x Jamel's Shortcake). Breeders, Jackie Towbin and Barbara Hampton. Photos courtesy of owner Roger Kaplan. Breeder-judge, Jim Sailer.

perfect) and taking care not to hit the television set, let fly your missile. If you're lucky enough to hit the crate, he will be startled into silence but more importantly, he will spend the next few moments (quietly) wondering if you were in some way connected with this mysterious event.

It may take a repetition of this sequence but when the second missile clatters on his crate, a marvelous thing happens. He begins to understand that his human is not his slave but is something more akin to a god. Not only can you rattle his whole world but you can cause objects to sail through the air! Even his mommy was never able to do that.

This may sound harsh, and for some breeds, it might be. But remember, wild whelps are taught in no uncertain terms, the meaning of "be quiet" and "stay hidden." In this case, there is no swooping eagle to snatch him away, but deep in his psyche, a long dormant instinct awakens and he will respond. So OK, the sky isn't really falling. But the puppy doesn't know that and you've been fair in warning him with the "No" bark.

Sit quietly in the room for a few more minutes, and chances are very good he will snuffle himself to sleep. You've won. Not the battle, but the first contest of wills. Don't leave the room until you're satisfied you've outlasted him and he's fallen asleep or become completely occupied with his chew toy.

You may use the smaller crate to begin with but will soon want to purchase an adult-size crate. While it's true that we don't miss what we never had, you'll wonder how you could have gotten along without a crate once you've used one. The correct size for an adult dog is 36 inches long, although a big male will prefer 42 inches. Either length will still fit in a full-size station wagon or mini-van. The height will be 26 to 28 inches, depending on the length. This is quite large enough. The super big crates are for Danes and St. Bernards and such. Be sure to select a good heavy "bench" type wire crate with two strong locks. Remember that his middle name could be Houdini.

In warm weather, do not put a rug or crate pad in the bottom of the crate. He will hate it and probably scratch or chew it into a rag. Use perforated rubber interlocking squares or one of those heavy grass doormats. Either one will keep him cool while it allows soil or urine to pass through, keeping the dog clean.

The Akita, The Enigma

POSITIVE/NEGATIVE

"Fierce as a Samurai, gentle as a kitten." "Gentle when stroked, fierce when provoked." "Tender in heart and strong in strength." That is how the Japanese describe the Akita.

The Akita is a dog of many contradictions, a complex creature with great depth of personality. He is a dog for the true dog lover for he can never be taken casually. As we explore the breed, you will begin to realize that the most unique characteristic of the Akita dog, is in fact, his uniqueness!

Naturally, most of this book will present the positive side of the breed but it would be a disservice to both the reader and the dog if we failed to point out what many people would consider the negative aspects of giving your heart to an Akita. Most of you will already have some liking for the breed or you wouldn't be reading this. That being the case, you'll probably perceive even the bothersome aspects of Akita ownership as tolerable and, indeed, most of us who live with one of these magnificent beasts are able to find a positive side to just about every breed characteristic! But please, for the sake of the dog and your own peace of mind, take your time and carefully consider whether or not this breed will fit into your lifestyle. Do it before you buy. A major advantage in purchasing a purebred dog is knowing what the breed should be like at maturity. How big, how hairy, how active, how protective, how trainable, and so on. In this chapter, we will tell you, perhaps not just what you want to hear, but certainly what you need to hear.

First let's look at some of those Akita contradictions. Among the large-to-giant breeds, the Akita is unique in that his size is coupled with the alertness and inquisitiveness of a terrier-sized dog. Even

Akita Tani's Kuma-san (Akita Tani's Shoyo-Go x Hairre Kitsune) was the first Akita owned by television star Pat Harrington. (Bear) appeared on the Steve Allen show with Pat, and the baby in this photo now dances with a ballet company in San Francisco.

so, he isn't a busy dog. He's not hyper, but he is energetic. He is not placid, but he's calm. He's not aggressive, but he is dominant. Not a barker, but oh! can he talk to you. He is not stubborn, but he is determined. He is precocious and he expects answers. Almost all canines are loyal and, of course, the Akita is no exception. But this loyalty can be and often is taken to frustrating extremes.

His physical characteristics must also be considered. What may be attractive to one family may not be so well appreciated by another. He is large. More suited to a station wagon or van than the back seat of a compact car. Although he fits quite comfortably into a small apartment, he can completely cover the working floor space of a small kitchen. He has been known to appropriate the cool tile of the only bathroom as his resting place and some Akitas eventually discover the perfect proportions of the master's bathtub. Conversely, unless taught to do so as a spoiled puppy, he will not want to nap on the sofa.

A proud father. Frisco is shown with two of his 4 month old female puppies, "Copy" on the right and "Ditto" on the left. Owned by Cathy Sartor.

What about coat you say? Well, the Akita should have a luxuriant, triple-layered coat and, like all other northern breeds, he changes coat twice a year. Be forewarned, it's like a blizzard! The shedding lasts about two weeks if you go ahead and brush out the dead coat and do a couple of warm baths to speed the process along. But please, if you are an immaculate housekeeper who can't abide hairballs wafting under the living room sofa, choose another breed.

To most dog lovers, blowing coat is an unqualified negative. Ahh, but to many lovers of the Akita, the shedding is regarded less as a detraction than as an indication that a brand new glorious show coat is about to emerge. To the anxious owner anticipating that long-awaited litter, it's a welcome sign of the hormonal activity which precedes estrus.

Even though the dog throws off an amazing amount of coat during the twice-annual "blow," to most people, this is preferable to the year-round shedding of short-coated breeds. The fine undercoat (that portion of coat which gets in your nose and on your best dark suit) is trapped by the second layer and the guard coat. For the most part, it's held there until you take brush and comb in hand and remove it. Quite handy actually. Better it stay there on the dog than to pass the butter dish to your mother-in-law and have her discover one of those short little hairs from a single coated dog.

The triple coat does not mat but should be groomed at least once a week. It doesn't take long, and it is one of the most pleasurable and stress-reducing activities connected with dog ownership. Unlike training, showing, or even a relaxed stroll with just a dog for company, you don't have to "go" anywhere, it doesn't take a lot of planning, it costs nothing, and you don't need anyone's help in order to experience the benefits. Seeing the coat shine and each hair lift and respond with glowing vitality provides the same sensual pleasure many people derive from wearing a fine fur. Thankfully, this isn't a dead fur.... Not only is this animal alive and happy, the best part is that he's yours!

Most prospective owners want to know how the breed compares to something they've owned before. Allow me to help with some comparisons,

into more independent thinkers. They are genetically programmed to work with man, but not necessarily for man.

For instance, a German Shepherd Dog will protect his flock or family and his immediate territory but is somewhat less inclined to guard inanimate objects or more abstract territory. Herding breeds rarely had to defend a flock against people, therefore, they usually exhibit an ingrained reluctance to bite a human. Their primary defense against trouble is to bark steadily, thus sounding an alarm to alert their human partners. The northern-type dogs were expected

Shogun's Yukitama of Jade at about 8 weeks. This would appear to be a standoff between the two babies, Snowball the Akita and her tiny friend, a Pygmy goat. Both youngsters owned by Terry Arndt.

none of which should be construed as derogatory toward any other breed nor applicable to each and every dog.

The Akita is a little stronger in character than say, a Collie. He's a little more independent than the German Shepherd Dog, or most of the other herding dogs. There is good reason for this. Most herding breeds were developed to work for man and to follow his directions; consequently, they excel in obedience. Conversely, those working and terrier breeds which trace their origins back to a time when they were used for war, fighting, solitary guard duty, or confronting large game, evolved

to sound the alarm first, then investigate. Here the Akita differs from his spitz-type ancestors for he is more than an alarm dog.

Most of the true guarding breeds go very quietly about their job. Like his Mastiff ancestors, the Akita rarely barks and when he does, it isn't in hopes of scaring off something he's afraid of: it's a clear statement which warns against trespass. The guarding breeds were often called upon to protect their owner and premises from human intrusion and therefore they may be expected to stand ground against a human, even to the point of biting. The guarding dog will become more aggressive when confronted by a direct challenge. On the contrary, most herding breeds will bow to an authoritative and forceful human approach, as is their heritage. Both groups of dogs are doing what is proper and deliberately encoded by man, in service to man.

Like many of the terrier breeds, Akitas were also used to confront big game and, in a more sordid time in history, their own kind. There is therefore a subtle distinction between ownership of, let's say, a Belgian Shepherd or Great Pyrenees, compared to an Akita. The former will have strong instincts to protect the flock (you) but will work at your command. The latter is inclined to go about taking care of you, independent of your wishes, and sometimes, in a most inconvenient manner. The Akita's heritage is to protect. His way of fulfilling that role must be channeled by a conscientious owner.

What some trainers perceive as stubbornness, the Akita owner recognizes as the independent will of a self-thinking creature. When dodging the tusks of a charging boar, the dog isn't listening for nor would he heed his master's commands. (His smart owner was probably scooting up the closest tree anyway!) The dog had to make instantaneous decisions with split-second timing in order to survive. He did not wait for his owner to shout instructions; indeed, his owner was more often only his keeper and not his heart-mate.

Confusing to some owners is this Akita-thing called rank. Akitas are very conscious of stature. Those who have more than one Akita come to understand that the breed has a finely tuned sense of rank —and they can count! Each wants to be fed first, watered first, taken out first, first in the car, first through the door, and always made to believe that they are first in their special person's heart. This is not just a melodramatic observation: it is part of the dominant nature of the breed and a characteristic which new owners need to be aware of. It's easy to slight an Akita, i.e., not grant him the respect he feels is his due. While that may sound corny, anyone who has owned Akitas and has developed a close relationship with the breed will nod at my comments and say, "Yes, that's right."

Let me give you a delightful example, retold here as it appeared in a 1962 publication of *The American Akita Breeders.*

"Watching' The Back Trail...." Polar Ranger O'BJ keeps an eye on things while breeder/owner Jim Witherby takes a coffee break. Ranger is by Ch. The Widow Maker O'BJ x Ch. The Coca Cola Cowgirl O'BJ and is an important sire for Paladin Akitas.

"An Akita Tale"

by Mrs. Robert Wonderees.

Mr. and Mrs. Ed Reynolds, now living at Bermuda Dunes in the Palm Springs area, were delighted to make the acquaintance of our black male Akita, Kami. Several years ago Mr. Reynolds had a hauling contract at the north end of Vancouver Island, B.C. He was hauling iron ore from the mines to the dock and dumping it into hoppers which fed a conveyor belt loading the Japanese freighters. He was acquainted with the Akita and told of this incident. One day the Japanese cook from a Japanese freighter came ashore and wanted to get some fresh meat from the camp cook at the mines, offering in trade an Akita pup they had on board. Although neither cook spoke the same language, the trade was effected and everyone was happy.

In succeeding weeks many freighters came and went and the growing dog was interested in the ships but didn't bother them. One day, however, the dog discovered his "home ship" in port and promptly tried to go aboard. This effort was not tolerated; when the captain discovered him, he was promptly thrown off. The Akita tried five or six times to board, each time being unceremoniously put back on the dock.

The second day the dog was again at the dock but made no effort to board the ship. Instead, he cocked his head, watched, and was apparently trying to figure the whole thing out. In about 30 minutes, he found his way to a point where he could jump to the moving conveyor belt. He rode it to where the iron ore was dropping into the hold, gave a magnificent leap, and cleared the hold, landing on the deck. Mr. Reynolds watched with fascination and was astounded to see the dog's determination to carry out a plan. This Akita promptly made his way up the stairs to the bridge, sought out the captain, and stood perfectly still facing him. The captain was speechless.

When the dog apparently felt he had made his point, he turned and with great dignity and a slow, measured walk, calmly returned to the lower deck, and majestically walked down the plank to the dock. He never looked back or made any further attempts to board another ship. Obviously, this Akita was not to be despised.

Today he is still at the mine and considered invaluable. He is the only adequate control they have ever had against the large, marauding bears in the area. The bears were constantly rifling the garbage cans and presenting a real menace to any of the men walking around after dark. This is certainly one Akita who not only is loved and appreciated but earns his keep as well.

Determined? Yes. Acutely aware of his rank and right to board his home ship? Well, you decide.

The Akita-inu is the product of many generations of breeding for strong will, courage, determination, and intelligence. While today's Akita is far removed from the fighting dogs behind him, and it's true that we can socially condition and train a dog, we cannot change the breed's self-determination any more than we can rewrite his history. The fact is, many owners are attracted to the breed because of their independent, self-assured character. Those who are not should select another breed rather than attempt to change what, to many, is the ultimate canine companion.

And about trainability. Having trained professionally, I can speak with some authority about formal obedience training. The Akita is a quick study. They learn rapidly, but, having grasped the basic idea, they just as quickly become bored. Many trainers fail to understand that schooling an Akita is like working with a precocious child who refuses to learn by rote but instead, wants an explanation from the teacher. Some Akitas simply refute that which makes no sense from their uncannily logical point of view. Like clever children, they will work and learn better when given justification along with the traditional incentives to perform.

Take the heeling routine for example. Having quickly grasped the basic idea, the Akita is quite likely to plunk his big butt down and say, "Why? Why do you want me to walk in this precise position by your left knee? We're not really going anywhere... I've quickly caught onto that. And why do you keep stopping? Why do you want me to sit down every time we stop? I'm not tired, I'm bored!"

If you understand "dog talk" you'll find it a little hard to justify to a dog why you're going in circles, seemingly unable to decide where it is you want to go. Can you blame him when he looks down at the ground, head pulled into his shoulders (the classic Akita-sulk) and clearly registers his disdain for your good judgement?

Don't laugh! This will take place at some point in every training relationship. By now, Akita owners will be smiling. You know.

Good owners are like good parents.

more reason for doing it than the fact that his owner considers it to be fun. The Akita is apt to reason that going around the jump is more expedient and, yes, he may resent it when his owner insists he keep going over the obstruction. The same instinct which commands the wolf to conserve energy for the hunt, may make your Akita think you wouldn't last long on your own!

Akitas want to please you, don't misunderstand me, but they also want to see the sense of something. It will be next to impos-

A stunning collection of well trained Akitas owned by Maria Heldman, this impressive group is "Halston," "Turbo," "Aspen," and "Mirage."

They may sometimes find ownership "inconvenient," but the truth is they are immensely proud of their "gifted" Akita. Other dog owners don't have the patience or are uncomfortable by this sort of behavior. Admittedly, the Akita isn't an easy dog to live with if you want the more traditional master-dog relationship.

It takes a talented owner to go into the repetitive training necessary to achieve high scores in the obedience ring. A Golden Retriever will sail over the jump because it's satisfying to the dog, and he needs no

sible to convince your Akita that doing the figure eight is anywhere near as exciting as stalking the neighbor's cat.

Speaking of which: Cats are one of the few animals which can dominate an Akita. The most macho male or would-be huntress will usually get along great with the family cat even though we all know cats don't agree anyone else is boss! The Akita will often just sigh and accept the cat's insolence. One would almost think they respect the irrepressible self-sufficiency of the cat! Seriously, if it's of Persian type,

"Gentle Giant". Casey, a seven year old male Akita keeps a watchful eye over four week old orphan kittens, owned by Margie Rutbell.

(mellow, dignified) and not given to running up the drapery and across the ceilings, the Akita often forms a close bond with the family feline. Be aware, however, that this does not mean he will extend the same friendship to the neighbor's cat.

Are Akitas good in the house? Well, stop and think. Paper walls and rice-mat floors. The ornate palace of the Shogun. The Akita not only was at home in either abode, he was welcomed there. When it comes to adapting to living with people, in elaborate or humble surroundings, the Akita dog puts

the bear side of his personality aside and becomes an overgrown cat!

First, he's incredibly clean. Perhaps that's one reason they accept cats as friends. Not only are they a snap to housebreak, they are equally as clean in their personal grooming. They will often wash themselves like a cat, bury their feces like a cat....and dance like a bear!

If a puppy has been reared under sanitary conditions and his mom was reared in a like manner, he will come to you virtually "house trained." The proper mother will keep her babies immaculately clean. By the time they're old enough to toddle about, the puppies will waddle to the far end of the nest to relieve themselves. From about four weeks on, with a wise breeder's cooperation, the pups will use only a designated area of their surroundings. The unknowing breeder may have accustomed them to newspaper but please, even in an apartment, do not continue that practice. An adult Akita can release half a gallon of urine—more than even the *New York Times* Sunday edition can handle!

Apartment dwellers want to know about exercise. Akitas do not require a tremendous amount of space. They do need a minimum of four toilet walks per day to

Ch. The Silver Chalice O'BJ (Ch. Aitochi's Stinger of Sugar Run x Ch. Okii Yubi's Dragon House Ko-Go) owned by Elaine Nussbaum. "Tomo" is shown at 11 years of age. Akitas make wonderful house dogs at any age.

avoid bladder or bowel problems. And be sure to take a small plastic trash bag along. It's easy to turn the bag inside-out with hand inside, and literally pick up the stool, reversing the bag so that the contents never touch your hand. Tie shut and dispose of in a proper receptacle. Bingo! You're a good neighbor and a responsible dog owner.

If you have a balcony, do be careful. Akitas have no fear of heights and young males have more bravado than judgement. They have been known to sail off a second-floor balcony or window ledge. We once came home later than expected and were greeted with the sight of a dog on the roof! BigSon had wriggled through the attic window and was pacing back and forth on the first-floor roof. It was a tense couple of minutes until Bill got into the house to call him down from inside. We knew if we said his name, he'd leap from the roof to come to us. Now

Clancy, a longcoated Akita puppy and his good friend Logan, a Welsh Corgi, both owned by Steve and Julie Bolding. They remain good friends because Clancy is altered.

you know why our friends called him "Superman" for indeed BigSon thought he could fly.... and he's walked through a wall or two!

Generally speaking, just patrolling your back yard, checking out the neighbor's cat, and playing with another family pet are sufficient exercise to keep an Akita in reasonably good muscular condition. Like the Bull Terrier or racing Greyhound, a properly structured Akita is born with good muscle mass. If you can take him jogging or for a run on a private beach or out to the country

for the day, he'll love it. It's not only the sense of freedom and the extra exercise your dog will love, it's the chance to encounter and catalog all those exciting new smells!

If you will allow him in the family pool, that's wonderful exercise although the chlorine is hard on the coat. The double coat lends buoyancy in the water, and his strong swimming skills and very soft mouth make him a natural for retrieving. Despite these assets, my personal observation is that most Akitas do not really care for swimming. They love water, love to play or wade in water, but rarely strike out to swim on their own initiative. As for retrieving, they are not naturally inclined to it. A youngster can be encouraged to retrieve a ball or toy a few times, but will rapidly tire of the game.

Unique to only a few breeds, Akitas have a very high pain threshold. Although they are exceptionally sensitive and easily wounded emotionally, they usually ignore physical pain. This can be dangerous for they tolerate illness with such a stoic dignity that the owner may be unaware of a serious health problem. Young puppies will be seen playing during the onset of parvo virus, oblivious to the warning symptoms of diarrhea and vomiting. By the time your Akita actually lays down and signifies that he is sick, he is very, very sick. Your veterinarian must understand this oddity. It will better enable him to accurately diagnose the seriousness of any condition.

Not only do Akitas tolerate pain, they usually maintain an unruffled attitude, even when subjected to intense agony. No better example comes to mind than the time Widow-Maker managed to hang a front toe in the door of his crate. In trying silently to free himself, he had turned halfway around and became wedged facing rearwards in the crate with his front leg drawn back under his belly. When he finally yelped and I ran to the back of the motor home, I found him with the toe not only trapped but severely twisted in the vice-like grip of the door framing. I yelled to Bill to pull over and tried to speak calmly to the dog. He was in a terrible fix, but he remained confident that we could solve his dilemma.

Without waiting for the motor home to come to a stop, I tried to unlock the crate, thinking that would free him. No go. The twisting of his toe had jammed the latch and I couldn't budge it! Struggling to maintain my footing, I shouted a warning to Bill to take it easy as the motor home left the roadway and bounced over the rough shoulder. I was sure the jostling would cause the toe to be broken as the dog was in a precariously off-balance position.

"Easy, stay, stay...." I breathed in what I hoped was a reassuring tone. His tail gave the slightest side-to-side movement and although I couldn't see his face, there was no doubt he said, "You've got to be kidding!" He had ceased to struggle and was bracing himself as the motor home bumped to a stop.

Now, he knows what "get back" means. It's a common enough phrase but who could guess it would prove so useful? Desperate for some way to turn him, I commanded "get back, get back" and motioned towards the front of the crate. Through his pain, he looked at me as though I had asked him to walk through fire. He looked betrayed. Frantic, I commanded again, "get back, get back". His eyes met mine, and I could see his confusion, yet he shifted his weight backwards! Instantly, he realized the pressure had eased. "Good boy, get back, back." He turned his body a bit to-

Awake or asleep, Akita puppies are huggable. This 8 week old Coal Miner son is owned by Fran Cox, bred by Myra Addington.

wards my fingers and scrunched further towards the front of the crate, thus taking even more pressure off the trapped limb.

Bill shoved me aside and, with what seemed to be super-human strength, lifted the door section of the heavy crate just enough so that, by pushing and twisting his toe (while my stomach roiled at the sight of what I was doing), suddenly, the toe was free!

Through all of this, the dog had not uttered a sound. More incredibly, he had remained responsive. If he had continued to struggle or had he panicked, the toe and probably the pastern joint would have been broken. We could never have turned him enough to free the pressure on the door frame.

An emergency clinic x-ray assured us nothing was broken so we went on to the show grounds. He hobbled on three legs the rest of the day but by the next day, when challenged by a Rottweiler, Widow-Maker squared off with his weight on all fours. We laughed, knowing the foot would be OK.

Ch. WW The Coal Miner's Daughter at six months. Her most important job is watching over the house and children at Wishing Well Akitas. Bred and Owned by Myra Addington.

As in most breeds which have at some time been used for combat, natural selection was predicated on ability for rapid healing. A wound which might plague the average dog for a week will be hardly noticed by an Akita. Vets are often surprised at the speed with which an incision will heal. Conversely, the Akita has a low resistance to anesthesia and owners should inform their vets to be watchful as to the amount of drug administered.

How is he to live with? Is he affectionate? Oft-asked questions; they deserve an an-swer. One of the many reasons people love dogs is because they boost our ego. They love us, they need our approval, and they seek reassurance of our love in many sweet and flattering ways. The Akita is a little less demonstrative, seeking your approval in more subtle ways, and he wants only your love. He seldom cares about non-family members.

In some breeds the term "standoffish" is used to describe the breed's relationship with strangers. One breed's standard says "chary of strangers." The Akita is anything but wary, but he might rightfully be called standoffish. Actually, he couldn't care less what a stranger thinks of him. The gushing and oohing and ahhing often seem to embarrass a male Akita, although, as might be expected, the female always appreciates admiration! She will accept petting and attention from strangers much more readily, whereas the male doesn't care for any form of physical familiarity. One might think he doesn't need assurance that he's the most handsome, biggest, strongest or most awesome dog. He knows it!

Owners who enjoy the subtle devotion of the cat family will immediately understand the undemonstrative loyalty of the Akita. The Akita doesn't pester you for attention. He won't nudge your newspaper out of the way every time you sit down, he won't sit in front of you with a paw on your knee, he won't parade back and forth in front of the television screen during your favorite movie. The mature dog is content to lie quietly across the room, seemingly asleep, but very aware of your every movement. And when you get up, you'll find that you have your Akita shadow behind you as you go from one room to another. And no, it isn't because you feed him!

As dominant as he is, he's rarely intrusive. He is quite likely to put off the urge to relieve himself until you have decided to quit whatever you are doing. At the first sign of a break in your concentration, he'll be quick to tell you that he would like to go out, please, thank you very much. Now what could be more charming and considerate than that?

Without your company, he'll be lonely, he will be bored, yet he will wait patiently for your return and rarely will he vent his frustration on your belongings. Most observers swear the Akita is imbued with the calm patience attributed to many people of the Eastern countries.

Ch. E Oka's Broadway Bear with his pal, Miss Dana Balitzer. Bear is owned by Cheryl and Mark Balitzer.

On those mornings when you would like to sleep in, he will respect your wishes. Many owners will tell you that the first thing they see upon opening one eye to peer at the day's possibilities is the devoted face of their Akita. He's been sitting there quietly, watching, waiting for his best friend to awaken. It is this unassuming and undemanding friendship which Akita owners find so special.

Within the privacy of his home, he may be a clown, a cutup, and a willing partner in whatever games you devise. In public, he is the epitome of a dignified, noble companion.

Most of the larger breeds are seen as powerful, awesome, imposing, but few are described as pretty. Many Akitas are indeed pretty, and you will often hear owners say that the first thing that attracted them to the breed was the beauty of the beast! The senses are intrigued by the unusual combination of size, power, and elegance. Is that not the appeal of the Black Stallion or the Concord jetliner? So it is with the Akita.

Are they OK with the elderly? What about handicapped family members, will they accept a wheelchair or your grandmother who uses a walker? Good questions. But allow me to defer to someone who is so much better qualified to answer them for you.

Excerpt from *HEADline News,* Volume II June 8, 1990. Guest article by Maria Heldman, Mariah Akitas.

"The patients that we see have had a serious accident or injury (i.e., stroke, head trauma, automobile accident, fire/swimming accidents, spinal injuries, etc.). These people may or may not be able to see, speak, hear, walk, and may be scarred for life due to injuries.

"When these people meet our dogs, they respond! Our dogs don't care what condition the patient is in or what they've been through but accept them the way they are with a lick, tail wag, or even a smile. We usually visit two floors of patients, and they are waiting in the reception area or in their individual rooms (with a doggie snack, of course) for a dog to visit. Sometimes the dogs are allowed up into the patients' beds! Every dog that enters the hospital has been tolerance-tested to wheelchairs, beds, canes, heavy hands, and hair pulling. They must also be bathed and free of parasites as most of these patients have had surgery and their environment must be germ-free.

Registered Therapy Dog, O'BJ Kati A Maker of The Pace (Ch. The Widow-Maker O'BJ x Overhills Pacer) waits by her harness and credentials. Kati is a true "working dog" owned and trained by Richard and Lynda Oleksuk.

"My husband and I have very demanding jobs and busy schedules, but we always try to make time to visit the hospital with the Akitas. It is very rewarding and uplifting when we come home and know that we have made a difference to someone who is not as fortunate as we are. Please try to live your life the fullest and love and respect those not as fortunate."

Mark and Maria's Akitas are obviously dual-role dogs. They excel in the show ring, but their dedicated owners make sure that the many facets of the Akita personality are appreciated by people other than show buffs!

If you've read this as more positives than negatives, you are probably going to purchase your first Akita. If you already own one, you could have no doubt written twice as many pages on his or her intriguing contradictions! You also know there's something we really haven't explored yet: Aggression.

The best therapy of all! Akitas owned or bred by Maria Heldman doing a wonderful job as hospital and nursing home therapy dogs. They are Bonzai, Kuma, Keisha, and Reina, ranging in age from 6 months to 11 years. Maria and Priscilla McCune enjoy taking the dogs as much as the patients enjoy having them and the dogs are delighted with the opportunity to interact with so many wonderful new friends.

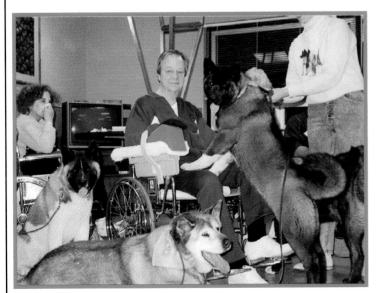

STEEL GLOVE—VELVET MITTEN

The Akita exudes a haughty superiority that is backed up by the ability to enforce his supremacy should any other dog fail to recognize him as Akita-inu. The contradiction is that the Akita will often tolerate and even protect a much (much) smaller dog with a dominant personality! Many strange liaisons have been formed between small, yappy, possessive dogs and their big buddy, the family Akita. Do not, however, expect your Akita to tolerate such behavior from a non-family dog! While he might step over a pesky little dog and continue on about the important business of being "Ak-i-ta," he's just as likely to decide enough is enough. With one swift movement, he may reach down and severely shake the bothersome tormentor. I have seen a male Akita throw a small dog over 50 feet. Even though the action isn't meant as an attack, per se, it will almost always result in injury to the smaller dog.

Responsible Akita ownership is realizing that no amount of training can truly guarantee that an Akita will not be an Akita given the right provocation or (let's face it) temptation.

He—or she—will be dominant over other dogs and even other species. It's an essential breed characteristic. You've all heard the saying about changing a leopard's spots. Any big cat trainer will tell you that no amount of training can ever make a tiger spotted instead of striped. He can be taught to jump through flaming hoops and he will usually love his trainer, but he can not be caged with another of his species and sex. Do not be misled by breeders who would try to convince you that training can transform an Akita into a Cocker Spaniel. If you want a dog who will get along with other dogs of the same sex, make yourself happy, buy a sporting or hound breed.

Most people see the inherent aggressiveness as a drawback. Others see it only as strong character and are proud to call the Akita their friend. You must accept that they are usually intolerant of other sexually intact dogs. You can not have two uncastrated or unspayed Akitas of the same sex together. Nor can you have a sexually active Akita with any other bossy dog of the same sex if it is of a size to be considered a worthy opponent. No matter what other people

A well-trained group of Akitas. Aspen, Keisha, Winnie, Revo, Vauarnel, Bonzai, and Kuma. Courtesy Mariah Akitas.

may tell you, Akitas will only get along with another dog who understands the pecking order and is willing to grant the Akita the respect which, rightly or wrongly, he considers his birthright.

The adult Akita will rarely tolerate trespass by strange dogs or cats and may react swiftly to banish them from the home territory. So although all dogs should be restrained by fence or leash, it's essential that the Akita have a secure exercise area free from possible intrusion by other animals.

Since the Akita believes any place he stands is his, one must also take care when exercising the dog in a public place. Dogs communicate through very subtle signs and body language. If your Akita is insulted by your jogging buddy's dog, he (or she) may be quick to take up a challenge which you didn't even realize had been issued! You could lose a friend because neither of you realized it was the other dog which actually precipitated the fight.

The mature male should be discerning. He won't be an exuberant happy tailwagger upon meeting a stranger. We like the bitch to play the part of the perfect hostess and be more amenable and welcoming of strangers, but we expect a male to go about the business of observing the stranger—i.e., guarding. To other breeders, a male Akita who fails to climb in your lap might be considered mean or ill-tempered, yet it's not really a matter of interpretation or even of personal preference. The Akita is a guard dog. He should be watchful of strangers until he's made his own decision or until his owner has indicated that the person is a welcome visitor. To do less would be unfitting for the breed . . . sort of like a pointer which ignores the flutter of wings or a terrier that passes by a burrow without checking it out.

Will he bite? Yes. Surely you gathered that by having read this far. Will he bite indiscriminately? Not if well bred and properly reared. We must be realistic in order to be good owners. In today's crowded world and with the anti-pet legislation flurry in so many areas of the country, it is the duty of every dog owner to set a good example. To treat the guard-working breeds as though they were stuffed toys is not fair to the breeds involved and certainly not fair to the public.

Sea Breeze Excalibur at sixteen months of age with Officer Charles West. "Kato" was a canine cop before returning to the show ring where he completed his Ch. title with breeder-owner Linn Greene.

"Tika" waits for her owners, Donald and Janet See. The intense loyalty and devotion of the Akita is legendary.

threatened. Even fewer families who own one of the guarding breeds are ever intruded upon. Such a dog is a visible deterrent to the would-be burglar or assailant. So be reassured. It's perfectly OK to be comforted by the knowledge that, should the need arise, the family Akita will fight to protect his loved ones. Wouldn't you?

HOMEBODY/HOUDINI

Will the real Houdini please "stay put"?! Just as cat owners will pretend anger

Some breeds have a natural inhibition against ever biting anything other than a dog biscuit. This has been carefully developed over centuries of selective breeding. They excel at what they were bred to do and are wonderful companions. Other breeds have been developed for specific purposes and just as carefully selected to fulfill those roles. A calm, stable, well-mannered family watchdog is of far more assurance when one is home alone and hears those strange noises than is the pistol, unloaded (hopefully), and stored on top of the closet shelf. A confident, sensible dog of the guarding breeds is also far safer than a loaded gun. Properly reared, well-disciplined family protectors serve a needed and much appreciated role in today's society.

Problems occur when careless or uninformed owners fail to respect the instinctual capabilities of their chosen breed. We get far more calls from owners of the guarding breeds wanting to know what is wrong with their dog because it shows no sign of protectiveness than from those who are concerned because a dog has actually shown teeth without justification! The good dog will hopefully never, ever, have any reason to demonstrate his guarding capabilities. Most families, thankfully, are never

at their cat's finicky appetite, Akita owners can hardly conceal their pride as they try to top each other's stories of how, when, and where their Akita did a disappearing act! It's a sometimes funny part of Akita ownership but caution is warranted. Although most "escapes" end happily with the dog finding his owner (so as to make a point about being left behind), there is a very real danger in the dog's ability to escape confinement. Most escapes are from crates.

Please don't routinely confine your Akita in an airlines-type crate. The closed-in aluminum crates, though difficult to escape from, are not suitable for shipping as they transmit heat directly to the dog and can quickly become a dangerous oven. The plastic crates are great for shipping, but are not the best everyday choice. Firstly, they don't allow for proper air circulation. Secondly, the male likes to see and feel that he's in control of his surroundings. And male or female, most Akitas come equipped with a mild case of claustrophobia! While some less confident breeds might appreciate the facsimile of a safe, closed in den, the adult Akita neither needs nor seeks this sort of security. Of more concern, most standard airlines-type crates are no match for a determined Akita.

Rare is the instance of an Akita coming out of a crate during shipment. Only those familiar with the breed might understand that the dog must somehow know there would be no way to find his owner. Even so, when shipping an adult, it's wise to secure the top and bottom halves together with heavy bungee straps and to be really safe, drill a hole through the door facing so that you can affix a padlock joining the wire door to the plastic frame.

If this seems a bit extreme, allow me to share a couple of our first experiences, which will hopefully better prepare you for your first encounter with the supreme escape artist.

Although Sachmo had always agreed to ride in an airlines crate in our bus, he took strong exception the first time we stuck him in a handy plastic crate at home. Two families arrived, each with unruly children in tow. To protect the dogs from the children, we crated Ko-Go and Sachmo in my office. Five minutes later he strolled into the living room!

Assuming the latch gave way, I took him back to the office and, for once, he entered the airlines crate willingly. That should have tipped me off because he had always resisted going into that type of crate. With my mind on our guests, I made sure the locking rods were securely in place, told Ko-Go she was a "good girl" and returned to the living room.

It was only a couple of minutes until once again, Sachmo appeared in the doorway. This time we allowed him to check out our amazed guests before I locked him in the bedroom!

We all went to "check the crate," whereupon we found the top rod still properly through the hole in the door frame but the bottom rod dislodged. Those of you who have used an airline crate know precisely what I mean. We all agreed it would have been impossible for him to get out of that narrow gap and yet, we were faced with the irrefutable fact that he had done just that! Someone pointed out that if he had tried to back up into the crate after forcing his head and neck through the opening, he could have panicked and strangled himself. I saw Bill smile. Sachmo? Panic? Not likely. Just the same, we never again put him in an airlines crate.

You would think we had learned better but, after all, he was our first male Akita. Orca was purchased as an adult, and having been raised with Golden Retrievers who never informed him of the Akita's proclivity for spectacular escapes, dear sweet Orca was always content to lay in his crate, front

Nothing like having your own wheels! Crown Royal's Tokiami Go (Ch. Noji's The Count Crown Royal x Subo's Hoshii Niiki Nokoru) at six months. Toki is owned by Doug DuVon and Ingrid Linerud, bred by Lee and Kris Wacenske.

feet crossed wrist-to-wrist with a philosophical expression on his face.

But BigSon was his father's son. As a youngster, he had seemed quite willing to ride in an airlines crate and, OK, I suppose Orca had lulled us into forgetting the lesson Sachmo had taught us. When he was about two years old, BigSon decided it was time to remind us of his heritage. We left him alone in the van while we took his visiting girlfriend into the vet's office and had been inside less than five minutes when Bill happened to glance out the window. There was BigSon sitting in the driver's seat with a front leg over the steering wheel just as though about to switch on the ignition! The whole staff came to peer out the window and our vet, who knew him well, said we were lucky he hadn't driven off and left us stranded. We just assumed the crate hadn't been latched securely and we forgot about it. We shouldn't have assumed. And we shouldn't have forgotten the incident.

Checan's Ko Guma, demonstrating the retrieve for owner-trainer John Seaborn.

About two weeks later BigSon topped his "Opening Act." Bill had decided to walk a puppy while waiting for me to try on moccasins at a favorite shop in Cherokee. Apparently that was OK with Bigson as long as Bill and the puppy were by the van. It wasn't OK when Bill wandered off down the crowded street, amid throngs of curious puppy-petters. How did BigSon know they were no longer "there" with him? Don't ask me. Perhaps the Chief, there to provide photo opportunities for the tourists, could have told us. If he hadn't been so embarrassed...

Hearing a commotion, Bill looked back to see tourists scattering and a 20th—century warrior doing his best to call up that traditional wooden expression as a big wolfish appearing dog suspiciously checked out his ankle-length feathered headdress! Satisfied, BigSon lifted his leg, about to make a clearly masculine comment about men who wear feathers and bells. Running with the puppy, Bill shouted "BigSon, No!" The leg went down. BigSon stalked over to anoint the shrubbery as, gasping for breath, Bill skidded to a stop and began to apologize to the full-blood Cherokee. Regaining his composure, the Chief finally smiled as someone in the crowd yelled "great show" and the cameras started clicking. ... BigSon thought it was all great fun, even hammed it up for the crowd.

Well, that time we figured out how he performed the trick and, since it seems many Akitas are born with an inherent knowledge of plastic airlines crate construction, we shall forewarn you. Standing very tall, the dog pushes against the top with back and shoulders. Lifting the top half of the crate will spring the door just enough to allow the rods to pop loose, freeing the door so that the cat-like Akita can wriggle out. Some owners have also speculated that they lift the rod with a lower canine. I wouldn't doubt it if I were you.

Non-owners or new owners will read in disbelief. So be it, but don't say I didn't warn you and the point of this little story is exactly that: to warn you. We were very fortunate in that neither BigSon nor Sachmo suffered

Ch. O'BJ A-Head of The Game (Ch. O'BJ King's Ransom, ROMXP x Ch. The Dame's On Target O'BJ, ROMXP) doing her dancing bear act. Owned by Howard Carlton and the author.

While it's true that youngsters may never realize they can get out and therefore may not try, it's equally possible that while laying bored and just a bit resentful, your Akita will look at that door or the not-too-secure construction of collapsible crates and ergo, he knows he is Mr. Akita-Houdini. Please, don't take chances with your best buddy.

THE JAPANESE-AMERICAN AKITA

There exists much confusion about "import" type. Let's talk about the subtle differences in behavior and attitude between the Japanese type and the American type.

Each dog is an individual, and while certain personality characteristics become quite distinct within a given line, there are inborn habits and instinctive quirks attributable to the Japanese lines which clearly demonstrate the more primitive side of the Akita's background.

With the political atmosphere of the '90s, cultural and political walls are crumbling, and thankfully so too has the wall between AKC and JKC. Personally, I have mixed feelings about the flood of Japanese imports. We've seen the results of this in other breeds and they were not always favorable. Unfortunately, importing quality specimens is synonymous with importing pets and problems. While some breeders have been blessed with great integrity combined with an understanding of genetics, and are therefore able to sort out and overcome the new problems, others are not.

And yet there are so many endearing characteristics exemplified in the Japanese lines that we would hate to see them lost through the simple process of a forced evolution in the States. As the physical differences in type become ever more distinct, the latent personality traits become more obscure and more difficult to preserve. Yet, it is precisely these fascinating characteristics which truly separate the Akita dog from other breeds common to the North American continent.

Dancing on the hind legs is an odd trait which Akita owners of the 1960s and '70s took for granted. It's rarely mentioned to-

"Nicholas In Harness" photo by Kelle Clinton. Am/Can. Ch. Seawood's St. Nicholas, (Ch. Akita Tani's Daimyo, ROM x Ch. Golden Sun Seawood Wa Wa L'Wilac, ROM) is owned by Frank Clinton, bred by Kelle Clinton.

injury. It could have been otherwise. We now use bench-type crates and, although all of them are designed to be collapsible, we have found (through experience) it is much safer to permanently wire the top and sides together and secure the door with large bolt snaps. Akitas have been known to easily disengage the partition hooks, collapsing the crate in upon themselves and of course, factory door latches are seldom strong enough to thwart a determined dog of any breed.

day. Males are as adept at this delightful bear ballet as are females. While the American Akita is of a more serious nature, he is still known to let his hair down in the privacy of his own home. Students of wolf behavior will recognize many of the classic postures, gestures, and centuries-old games which the Akita instinctively employs.

There is a distinctly different twinkle, a smiling, squinting expression in the eyes of those dogs only a generation or two removed from Japan. Odd mannerisms such as rotating the head like an owl while performing the dancing bear act is a distinctly Akita gesture meant to convey extreme purely primitive behavior. Even when establishing dominance, the wolf can be a hilarious comedian. Males have been known to very deliberately mount a subordinate male in order to evoke a downright comical submission. Urinating to mark territory is well understood by all animals, including the human one. Less understood is the wild animal's use of urination and defecation to express frustration, love, anger, and not infrequently, a poignant disdain for certain humans.

The wild canine, despite his daily struggle to survive, seems to find time for pure fun, sexual and dominance displays, and play-

A 14-dog team comprised of 6 Huskies and 8 Akitas. Owned and trained by Phil Gray, Anchorage, Alaska.

pleasure at your arrival. Even understanding how supple the Akita dog is, this bird-like ability to cock and turn the head so far around defies the limits of canine neck structure! This unique display is most often performed by the female.

The forthright sense of humor demonstrated by some individuals is also indicative of their not-too-distant past. The sly, often cunning ways in which they so effectively put us in our place are easily traced to ing tricks on other members of the pack. Because the 20th-century Akita does not lend itself to pack living (due to man's enhancement of its dominant side), it depends on its human pack members to be the recipients of doggy practical jokes. Young Akitas love to parade through the living room with underwear trailing from their smiling mouths . . . especially when company is present. Perhaps it's only because you were paying more attention to your guests. Or perhaps the dog is playing a very deliberate joke, already having learned that you get upset-amused when he robs the clothes hamper.... Unwinding the toilet paper is a favorite puppy pastime. Why? Because they see you do it and figure they can do it better. And they can!

Most young dogs have a special love for your socks. Not the freshly laundered ones. Nature gave the human animal some pretty strong scent glands in the feet (so we could be easily tracked I suppose). Whatever the reason, it's funny-flattering for we know how strong our scent is in our shoes and socks. This may be a form of imprinting such as that used by mother seals and their babies. It's mostly scent which enables her to return to the rookeries and find her baby amid thousands of crying infants. I doubt that your Akita will ever have to track you through downtown Manhattan but just in case, instinct tells your puppy to snuff up your scent and catalog it forever. Pretty amazing, eh?

Now that you know that, you'll be better prepared and maybe just a teeny bit more tolerant if, Heaven forbid, your Akita soils your pillow. It's up to you to figure out if it was because he meant to do you a favor by marking your resting place so you could find it that night, or if he was deeply hurt by something you did to him. If you left him at a time when he has always been allowed to go, perhaps on the morning walk or the trip to the market, he knows. He'll be hurt and worried about you. The place strongest with your scent, the one place he knows you will return to, is your bed. Need I say more?

The closer the genetic makeup of your Akita is to the modern Japanese lines, the less inclined to guard effectively. You can't have the sweet, happy-go-lucky, innately primitive side of the canine personality along with the boldly dominant, fierce-if-needed side. The contrast between the old-style guarding, serious minded, Chow-Mastiff-Tosa Japanese Akita and the more ornamental, Shiba-like personality of the late 20th-century Japanese Akita is intriguing. For most owners, the ideal Akita is some-where between the two extremes and that, my friends, is the appeal of the American-Japanese Akita!

Akita owners are often astounded when their hundred-pound dog leaps a three-foot fence or jumps up on the vet's table unaided. This is but a practical application of the primitive hunting leap. Many other smaller breeds might be physically capable of this feat, but, of the large breeds, only the Akita knows he can do it!

The classic hunting leap is an extraordinary maneuver in which the dog springs into the air and comes down with all four feet and muzzle "on point," thus trapping and grasping a mouse or other small prey. A few lucky owners have witnessed this strange behavior but failed to understand the origin of the fascinating action. It seems to most often occur in high grass or snow when bitches are playing with weanling pups. To me, it's obvious they are instinctively teaching their youngsters how to hunt just as the Arctic fox or wolf would do. Your Akita doesn't need to catch the imaginary mouse any more than she needs to turn around and around to flatten a grassy bed or to bury her food for a time when hunting is poor. She does it because her ancestors did it. Let us hope that domesticated canines will continue to provide us with a glimpse back in time as they perform these instinctive actions in our living rooms and our back yards.

It's unfortunate that such natural abilities are at risk by the demand for excessive bone and the corresponding loss of muscular development and agility which has evolved in most American lines. This need not be so for in fact there's a happy medium long recognized by breed purists. It does not excuse light bone or a dog generally lacking in substance as being "Japanese type." That is most definitely not typical of Oriental type of the past or of today. The perfect Akita has yet to be born but when he is, he will be big, strong, powerful, with good bone and substance. And he will be the perfect athlete.

The point is, if we lose only physical characteristics, we may be able to recapture them by sneaking in a Japanese dog or even crossbreeding. It has been done. But if the age-old instincts and behavior patterns are lost, they are gone forever. We are steadily reducing habitat and destroying wildlife all over the world. Soon there will be no more wild things within reach of man. Animals behave differently in animal parks and zoos, no matter how much we try to recreate their natural habitat. The day will come when we have only worn-out films to illustrate the Arctic fox's uncanny ability to capture a tiny mole under a deep drift of snow.

For example, all dog owners are intrigued by the cute way a dog tilts its head at a strange noise. It's an enchanting little mannerism. Few of us stop to think why the dog does it and perhaps it's just as well. Some owners would not care to picture their little lap dog as an accomplished hunter. Even though unable to scent a mouse because of deep snow or wind direction, the wild canine is unlikely to pass it by. Hearing a squeak or rustle which even a good microphone would fail to pick up, the predator lines up the sound with each

ear, then by tilting the head. He causes those two lines to converge on the exact location of the prey. This canine sonar is a remarkably fine-tuned technique, not something dogs do to amuse us. We may smile at our dog's head-tilting attention to the sound of the can opener without realizing that the mannerism is vital to the survival of his wild brothers. We just scrape out the can of dog food and accept his appreciation without realizing the dog admires us for our keen senses in knowing the "mouse" was in the can!

In most industrialized countries, we are only 200 years removed from nature. Yet today we watch a nature program on television and are amazed to see an Arctic wolf formally bow to the pack leader or a vixen perform the hunting leap. How can we tell our children's

Ch. O'BJ Remus Of Sachmo, inbred son of Ch. Sachmo out of his daughter, Ch. O'BJ Nikki No Nikki, ROMP. Owner, Tamara Warren.

children that we once had a dog who could do that same incredibly beautiful aerial ballet? It's only too possible that they may not know the beauty of the wild and the fascination of having a wolf-creature in the living room. Our grandchildren may think we are senile, only dreaming the dreams of the old people.

Let us hope that the Akita-inu never joins the Endangered Species list.

The Path of Greatness

Nothing is so boring as history without substance. Tracing the path of a breed's development is vital to any in-depth breed book, but it's a lot more fun and the route is easier to remember when it's marked by friendly sign posts—individual dogs and people you can relate to!

So, along with all the names, facts, lists, and statistics, we have chosen to take you on a few side roads. In fact, we're going right into the kennels, living rooms— and hearts of many of the people who shaped the Akita, both in the U.S. and in other lands. You might even call this a trip down memory lane....

On behalf of all who love the Akita, I want to thank these kind owners for their wonderful response to my request for photos and personal information. In spite of busy lives or a shyness about writing something themselves, they gave in to my pleading and came through for future generations of Akita owners. I must also apologize for those few who declined to share information about their successful breeding programs or their famous dogs.

In other cases, I've dug deep into my own memory banks and dog files in order to

Goromaru-Go, born in 1948, is renowned for his consistent ability to produce excellent puppies. His name can be found on many of the pedigrees of important early dogs. Owner, Susumu Funakoshi.

provide you with a bit of background on interesting dogs or people.

Alphabetizing this chapter is an impossible task. Many of the dogs are better known by their "call name," some are not. Ditto for the people; some would be easy to look up by their kennel name, others by their last name. Well, that makes it easy for me and a bit more interesting for you because you'll just have to take a more leisurely stroll down the path of greatness. We've helped you a bit by capitalizing the name and route signs....

Our trip begins in Japan and meanders through several countries. What better place to begin than Futatsui Village, Akita Prefecture? It's the birthplace of **GOROMARU-GO,** born January, 1948. His sire was Ichinoseki Goma, whose owner, Mr. Sato, was walking from Tsubaki to Mr. Ichinoseki's. On his long walk, he rested with the Narita family. As fate would have it, their female Futatsui Goma was in season. The breeding took place during that fortuitous visit and so began another entry into the history books.

Goromaru was from the litter of three males and a single red and white female. Mr. Susumu Funakoshi purchased the red and white male puppy and his words describe Goromaru better than any:

"The most memorable scene when Goromaru first came to my home was a long-haired puppy with large head running from one person to another in the living room of our home. What made him outstanding was his eyes. They were rather small, triangular in shape, deep set and well balanced with the black mask showing the strong character of the dog even at that early age. However, we had difficulties with his diet because of his stomach."

As was common during that period, Goromaru was raised without any exercise for the first six months. Young puppies were not shown, just fed generous portions of food in order to develop a huge youngster. This would seem to indicate that the Japanese breeders of the day not only sought to increase size and substance but were aware that rapid growth combined with the rigorous exercise regime previously used for young Akitas, could be hazardous to big pups. Mr. Funakoshi comments, "I also think that there was no need for vigorous exercise because Akitas had less problems with their hind legs in those days."

Mr. Funakoshi notated that Goromaru's left ear began to stand at six months, and by eight months both ears were erect. They were thick and well formed, but his cheeks were not fully developed, which made his ears look a little too large. His owner describes his chest as being a little narrow, but considering the youngster had no exercise, this is understandable, as was his weak topline.

Mr. Funakoshi's mention of coat texture is interesting, "...his coat, which tended to be a little soft, became stiffer and developed to perfection."

In May of 1950, Goromaru was entered in the 13th Akiho Headquarters Show. Once again, the two predominant lines, Ichinoseki and Dewa, were represented by Ichinoseki Gomo and the heavy, well-built bitch, Tatemitsu-Go of the Dewa line. Goromaru's litter brothers, Jiromaru-Go and Long-Go, were also competing.

Goromaru-Go placed third in the class, but was unplaced in higher competition. His owner said his popularity with the crowd was overwhelming despite his loss in the ring. He describes the reasons for his defeat as his narrow chest and his tail being too long. Considering that tails today are often too short, one has to wonder how long was too long?

Mr. Funakoshi stated that Goromaru's markings (red pinto) were his greatest fault. He says, "at that time, pinto was not an accepted color of coat." Despite the unpopularity of his coat color, Mr. Funakoshi notes that his other excellent qualities were so evident that many breeders sought his stud services, and his popularity continued to increase.

Kongo-Go (Taishu-Go x Tatemitsu-Go), owner-handled by Mr. Hashimoto, was a silver sable dog of great nobility. One of Goromaru-Go's main competitors, Kongo-Go was well trained by his flamboyant handler and would dance on his hind legs during conformation shows.

Goromaru became known for his consistent ability to produce quality puppies. He was crossed to the Dewa line as well as the Ohira and Yurihi lines and can be found behind most of the more popular old pedigrees. One of his famous sons was **BANKOMARU**, who is described as only 25 inches tall but of such immense character that he appeared just as tall and impressive as 27-inch dogs. Bankomaru was winner of Akikyo's highest award, the Kinsho Meiyohai.

One of the most interesting stories about Goromaru also gives us an interesting word picture of **KONGO-GO** as well as an accurate description of the manner in which these two mighty dogs were shown. Goromaru and Kongo-Go competed at the Akikyo Show held in Tokyo. Kongo-Go was a silver sable and was characterized as a city slicker, a prince of a dog. Goromaru was, of course, a red pinto and today he might be called a bit of a country bumpkin. Mr. Funakoshi, described as having a dark thick mustache and a very serene personality, was himself considered something of a country boy, particularly when compared to the gaudy attire and flamboyant style of Mr. Hashimoto, Kongo-Go's handler. Thus, the stage was set for the classic story of country boy meets city slicker.

Quoting Mr. Ichiro Ogasawara, "The show was judged by Mr. Kiraizumi and myself. We were all impressed by the two Akitas simultaneously shown at the center of the ring. Mr. Hashimoto, the handler of Kongo, threw his hat in the air several times. And each time, Kongo would stand on his hind legs. On the other hand, Mr. Funakoshi, who was handling Goromaru, would advance Goromaru one step toward Kongo, then another. Both Akitas squared off, each staring each other in the eyes. Then suddenly, Kongo backed off. The match was decided."

This is just one of many interesting stories which describe the face-off. Courage and bravery was as revered in the national dog as in the kamikaze pilots.

Goromaru became ill at nine years of age. It appears that his death may have been due to bone cancer for he was said to be suffering from an ailment of the shoulder bone. He quietly passed away September 19, 1956 with his family standing by. Not uncommon for dogs of high rank, a funeral was held. There were many famous people in attendance, including the current managing director of Akiho, Mr. Matsuyama. It was a formal funeral befitting of such a famous dog.

There's a valuable lesson in Kichijiro Funakoshi's words and his reference to the words of another, "I for one hope that someone may succeed in producing an Akita as great as Goromaru one day. Mr. Gisuke Yamamoto, the great master, said 'we Akita lovers fancy all sort of dreams. We try to produce Goromaru with Tamakumo's coat. We fancy Tamakumo with Goromaru's spirit. We imagine having Bankomaru with Kumohibiki's coat, and such dreams drive us on in trying to breed better Akitas. Such efforts, indeed, are the foundation and basis for the production of Champion Akitas."

KINCHO-GO was bred by Mrs. Hiroko Abe and handled by Mr. Hashimoto, the owner of Kongo-Go. They proved to be an unbeatable team in the show ring. It was not common for women to be so openly involved in the sport in Japan, and Mrs. Abe's success is noted as the beginning of a new era for women.

Women also never handled in the ring, and it is significant that Japanese history records women handlers of this time as "flowers in blooming glory." Every dog lover must know that women have always nurtured litters and had great influence in the studious decisions on which dogs would make the best breeding pairs. Although women are still not so commonly seen in the show rings of Japan, Mrs. Abe's active involvement with the show career of Kincho-Go was prophetic of a changing show scene.

TAMAKUMO-GO was, according to Katsusuke Ishihara, the greatest Akita in the Tokyo area, whereas the top dog of northern Japan was Goromaru-Go. Tamakumo-Go was a rich black brindle with well-shaped ears, dark, deep-set eyes, and tight mouth. "The stop was a little too pronounced but did not detract from the overall quality of his facial features. Some people felt the pronounced

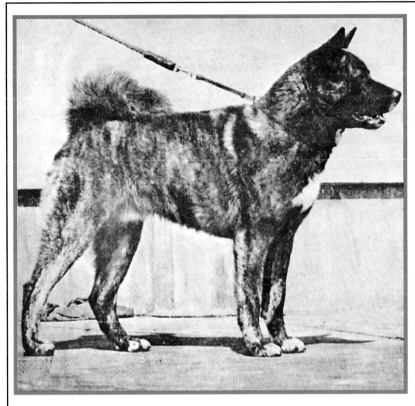

Tamakumo-Go, Meiyosho Award Winner (Arawashi-Go x Sansho-Go) was declared by Japan to be representative of the best large size Japanese dog even though brindles were unpopular at that time.

stop gave Tamakumo a more distinct appearance."

He is described as having a neck strong and powerful with a wide, deep chest, well supported by powerful legs. His most outstanding feature was said to be the condition and color of his coat. According to Mr. Ishihara, before Tamakumo, the Akita lacked distinction between the coarse guard coat and the wooly undercoat. "The beautiful black brindle coat of Tamakumo was most impressive, but the quality of having two distinct types of coat was, without question, the most outstanding feature, which I was determined to pass on to future Akitas."

Tamakumo-Go was shown in the six- to nine-month class, and did not do well, much to the disappointment of his owner, Mr. Tadamoto. According to Mr. Ishihara, "It was generally believed, at that time, that the true large- size Japanese breeds should be large and heavy. Therefore the more lean, muscular Tamakumo-Go was considered below standard. Tamakumo's lean musculature was a result of a training and exercise

program where Mr. Tadamoto, utilizing a small-wheeled bicycle, ran Tamakumo about 15 kilometers daily beginning in the fifth month."

Please note that Tamakumo was of much smaller structure. Do not begin road working your five-month-old puppy! The size and substance of most American dogs do not lend themselves to early roadwork, and premature stress on soft tendon and bone will likely cause the pasterns, feet, and topline to break down.

Tamakumo's photograph was sent to all the kennel clubs of the world, including the AKC, as representing the best large-size Japanese dog. There is no question he is thought to be the best Akita by at least a few people. His brindle color was not popular at the time, perhaps because most of the top dogs were red or white. Even then, there was much discussion about standardizing coat color. As has been pointed out, color fads are not uncommon whether one exhibits horses, cars, or Akitas.

Tamakumo was later shown at the Akiho

Headquarters Show where he won the Meiyosho Award. It is said his successful show career marked the beginning of the brindle popularity, even though there were people in the western regions of Japan who said the brindle was not a true Akita!

Just as controversy once raged here between "east coast" and "west coast" Akitas, similar discord occurred in Japan. People of the western region of Japan criticized others for not using Tamakumo in their breeding programs. There were wide differences of opinion between the breeders of Akita City and the Tokyo area.

Tamakumo-Go's sire was Arawashi-Go, a dog selected for his greater degree of angulation, front and rear, probably because he was not as large and heavy as some dogs popular during that time. He was not considered a valuable stud dog by most people, perhaps due to his round, light-colored eyes and his shallow stop. His disposition is described by Mr. Ishihara as "not gentle, especially toward strangers." His dam was Sansho-Go, a large bitch with good facial features, but described as shy.

Tamakumo was one of a litter of several famous dogs, but when Mr. Ishihara visited Mr. Tadamoto, Tamakumo's owner, they were surprised to find his ears not standing and the five-month-old puppy to be in a general state of poor health. It was remarked that Tamakumo's diet was too rich, too much beef, but I wonder too about all that roadwork! That he recovered is evident in his final reputation and the many fine progeny he contributed.

No trip from Japan to America could be more significant than that of the Akitas owned by the world famous **HELEN KELLER.** Miss Keller visited Akita City with her secretary, Miss Thompson, in June 1937. While there, she asked to meet an Akita. There was a bit of scurrying about in order to come up with an Akita of proper coat and kind temperament, as it was known that Miss Keller was blind and could only meet the dog through her sense of touch.

It was therefore decided to show Miss Keller a two-month-old puppy by the name of Kamikaze-Go. Following a lecture at the Akita Memorial Auditorium, the puppy was brought to Miss Keller. She fell in love with him and arrangements were quickly made to give that puppy to her. Kamikaze-Go was very young and so arrangements were made for him to be kept by the owner until Miss Keller completed her tour of Japan and Manchuria.

Unfortunately, Kamikaze died of distemper not long after returning to the States with Miss Keller. Quoting from a letter by Helen Keller to Mr. Ogasawara, dated November 1937, "How dear and loyal Kamikaze was! Every time I went out into the garden he would jump up to greet me with big affection. Nothing pleased him so much as to follow me round and round while I walked. I never saw such devotion in a five-month-old puppy. Whenever he was with us in a strange place, and Miss Thompson went out of the room for a few minutes, he would stick close to me. Once I shut the door not knowing he was outside in the hall. I felt a loud noise and wondered what it was. Presently I learned that it was my faithful protector banging against the door and barking until someone let him in. He made friends with everyone, and all who saw him were enthusiastic over his beauty and his adorable ways.

"If there ever was an angel in fur, it was Kamikaze. I know I shall never feel quite the same tenderness for any other pet. The Akita has all the qualities that appeal to me—he is gentle, companionable and trusty. But I cannot bear to write longer on the subject. I am so distressed. I can only thank you again for a gift which was a precious part of my home and an unfailing source of happiness."

This touching story was picked up in a news article in Japan, and the Minister of Foreign Affairs, Mr. Arita, arranged to have Miss Keller sent another puppy, in fact, he was a litter brother to Kamikaze.

It should be noted that this took place not long before World War II, and we can only assume that relationships between the two countries were becoming strained. But the youngster Kenzan arrived safely at his destination in New York. There were many write-ups and photos published in the *New York Times*, and the exotic Japanese dog received much publicity.

Again quoting a letter from Helen Keller to Mr. Ogasawara, dated April 1940, "You

"It touched me greatly when I heard from Mr. Fleisher that you had given up your favorite dog for my sake, and he meant all the more to me. I thank you every time I stroke his beautiful coat or touch his tail waving like a pine bow in the breeze. I love him not only as your dog, but also as a

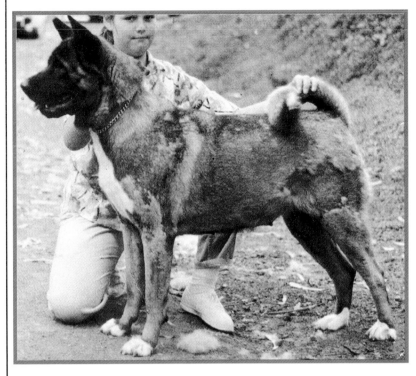

Akarui Kokoro, Shoyo and Ningyo's dam, a foundation bitch for Akita Tani Kennels. She is "blowing" a good thick coat.

will see that Kenzan-Go is as handsome as ever and full of life, but he is infinitely more than that. He has become a splendid protector and companion and is a precious part of my daily life. He lies beside me all golden in the sun while I write or read. Now and then, he rises and lays his noble head on my knee with great affection. He is never so happy as when Miss Thompson and I take him out for a walk.

"We have had deep snow drifts here all winter, and it has been a delight to watch Kenzan-Go rolling and leaping over them. Sometimes with a powerful paw, he would break the ice in a brook for a drink, and away he would go following the tracks of a fox or a deer in the snow. But he always came back telling me with nose, ear, and tail to play with him.

message from the Japanese people whose friendship shines among my brightest memories."

Following the war, Miss Keller again journeyed to Japan in 1947. While traveling from Hokkaido to Tokyo, she made a point of meeting with Mr. Ogasawara and again, she eloquently expressed her appreciation to him for both Kamikaze and Kenzan.

Since so many of those first Akita immigrants landed in the western half of our country, that is where we'll begin this odyssey. One of our first stops is California and the famous **AKITA TANI KENNELS** of **LIZ HARRELL.**

Liz is as staunch a supporter of the breed today as she was over thirty years ago when she and her husband incorporated the Akita Club Of America in Los Angeles.

123

Known for her willingness to share her vast knowledge of veterinary and genetic matters as well as her sharp insights into the breed and its interesting people, Liz has earned the respect of all Akita fanciers. Although she and I have slightly different concepts of what the perfect Akita would look like, we are bound in friendship through the dogs we love. Wonderfully written, her articles were always the first I chose to read, and I was never disappointed for I always found something of great value in her teachings. My respect and affection for Liz have grown over the years and, when I sent letters to prominent breeders requesting photos and "word pictures," I knew we all could count on Liz Harrell.

Her love for the breed is her duty, and her

Japanese Gr. Ch. Teruhide-Go, owned by Liz Harrell. Although obviously blowing coat in this photo, this early Akita Tani import exhibits the size, strength, and immense coat of Japanese dogs of his time.

unselfish dedication to helping others appreciate the Akita is something Akita fanciers have always been able to depend on. When we formed the Akita Breeders Council, Liz was one of the first (and most objective) people I called upon. If there had been more people as unbiased and devoted to the breed as Liz is, the ABC would have flourished.

Read carefully the following. It is history at its finest and offers valuable lessons for the true student of the breed.

"We started our kennels in the spring of 1959. We started with three females and one male. The male was never used for breeding. He was a handsome fellow with a super temperament, but he also had questionable hips. The female named Mikoni eventually gave us two litters. The other two females were litter sisters and they gave us our foundation to build upon. Akarui Kokoro was bred to her sire and that gave us Shoyo. Shoyo was bred back to his dam and that gave us Tatsumaki. Haiiro Kitsune gave us three litters and all three sired by Shoyo. From this we got Ureshii Kuma (the first OFA Akita), Toyo Koshaku (the sire of Kuro Chikara) and several other animals such as Hayashii Kuma, Waka Ningyo, etc. Using these animals with the Shoyo/Kokoro male, Tatsumaki, gave us a broad base to work with.

"In those days we showed in the Miscellaneous class, which meant we could not win championship points. All of the people at that time got out and supported the breed. We knew some day we would see the Akita in the championship role and that was enough to keep us going. Also, we loved the Akita breed.

"I took Shoyo to the Chicago International where there were dozens of Shih Tzu as well as several other Miscellaneous breeds. Shoyo was the first male Akita to place at Chicago, which pleased me greatly. It was there that I met Lina Basquette, who told me that I had a good animal in Shoyo. She now judges Akitas.

"Toyo Koshaku, one of Shoyo's sons, was the sire of Kuro Chikara, ROM and Ch. Akita Tanis Yorokobi No Moto, CDX, TD, one of the first Akitas to place in the Working Group and the first Best Of Breed at Westminster. One son of Shoyo is Hayashii Kuma, Bear who belonged to actor Pat Harrington and appeared with Pat on the old Steve Allen show. The child with Bear is Pat's daughter who now dances with the Joffrey Ballet. Other sons include Waka Ningyo and Kosho owned and trained by Edita Van der Lyn to work with her Dachsies. Edita trained animals for the RAF during World War II and for Ivan Rors in Florida. Kosho once appeared in a movie with Faye Dunaway and Anthony Quinn.

Akita Tani's Jirocho, (Akita Tani's Bad Leroy Brown x Akita Tani's Satin Doll) a Kuro Chikara grandson bred and owned by Liz Harrell.

Akita Tani's Tatsumaki, ROMP. Liz Harrell's poignant comment on the back of the photo. "These are the only pictures I have of Tatsumaki. On those days, we were young and thought we would all live forever. Better these than none at all..." A reminder to us all to take photos or video, while we have an opportunity and our dogs are young and glorious.

"Another of Shoyo's sons was Kuro Yama, sire of the first Best in Show Akita. Kuro Yama had a litter sister named Kuro Shusu, ROM. Kuro Shusu was bred to another Shoyo son, Tatsumaki, ROM to produce Ch. Akita Tani's Daimyo, ROM. Tatsumaki's dam was Shoyo's mother, Akarui Kokoro. Daimyo had several champion siblings including Akita Tani's Yoru Bara, CD, the first Akita female to place in the Working Group. Her sister, Kyoko, was a multiple-BOB winner, and we still carry these lines in our kennel.

"In the first 15 years we made two outcrosses. One of these was to a Japanese Gr. Ch. named Teruhide-Go, which we owned. One of Teruhide's daughters was Meiyo. She was the first Akita bitch to win a first at the Chicago International.... again surrounded by

Akita Tani's Toyo Koshaku, another Shoyo and Kitsune son who was himself the sire of Akita Tani's Kuro Chikara and Ch. Akita Tani's Yorokobi No Moto CDX, TD, bred by Liz Harrell.

Shih Tzu and other breeds. Meiyo was bred to Shoyo and produced two get that we kept. They were named Makoto, a male who won an Akita match his first time out. More than 60 to compete with, so it was a big win for us. His sister, Mazu, was bred to Kuro Chikara and produced Ch. Akita Tani's Nishiki Ryu, who appears in many pedigrees both here and in

Akita Tani's Shoyo-Go. Even in this photo at 10 years old and blowing coat, one can see the balance and overall good structure of the Akita Tani Kennel's foundation sire.

other countries and that includes Best In Specialty and Best In Show winners.

"Kuro Chikara, a Shoyo grandson, was bred to Shoyo daughters and granddaughters. One of his granddaughters was Akita Tani's Kageboshi, winner of the first Akita Obedience Trial. Kageboshi and her sister, Akai, were both bred to Shoyo and from that came Akita Tani's Shorii San, who was the first Akita to get a CD at six-and-a-half months of age. She qualified in four shows held on weekends one week apart. Akai produced Kofuku-No's Shoga Hime, the dam of three-time Best In Show winner Holly Go Litely.

"Kuro Yama was bred to a Shoyo grand-daughter named Sumiko and that produced Ch. Akita Tani's Mitsu. The late Stephanie Gimbel showed her for me.

"Ichi Tokubetsu was our last champion. He finished in six shows with five Best Of Breeds. We then retired from showing but still occasionally produce a litter. Of the dogs we have produced recently, there is Jirosho... who lives with us... he is a Kuro Chikara grandson. 'Sam' lives in the Pacific northwest but has never been shown. You will note that families own these dogs. They live happy lives and stay with the family. They are not bounced from place to place like used cars.

Top left: Akita Tani's Kuro Shinju, owned by Peg Johnson. Top right: Ch. Jai-Laphans Zee, owned by Jasper White. Bottom left: Fuji, owned by the Nakashima family. Bottom right: Korhu at 10 months, owned by Liz

Middle: Ch. Akita Tanis Ichi Tokubetsu represents a special bit of history with Shoyo-Go four times in his pedigree. Bred by Liz Harrell.

One dog placed in Washington State truly enjoyed his life. His is picture appeared in the *Seattle Times,* so he got his 15 minutes of fame.

"We have enjoyed our thirty years with Akitas. Still have quite a few around us. I regret only that it is necessary for this regal breed to need a rescue operation."

Also in Washington State is **CROWN ROYAL AKITAS,** the home of **CH. CROWN ROYAL AKAI OKASHI, CD** and owner **INGRID LINERUD.**

Okashi's sire is BIS Ch. Asahi Yama No Kaminari, CD and her mom is Bondel Chuken Tokyo Rose. Okashi's achievements are many. She was the number one female all systems in 1984 and the number one female in Breed points in 1987. She was BOS at the 1986 National Specialty. Thrilling to watch in the ring, it was no surprise that she was also BOW at the Canadian National Specialty, and achieved her CD title in three consecutive shows with scores of 191, 192.5 and 194. Okashi is the dam of ten champions. The person who can tell us all about Okashi is her owner and biggest fan, Ingrid Linerud:

Ch. Crown Royal Slugo Go, ROMP (Crown Royal's Samurai Joe x Bondel Chuken Sammie) owned by Ingrid Linerud.

Ch. Crown Royal Akai Okashi, C.D., BB winner and #1 Bitch 1984, Ch. Bondel Chuken Benson Jo, winning BOS, and their six months old daughter Ch. Crown Royal's O Okii Ashi Kuma, taking a five point major at her first show! Owned by Ingrid Linerud.

Ch. Crown Royal American Dream Boy, ROM and litter sister Ch. Crown Royal's Autumn Fujin, taking their second B.I.S. Brace at Region IV Specialty, 1988. Bred/Owned by Ingrid Linerud.

"Okashi was born March 17, 1982 on St. Patrick's Day, a very lucky day for us. She is a breeder's dream come true. She had soundness, type, movement, and that true 'look at me' attitude that makes a special dog really special.

"Her show record speaks for itself, and this includes her CD title in three shows. But Okashi is more than just a show dog. She is my girl, a wonderful companion, always with me, and so very, very loyal. She loves to go to the river and swim and chase ground squirrels. Even now at eight-and-a-half years, she is fit as a fiddle.

"She was always the best mom, having four litters and not losing one pup! But her biggest feat in my eyes was being a surrogate mom to Ch. Toku's nine babies, after I lost Toku when her pups were two days old. Okashi seemed to know when I came home from the vet's without Toku that a task had to be done. She got in the whelping box and

Am/Can. Ch. Crown Royals Akai Okashi CD, ROMXP (Ch. Asahi Yama No Kaminari CD x Bondel Chuken Tokyo Rose). Breeder-owner, Ingrid Linerud.

Ch. Yamashita's Aka Khan of C and L, CD (Ch. Cee Jays Rocky-Road of Kibo x Ch. Yamashita's No Aiko Amy Go) bred by Masaru and Ayako Yamashita. Owner-handled by Lynnmarie Yamashita-Doran. Co-owners, Charles E. Doran, Jr. and the breeders.

mal devotee who was raised with 11 different breeds of companion dogs. Her kennel name was formerly Yamashita's Akitas, established in 1978, and still carried on by her parents.

In 1982, Chuck and Lynn were married, the two kennels merged, and C and L Kennels came into existence. The merger also included the dogs, so they now have Akitas, Great Pyrenees, Pembroke Welsh Corgis, Shiba Inus, and Brussels Griffons. They have produced 29 homebred Ch. Akitas and Pyrs and 11 Companion Dog (CD) titleholders. Both are active club members and completely devoted to the sport. They have fun match get-togethers for their puppy people (what a great idea!) and are known as solid dog people. Asked to tell us about one of their favorite dogs they elected to share with us **CH. YAMASHITA'S AKA KHAN OF C AND L.**

"The dog we would like to be remembered for all his wonderful qualities was Ch. Yamashita's Aka Khan of C and L, CD. He was well into his CDX work when he passed away. Aka Khan was one of the most loving and outgoing Akitas we've ever known. Everyone who met him remarked on his personality and luxurious orange-red coat. He had the brilliant color noted in the standard, but not found in the rings today. He gave us our reds and always produced at least one all-white puppy per litter.

"With limited breeding, Aka Khan produced three champions and half a dozen get with points. He gave us Ch. C and L's Cha-Cha Khan, who finished at the tender age of eight months and 12 days, breeder-owner-handled. Not only had she won consistently over other bitch specials but she also took some breeds away from the boys. Cha-Cha's litter brother, Shiro-Khan, is an impressive, large white male, sporting the

tried to nurse all nine babies. She came into some milk, but didn't have all the milk needed; but she was a true mother to those pups. All nine are healthy and thriving.

"There will never be another Okashi. None could ever compare."

Traveling down the Pacific west coast, it would be fun to drop in on the very interesting **C and L KENNELS** of **CHARLES and LYNN DORAN.** C and L is a familiar kennel name all across the country. Charles 'Chuck' E. Doran, Jr. is an AKC judge licensed for the entire Working Group, Norwegian Elkhounds, Pembroke Welsh Corgis, and Cardigan Welsh Corgis. His kennel name was formerly De Fer Great Pyrenees, which was established in 1964.

Lynn Marie Yamashita-Doran is an ani-

most beautiful black pigment you can find on any Akita, let alone a white one. He had both majors and one BOB win by a year.

"Aka Khan always greeted everyone happily and never had an enemy. Not only was he a purported producer of beautiful puppies, but his wonderful personality was passed on to his get and made him an admirable ambassador for the Akita breed."

Going way back in West coast history, we couldn't overlook **CH. RYUJIN'S HOTEI and BOBBI WELTLICH.**

By Ch. Kuma Ryoshi x Ch. Arigato Miko's Brandy. Hotei is described for us by his good friend and the owner of his sire, Tiare Arndt:

Ch. Arigato's Mikos Brandy, (by Rowdy San x Miko Go) was bred by V. Clifford, owned by Bobbi Weltlich.

"Hotei was sweet, sweet, sweet, just like his dad Kuma, and he was a hulk at 28 inches and 135 pounds. He lived on a houseboat, and he and his mom are in a book on houseboats! His owner Larry built a three-story gorgeous boat featured in a book on the subject. Hotei's mother became a champion at age six after whelping her litters on the houseboat. They filmed scenes from the movie *The Killer Elite* on Larry and Bobbi's houseboat. Brandy's mom was a litter sister to Ch. Gaylee's O'Kaminaga. Hotei was special!"

Let's now move a bit further south because we're about to have the honor of meeting the breed's first Best In Show winner, **CH. WANCHAN'S AKAGUMO**, sired by Akita Tani's Kuro Yama x Tusko's Star, owned by Pete Lagus, co-owner, Carol Foti. "Brownie" was the first Best In Show Akita in the United States. I'll never forget when Carol called me, her voice quavering with excitement. "He's done it! He's done it!" she exclaimed and even as she told me he had just gone BIS under Anna Katherine Nicholas, it was just too wonderful to com-

prehend. Carol then went on to describe the historical event. She said the temperature was well over 90 degrees and Best In Show was judged on black asphalt in some sort of parking lot. She said the magnificent "Brownie showed his heart out" and with great pride in her voice, she said he never once dropped his tail or showed the effects of the extreme California heat.

Ch. Ryujin's Hotei, by Ch. Kuma Ryoshi x Ch. Arigato Miko's Brandy, breeder/owners Larry and Bobbi Weltlich.

I could believe that for we had gone with her to road work Brownie up what she called "Jesus Christ Hill." It was a very steep incline which she drove up in low gear with Brownie trotting effortlessly beside her car. She told us she kept his coat in oil and Bill and I agreed it was a glorious, shiny coat. Although we never saw him shown, I'm sure the big brown dog was indeed a sight to behold.

But wait, the person who knew and loved him the most is his owner, Pete Lagus, who says:

"Ch. Wanchan's Akagumo, known as Brownie, was the first Akita to win a Best In Show in America. He was bred by Dr. and Mrs. P. Lagus and owned by the Lagus' and C. Foti. Brownie was the quintessential showman and was legendary for his rapport with the crown around the Group ring. He is the sire of two ROM sons, Ch. Toyo-No Charlie Brown and Ch. Vaguas The Mean Machine. For a big dog, Brownie was an exceptionally fine mover and seemed to glide rather than move around the ring. He, more than any other dog, opened up the Group ring for the Akita breed in California."

No breed can progress without tireless people willing to work for the club. There have been many such selfless people who have devoted their time and energies to the Akita Club Of America. Two names stand out in the "highly capable" category as both club workers and premier breeders and exhibitors. Their most famous winner is the handsome "Mad Maxx" and **FRANK and SYLVIA THOMAS, CHIHEISEN AKITAS** give us a firsthand introduction to **BIS & BISS CH. NORTH STAR'S MAD MAXX:**

"I first laid eyes on Maxx in Denver in October of 1987. I had flown in to meet with the Rocky Mountain Akita Club and assist with their plans for the 1988 National Specialty. Naturally, my trip was planned to coincide with the Flatirons and Evergreen KC Shows... after all, why take a trip unless you can plan to attend a dog show at the same time?

"I spotted Maxx immediately; he was a bit rambunctious, but gorgeous. His owners, Mark and Cathy Schipper, had entered him in the six-to-nine-month puppy dog class. Tommy Mayfield was the judge, and it was quite clear...at least to me...that Maxx should take the points from the puppy class. Maxx was somewhat untrained and his handler, Marks, was inexperienced in the ring, but Mr. Mayfield set that aside and went with Maxx for the points.

"The next time I saw Maxx was at the 1988 National. He had developed into a very promising young dog,

Ch. Wanchan's Akagumo, known as Brownie, making history under Anna Katherine Nicholas—the first Best in Show ever won by an Akita in America. Brownie was bred by Dr. and Mrs. P. Lagus and owned by the Laguses and Carol Foti. He was an exceptionally fine mover for such a large dog and, on the auspicious occasion of this win, proved his showmanship by performing despite oppressive California heat.

and I was pleased that I still loved the way he looked and moved. Shortly after the National, I began corresponding with the Schippers and in March of 1989, I finally persuaded them to trust Frank and me with Maxx.

"We brought him to California and almost immediately began to show him. Maxx was entered in eight shows, of which he won six, and easily finished. All of this was not without incident. About two weeks after we got Maxx, we drove to Las Vegas for Silver State KC. Maxx was left in our van for the night; because it was warm, I felt 'sorry' for him and opted to leave him loose in the van rather than in his crate. When I came down the next morning, I thought I would literally have a heart attack. The side window in our van had been popped open and Maxx was gone! Usually the 'mistress of calm,' I was in a dead panic; I was crying and hyperventilating all at the same time. I offered a group of construction workers $1000 if they could find Maxx anywhere on the hotel property. Frank and I ran all ten floors of the parking lot of our hotel and the hotel next door. Finally, in desperation, I told Frank he had to rent a helicopter to look for Maxx. Bless his heart, Frank never questioned that decision, he simply rented a helicopter to the tune of $500 an hour to look for Maxx. An hour and a half later, there was still no Maxx. Fortunately cooler heads prevailed and Roger Kaplan, our dear friend, decided to make one more trip to the humane society to look for Maxx. Sure enough, he had been picked up in the Flamingo Hilton's parking lot and for a nominal fee, we 'bailed' Maxx out and breathed a sigh of relief!

Ch. Chiheisen's Take It To The Maxx (Ch. O'BJ Zack The Spotted Bear, ROM x Ch. Kuroi Kao Dallas Alice, ROM) shown taking one of his many Best In Show wins. He was also Best of Breed at the 1994 National Specialty. The striking red pinto is handled by Bruce Shultz for owners, Mark and Cathy Schipper, Frank and Sylvia Thomas, and more recently, Mr. Jose Mauricio Machline.

"As the saying goes, the rest of Maxx's story is dog-show history. Maxx matched every goal we set for him. He was campaigned for two years and defeated close to 3400 Akitas. In that time, he won in excess of 100 Bests Of Breed including two regional Specialties, a National Specialty and an all-breed Best In Show. He is a National Specialty and Westminster Award Of Merit winner and was ranked number two Akita in 1990 and 1991 and retired as number two in February 1992. Throughout his career, he was presented by Gretchen and Bruce Schultz. At the dog shows, Maxx never met a man, woman, child or dog he did not like. Because of his extensive show schedule, his availability to stand at stud has been extremely limited. In spite of that, he has sired seven champions to date and numerous major-pointed offspring. At home and on the road, he exhibits true Akita temperament and is courageous, loyal and loving. I love this dog for his gentleness and loyalty; I am awed by his beauty and massiveness; and I respect his strength and dignity. Maxx is six years old, but still exhibits the playful exuberance of a puppy, particularly when with his constant com-

BIS/BISS Ch. Running Bear's Sunburst (Ch. Big D's Akanboo Akai Palaccort x Am/Mx Ch. Kuma Yama's Palace Court Dani) winning under highly respected judge Richard Renihan, handled by Keith Pautz for owners Judy Gresham and Mark and Lisa Borlase.

panion, Kimmie, Ch. Chiheisen's Kismet of SMA. His gentle spirit and willingness to please have endeared him to us. I believe he is one of the finest representatives of his breed that I have ever seen and have felt privileged to know. When I am around him, I know how truly special he is. He's more than a great show dog: he's a 'gentleman!'"

Moving east through the desert of the great Southwest, there are interesting places to go other than the casinos of Las Vegas.

There's the sunny home of **BETTY and WALTER YELVINGTON** and **SABAKU KAZE** Akitas. They are the breeders of my first Akita, Sabaku Kaze's Asgard Kami and their line (based on Triple K) weaves through many top pedigrees today. It's always a special treat to see Betty at the Nationals.

There are some other stars in Vegas, they are billed as **RUNNING BEAR AKITAS.** Owners **BOB and JUDY GRESHAM** share their story:

"Our kennel was formed in 1984 and is located in Las Vegas. The name was chosen for the Akita's "bear" head and wonderful movement. Presently, five Akitas make their home with us and we co-own nine others. We belong to the Akita Club Of Las Vegas and the

Akita Club Of America and follow their code of ethics. We x-ray against hip dysplasia, and eyes are examined annually for any congenital problems. Written guarantees are given and all pet/companion dogs are sold under a spay/neuter contract.

"Running Bear Akitas has constantly striven for the perfect Akita. We do not breed litter after litter; each is well thought out and with purpose. The highest priority is an exceptional temperament. Next is over-all movement, soundness, beautiful face, tight feet, large heads with short muzzles and small tilted ears. If they happen to be brilliant red, all the better!

him Best Of Breed and a Group three at the Region V Specialty. The ultimate came November 11, 1990 where he was awarded Best In Show at the Cabrillo Kennel Club and became the 17th Akita to do so."

A trip to the opposite coast will be no less exciting. Let's stop first at the lovely Maryland home of **BETTYE and FRANCIS KRUG,** birthplace of **KRUG'S SANTO.**

Sired by Gyokushu Of Tojo Kensha out of Sheba, Santo was born December 7, 1963 and he died July 16, 1973. He was one of the most important sires on American soil but more than that, like all the great ones, he lives on forever in the words and heart of his

Am/Mex. Ch. Kuma Yama's Palace Court Dani and her six months old son, future Ch. and BIS winner, Running Bear's Sunburst. Dani was bred by Patricia Van Buskirk and is owner handled by Judy Gresham.

"Examples of our two best dogs are Am/Mex. Ch. Kuma Yama's Palace Court Dani and Best In Show and Specialty Ch. Running Bear's Sunburst (Buster). Dani has proven to be our foundation with wonderful temperament, movement and poise. She has been awarded through our local club top show puppy, dog and bitch and top brood bitch. Dani has produced two champions to date and has several others now on the show circuits. Buster finished his championship with all majors starting at six months of age. His first time out as a special earned

owner. Writing for *Akita Reference*, Bettye says:

"Santo made his appearance on Pearl Harbor Day and what an explosion his birth was to have on the Akita breed. Santo was one of 12 and, unfortunately, was the only one to live past two years of age. Ten died at birth or by age 6 weeks of distemper.

"The birth of this litter of 'unheard of royalty' made headlines—the story and picture being picked up by Associated Press and carried all over the U.S. The *Weekly Reader* in schools even picked it up too.

"Santo was cream, white front boots and a diamond-shaped crest on his chest. He had a black mask with a perfectly marked blaze down and around his nose. His head was absolutely gorgeous with small ears though you'd never have believed this by his large ear size as a pup.

"Santo was just too good to be true. After raising German Shepherds for eight years, I didn't know what to make of this puppy that never had to be house trained, never barked (what a joy) and wasn't a pacer. He was well aware of everything that was going on and was there to protect if needed. Santo was 'my' dog. Fran would tell him to do something; Santo would look at me to see if he had to do it.

"When people came to see the Akita, Santo would keep circling my legs and the people thought he was there for them to pet him. I knew that one move to harm me and he would have had them! I love the no-growling in the Akita. I loved Santo—did, and still do. There hasn't been and never will be another like him. After 11 years, there are still tears for him.

"He could be spiteful to me. If I scolded him, he'd make sure he mouthed some article of my clothing, just enough to say 'I could have chewed it.' Or after having been exercised and left at home with the kids, he would go into my bedroom, go around the bed, get up on my pillow and have *another* bowel movement. I sure got his message.

"Santo was raised with four of our children. He was their playmate and protector. He was with them in the woods, fields, wherever those five-, six-, seven-, and eight-year-old kids wandered—he was there.

"As a show dog, well, he wasn't. But he sure produced. I won't dishonor my dog by pointing out his faults in print. He threw very few of them. I'm no record keeper so I can't tell you what his get have done. I *can* tell you he's behind nearly every good Akita on the East coast. Krug's Sotto, a son, was Top Akita in the U.S. in 1968 and 1969. Another nice son was Ch. Krug's Daiyusei. Santo set the Krug look for us. I can see him in so many dogs even when he's five or six generations back.

"I love you and miss you, my protector, companion, and friend, Krug's Santo......"

A hop, skip and jump away to Pennsylvania, we'll find the famous **FREROSE AKITAS** of **FRED DUANE and DIANE MURPHY**

Am/Can. Ch. Frerose's Rev. Jesse is the early 1990's ambassador of one of the oldest and most successful Akita kennels. The champions and Register Of Merit Akitas owned or bred by the Frerose Kennels in Pennsylvania are legendary.

Am./Can. Ch. Frerose's Tugger The Slugger with his little Shiba friend, Freroses Beaver Dam.

One of my clearest memories is standing by Fred at ringside on the always-tough Florida winter circuit. I couldn't tell you who all the other "Specials" were on that circuit, only that there were some especially good dogs in competition. Even so, the other Specials might as well have stayed home. It had been Jojo and Sachmo throughout the circuit, and, as the week drew to a close, it was again a hotly contested showdown. Fred shook his head and muttered, "You got it today, B.J." but he was smiling. "I dunno, Fred, the judge really seems to be looking at Jojo." Fred sighed, his eyes riveted on the judge's face and his body tense with expectation. I glanced back at the ring as the judge took a few steps in Jojo's direction. Glancing back at Fred, I saw the lines in his face soften as he smiled and his eyes shone with pride and love for his dog. I knew then, it didn't matter which dog won for they were not only two of the greatest Akitas of their time, they were two of the best loved dogs ever!

When Sachmo became suddenly and seriously ill on the way to ringside the following day, it was Fred who was the most concerned. He was quick to offer help of any kind, and I have no doubt he would have sacrificed getting his own dog into the ring in order to help us find the vet and get help for Sachmo.

Am./Can. Ch. Frerose's Rev. Jesse, showing exceptional head, ears, and ear set.

It saddens me to hear people say that Jojo had a less than desirable temperament. I can say from many years of first-hand experience under the most stressful of situations, Jojo and his owner were both gentlemen of the first degree.

About his dogs and breeding accomplishments, Fred tells us

"In 1971, I acquired my first Akita after having bred and shown champion German Shepherd dogs.

"One of my first Akitas was Am/Can/Bda. Ch. Kenjiko Royal Tenji, ROMPX, better known as 'Jojo.' He was a great influence on my breeding program. He gave me what I was looking for; beautiful strong rears, good movement, and that winning attitude, while still maintaining that true Akita look and temperament. Jojo is in all my present Akitas several times.

"Another of my foundation animals is a bitch I bred, Frerose's Honey Bear, ROMP. She produced two ROMs with JoJo as their sire. They are Am/Can. Ch. Frerose's Gypsie Rose, ROM and Ch. Frerose's Sara Lei, ROMPX, who was tied for number one producer. Frerose has bred nine Register Of Merit Akitas.

"Am/Can. Ch. Frerose's China Doll of Kim-Sai, a Jojo granddaughter and multiple Best Of Breed and Group winner, is in all of my pedigrees. Although she is not an ROM,

China contributed much to my lines in the way of size, movement, and elegance.

"Jojo and China were my two favorite Akitas, even though I have loved many.

"When I go to a dog show, and most of the Akitas have Frerose in their bloodline, I feel that I have done a lot to improve the breed in North America, which I consider an accomplishment."

AM/CAN. FREROSE'S TUGGER THE SLUGGER is another top dog at Frerose. Fred says "Tugger is the sire of Group and Specialty winners such as Am/Can. Ch. Freerose's Rev. Jesse and Am/Can. Freerose's Mr. Moto. Tugger refuses to live alone and has always had the company of a Shiba in his run. He loves puppies and melts in their presence like any proud dad or granddad. Tugger is a wonderful Akita and a credit to his breed."

Am./Can. Frerose's Tugger The Slugger at 8 years old with his friend and handler, Diane Murphy.

AM/CAN/ BDA. CH. KENJIKO ROYAL TENJI, ROMPX Sachmo and Jojo competed frequently and both were "all Akita." Professionally handled, it didn't seem to matter to Jojo who took him in the ring as long as they showed him respect and just let him show! He exemplified the Akita in many ways, and I still chuckle about the time Fred arranged for a different handler to take him in the ring under Henry Stoeker. The rumor was that his regular handler didn't do well under Mr. Stoeker. Worried that Jojo might lose to Sachmo because of a personality conflict, Fred rounded up a different handler for the day.

There were several Specials in competition and Sachmo was in front of Jojo. Sachmo was examined and gaited and we then stood at the end of the line watching the judge go over Jojo. All went well and he gaited confidently around the ring to take his place at the end of the line. A moment later, I glanced back as I heard the handler scold him for not standing still. The handler gave Jojo a little jerk on the collar to correct him. Well, Jojo looked that stranger square in the eye and I heard him rumble.

Sachmo tensed but must have known it was the handler Jojo was "talking" to because he never looked back at them. Jojo's handler thought it over and then reaching into his pocket, he pulled out a piece of liver and offered it to Jojo. Jojo continued to look the handler square in the eye as though to

Am./Can./BDA Ch. Kenjiko Royal Tenji, ROMPX. Owner, Frederick O. Duane.

show flawlessly. After the judge had moved the lineup around the ring again, the handler was able to stack Jojo with no problem. Obviously, it wasn't stacking the mature male objected to, it was being disciplined about something he probably knew how to do better than the man who had attempted to discipline him! Tough? Yes. Overly so? Not at all. Just a wonderful dog with tons of character and, sure enough, he defeated Sachmo that day.

His fluid movement, hard topline, and great presence have made a strong contribution to the Akita breed. But, like all great ones, Jojo had another side, and that is what his owner, Frederick O. Duane, can share with us. Fred says:

"Growing up he was a good puppy, he only chewed up one sock. One of his favorite things to do to you, throughout his whole life, was stretched out on the floor and, when you walked by, he would stick out his paw and try to trip you. Then he would grumble at you as if laughing. All through his career he loved the applause people would give him and he would show and show.

make him say "Uncle." He ignored the bait. "Okay, big guy, do it your way," muttered the handler as he shrugged his shoulders and stepped back.

Satisfied, Jojo squared his stance (while my heart sank) and went on to

"He always slept under the bed and when I stayed in motels, he would slide under during the night. Then in the morning I would have to lift up the bed for him. Jojo

Am/Can Ch. Frerose's Shiraito (Ch. Frerose's Rock-N-Rye x Frerose's Samantha).

was the first Bermuda Champion and the first Canadian Champion. In the U.S. and Canada he was number one Akita 1978. He was number one Akita in Canada from 1975 to 1979 except one year he was number two. In the U.S. he was in the top ten every year he was shown.

"In 1982 Jojo, almost ten years old, went to the Akita National Specialty and won BOB from the veterans class. He went on to a Group second and beat 1000 dogs, the biggest dog show that year.

"In 1983, almost 11 years old, he went to the Akita National Specialty and won BOB from the veterans class and on to a Group first.

"Jojo has amassed over 300 BOBs, 49 Group placements, 48 of them in the old Group. (n.b.: Before the Working and Herding became separate Groups.) No other Akita living or dead has accomplished that feat."

Edward Israel served as president of the

Ch. Frerose's Dark Moon of Sho-Go, ROMX (Am/Can Ch. Kenjiko Royal Tenji x Am/Can Ch. Frerose's China Doll).

Akita Club Of America and both Ed and his wife, Adrienne, have been a strong influence in the breed, having produced some outstanding dogs. As I recall, Adrienne was a Samoyed person and she bought their first Akita as a wedding gift for Ed.

Adrienne was on my deposit list, but the co-bred litter we had hoped would contain a special puppy didn't really impress either of us. Feeling badly and knowing how disappointed they were, I called around, found a litter, and took them up to Terry Wright's kennel to have a look. Later, they purchased a Sachmo daughter from Tobe Kennels and again, I felt badly for them

Ch. Frerose's Happy Star (Ch. Kim-Sai's Buster of Frerose x Frerose's Lovin Molly).

when I heard she had failed to pass her x-ray.

We lost touch but it wasn't long before I began hearing of their success in the ring. Gifted owner-handlers, they became part of the winner's circle up and down the East coast. Originally located in Pennsylvania, let's stop at the **WINDOM AKITAS** of **ED and ADRIENNE ISRAEL.**

Ed shares the following: "Windom Akitas has been breeding Akitas since 1976. Our foundation bitch, Windom's All That Jazz, ROM (Ch. Krug's Red Kadillac x Lijo's Jasmine of Windom) is the producer of 13 champions as of this writing and is currently tied for the number two producing bitch in the history of the breed.

"We are a small kennel having produced numerous champions. We are proud that the majority of our champions are first and foremost pets and then show dogs. All but about three of the champions we have produced have been owner handled to their championships."

Throughout our journey we'll have to rely on memory because names which used to be well known have faded from the Akita scene and many of the famous dogs are no longer living. No visit to the East coast would be complete though without learning more about **SAKURA'S BUSHI, CD**, a strong influence in many eastern pedigrees. He was

Ch. Windom's Jazzabelle by Ch. Kin Hozan's Toklat x Windom All That Jazz, breeder/owner Ed and Adrienne Israel.

Ch. Windom's The Jazz Man (Ch. Kin Hozan's Toklat, CD x Windom All That Jazz) another show ring star bred and owned by Adrienne and Ed Israel.

Ch. Windom's Stardust, bred and owned by Windom Akitas, is shown taking an impressive B.O.W. award.

whelped October 4, 1967, sired by Prince Jo, CD, out of Michiko of Kensha, CD. Bushi's owner, Barbara Miller, described him as follows:

"What can I say about Bushi? He was a pretty puppy that continued to grow and develop to a beautiful specimen of an Akita. And as an added bonus he has a typical Akita temperament. Aloof and distrustful of strangers. Dignified in public. A virtual demon when fighting. And a loving, zany nut with family and friends.

"He is the lord and master of our pack of Akitas and demands and gets respect and attention from the other dogs. Being very male, all the bitches vie for his attention. He reigns supreme."

Bobbi not only had a way with words, she had a firm grasp on the essence of the Akita. One of her best writings was published in the AKC *Gazette* and it's easy to see that she based much of her feel for the Akita on her great love, Bushi. She said of him, "Bushi inherited his father's head and more times than not has passed it on to his sons. I've always felt that for a dog to be a good specimen for breeding it not only must have soundness and type but must have temperament. A male should be Dominant with a capital D. Nothing soft or feminine. And conversely, a bitch should be a dominant female. Sweet but with a gutsiness that equals that of a male. To breed less is doing a disservice to the breed by weakening it."

Windom All That Jazz, ROM, sired by Ch. Kin Hozan's Toklat, ROMXP, bred by Ed and Adrienne Israel.

Ch. Kin Hozan's Toklat, ROMXP (Ch. Royal's Benkei x Ch. Cripple Creek's Cotei Shinju) bred by Bea Hunt, owned by C. Harala.

It was Bobbi's wish that Bushi's sons would beat him in the show ring. She said then she would know that she had done a great job of breeding the Akita. Barbara is no longer active in dogs, but anyone who has dogs going back to the Sakura lines will agree that indeed Barbara Miller did "a great job breeding Akitas."

Summing up the Akita breed, Bobbi once said, "Bushi is a great beast of a dog to have for a friend!"

In the great state of New York, there's Coney Island but to Akita people, there's a more famous "island." It's called **ISLAND AKITAS. ROBERT** and **RUTH BROSKIN** are successful breeders of miniature horses and they seem to have applied their knowledge of genetics to the Akita breed, producing many outstanding specimens from their Grand Island, New York kennels. Ruth doesn't mind sharing some of the secrets of their success. She says,

"Our kennel was established in 1984. Am/Can. Ch. Allure's Island Shogun, our first Akita, is our foundation dog, and Ch. Tozu's Misty Morning, ROM is our foundation bitch.

"We have to date bred seven champions. Shogun to date has produced eight champions and has seven pointed get to his credit.

"With our foundation dogs, we take much pride in producing good type, soundness, exceptional movement, regal presence and show attitude with a desirable temperament.

"Our single most important goal in the sport of dogs is selectively breeding healthy dogs with exceptional characteristics of the breed for the conformation and obedience rings. We are proud of our dogs and their achievements and the success we have had with our breeding program."

The numbers of champions mentioned above have considerably increased since information was provided for this chapter. Obviously the Broskins are holding true to their convictions because the numbers of champions and top winners carrying the Island prefix grow each year.

Their most famous dog to date is of course, **AM/CAN. CH. ALLURE'S ISLAND SHOGUN.** Of this great competitor, the Broskins say:

"Shogun attained number one position nationwide two years in a row by defeating 1128 Akitas in 1986 and topped his own record by defeating 1437 Akitas in 1987. Shogun also attained number three position in 1986 by defeating over 5000 Working dogs, and number two position in 1987 by defeating over 6000 Working dogs. Shogun is the first Akita to have been honored by the Kal Kan Pedigree Awards in 1987 and appeared frequently in commercials on national television for Kal Kan in 1988 and 1989.

"In 1988, Shogun was a Top Producer of champions and has been an Award Of Merit recipient at the 1988, 1989, and 1990 Akita National Specialty Shows. In 1989, Shogun was BOB winner and Group winner at the Region 1 Akita Specialty

Show, defeating over 100 Akitas and over 1000 Working dogs. Shogun was selected to represent the breed and was the centerfold dog in the 1990 June issue of *Dog Fancy.* Shogun was also featured in the nutrition article in the 1991 *Dogs USA Annual.*

"Shogun is 27$^{1}/_{2}$" in height; exhibits true Akita temperament: aloof to strangers, but loyal, loving, playful and protective of his people and pets. Shogun's dignity, alertness and muscular structure combined with his powerful, balanced movement have made him well known in both the Breed and Group rings. Shogun is reproducing these same outstanding qualities in his offspring."

There are so many wonderful Akita owners that a whole book could be written about them. One very special lady I will always remember for her warmth and generosity is

Am/Can. Ch. Allure's Island Shogun (Am/Can Ch. Fu-Ki's Hideki Tojo, ROM x Am/Can Ch. Windrift's Orient Express, ROM) at six years old, handled by Kathy Mines Rayner under Robert Stein. Breeders Laura and Alan Armstrong, owners, Ruth and Robert Broskin.

ELAINE NUSSBAUM. As published in *HEADlines,* Elaine wrote a letter of comfort to another Akita owner whose dog had been diagnosed with cancer: "I just want to say be optimistic. Tomo has been through it all and she's just passed her 11th birthday! First someone poisoned her with strychnine while my husband was in intensive care at the hospital... She had seizures ... for more than 36 hours, at least 20 times. Tomo was in and out of hospitals for weeks and when vets gave up on her because she wasn't eating or drinking, we took her home and after a period of recovery, she became as bouncy as a puppy. That was four years ago!

"Then, Tomo had tumors, not benign, near the ovaries. The biopsy report read that it was the type to metastasize rapidly, nationally, meaning it would not spread locally, but throughout her body. She then was spayed and the anesthesia poisoned her liver! Again, she almost died and was very, very sick for a long time. That too was about four years ago.

"She still has those non-benign (malignant) tumors with a new one discovered just a few weeks ago below her ear. But, though the prognosis/diagnosis was horrible, Tomo is doing very well. She is 11 now and I'm hoping she'll reach 12, 13, and 14. When she's up, inside or out, she plays ball, soccer with her nose, flips mice, etc. Even if the labs don't make mistakes (and they do!), doctors can. Or else life fools us. Tomo was 'given up' by doctors in 1986! She is fine, if you don't keep thinking about the tumors. We check them for growth and, despite that horrible biopsy report (which practically had Tomo dead), they do not seem to be growing anymore. We did give Tomo vitamins on the advice of BJ. Megadoses, and perhaps that helped, if one believes in vitamins. We do."

Tomo is the beautiful white, **CH. O'BJ SILVER CHALICE OF TOMOKO** by Ch. Stinger x Ch. Ko-Go. Tomo was still doing well at 12 years but eventually Lee and Elaine lost her. To fill the emptiness, they did what so many Akita lovers have done; they opened their hearts once again, and this time they filled it with Akitas in need of rescue. Their lovely Maryland home is more than a stopping-over place for Akitas who needed help, it's a loving sanctuary!

I was never very good on geography but I do know one thing. *Dallas* is in the Rocky Mountains—and so are **CHRIS and AUDRY WEATHERMAN** and **NORTHSTAR AKITAS.**

Ch. Kuroi Kao Dallas Alice, ROM is a foundation bitch for Northstar Akitas and a dominant producer, unfailingly passing her many wonderful qualities on to her get. Chris and Audry have done exceptionally well as owner-breeder-handlers. Their decision to acquire a bitch of outstanding quality, and the

Ch. Kuroi Kao Dallas Alice, ROMX (Ch. Sherisan Ura Gin x Ch. Va-guas Kuroi Kao Kuma) during 1988 National Specialty judging where she won Best Opposite Sex. Dallas was bred by Priscilla McCune, owned by Chris and Audry Weatherman.

successful way in which they have used her, is a wonderful example for everyone who aspires to recognition in the dog world. Dallas Alice has proven herself both in and out of the ring. About her, Chris has this to say:

"Undoubtedly, the most influential Akita we've owned here at Northstar is our foundation bitch, Ch. Kuroi Kao Dallas Alice, ROM. We purchased Dallas as a three-year-old finished champion from her previous owner in Iowa. When I received the call that she was available, all they had to do was to tell me how high to jump; I dropped everything and drove all night into the middle of Nebraska and made the transfer on the

"Dallas has been everything we could have possibly asked for and more. While being actively shown, she exhibited a competitive, irrepressible spirit. An exemplary mother who shows the utmost in maternal instincts for her puppies.

"To date, Dallas has five champions and several other major pointed get, earning her the ultimate compliment, Register Of Merit. Her offspring exhibit the size, bone, soundness, and type we expect from an Akita. If a dog can be generous, Dallas is just that, not only in the form of genetic prepotency but also in that 'win you over' personality!

"If the eyes are the pathway to the soul, one has but to look into her eyes and see the

Ch. Kuroi Kao Aspen (Ch. O'BJ High N Mighty No Goshen, ROMX x Ch. Kuroi Kao Dallas Alice, ROMX) struts her stuff. "Aspen" was owner-handled to her Ch. at 14 months and is sure to carry on the proud tradition of her parents. Breeders Priscilla McCune and Chris Weatherman, owner is Priscilla McCune.

side of the interstate. I knew I had made the right decision on sight.

"At the 1988 National Specialty, Dallas was awarded BOS, owner handled. Her sons, Ch. Northstar's Mad Maxx and Ch. Northstar's Coors Silver Bullet, CD, placed first and second in their respective classes, also owner-handled. It was a thrill to do so well at a National, and Maxx has gone on to rank number two Akita for 1990.

gleam—the soaring of the eagle, the heart of the tiger."

Down to the plains of Indiana, we would find yet another dedicated couple, both equally involved with their dogs. Some of the zeal the Erwins once felt for showing their Akitas has died along with the great dogs they once owned. Their devotion to the breed has not diminished, and we thank them for sharing so much of themselves

Ch. Sleeping Bear's Teddybear Too (Can. Ch. Ursus Horribilis Kuroi Okanz x Ch. O'BJ Shelly's Brandy). "Teddy" was the youngest Akita to ever win the Group. In 1982 he ranked in the top ten Akitas for the year. Owner, Bill Erwin.

first Akita male. He was a pet, yet majestic and proud. Our first Akita puppy, sired by this male, was a Christmas gift—and so the story began.

"Our respect and love for this magnificent breed grew with our new Akita puppy bitch. We sought out information about the breed and visited as many breeders as we could find.

"Eventually, we purchased our first show puppy, Ch. Sleeping Bear's Teddybear Too. Teddybear stunned everyone, including us, by winning a three-point major and BOW our first time in the show ring. He quickly finished his championship, owner-handled, and went on to become the youngest Group-winning Akita (old Group) and a top-ranked Special. His incredible size and substance plus beautiful bear head turned many heads. His personality was that of a true Akita. He was all that an Akita should be.

"We learned with our giant Teddybear what it was to show and what it was to win! Akitas by Noji continued with Ch. O'BJ Kiowa of Noji, Ch. Daijobus Vampirella O'BJ, ROM (National Specialty BOW, 1983), multiple-Group winner Ch. Noji's Jack Daniels, Ch. Billie Jo of Noji, Ch. Noji's Dust Devilin, Ch. Noji's Mortisha Crown Royal, and multiple-BIS Ch. Mike Trual's Royal Tikara 'Pal.'

"Bill found Pal in the show ring as a class dog. In fact, he beat Teddybear at a regional Specialty for the breed. Bill fell in love with Pal's incredible soundness and type. Pal was owned by a Kentucky horse breeder. Bill spent months dickering with Pal's owner trying to purchase him. A deal was finally struck and a one-and-a-half-year-old Pal came to us as if he had been ours forever. He continued to show

with all of us. It has been said that Marcia should have been born a redhead instead of a beautiful blond, to which I must say that no person could have a better friend for like, their dogs, Marcia is fiercely loyal and will defend that which she believes in. Bill and Marcia always believed in their dogs, and more than one Akita was given a place in the sun through the love and determination of **BILL and MARCIA ERWIN, AKITAS BY NOJI.**

"Noji is an Indian word which means muscle. This seemed a fitting name for our Akita family," begins Marcia.

"Fourteen years ago Bill and I saw our

and win, becoming the first multiple-Best In Show male Akita and the number one Akita all systems 1985. Akitas by Noji has produced just four select litters of puppies which have included three National or regional Specialty winners and the breed's only all-champion litter of seven. With love and respect for the Akita, we are proud of our contribution to the breed."

We had heard about the gorgeous redhead from Kentucky, and that she was "doing it right" with a top handler and tons of love for her new hobby. A few months later, Vicki Fillinger asked us to evaluate a young dog she was handling for the Wishing Well lady, and, when Myra later contacted us, we knew that all the complimentary things we had heard about her were true.

BRUCE AND MYRA ADDINGTON of **WISHING WELL AKITAS** wanted to buy a "really good male." We didn't have anything for sale. But Myra doesn't recognize obstacles, she just breezes right by them. She came to visit and something magic happened.

He was a big, clumsy nine-months-old puppy when Myra Addington first saw him. We had kept him for his incredible size and bone, his perfect head and expression, and his wonderful personality. We called him many "pet" names and we loved the big ugly duckling but when he and Myra saw each

Ch. Mike Truax's Royal Tikara Pal (Ch. Kim-Sai's Royal Jikara Kuma, ROM x Smith's Princess Neisha). "Pal" was the breed's first multi-BIS male and was the #1 Akita in 1985. He won the Group 19 times, and sired six litters, two of which were all-champion (U.S. and Canada). Owner, Bill Erwin.

Ch. Daijobu's Vampirella O'BJ (Ch. O'BJ BigSon of Sachmo x Ch. Maxwell's Kuro Ban Kuma). "V" produced 12 champions including national and regional specialty winners. She is owned by Marcia Erwin and was bred by Charles Bell.

other, we knew we'd lost him. He was destined to become **CH. THE WW COAL MINER O'BJ**. His physical attributes have been proven over and over in Specials classes and Group rings throughout the country. But there's another side to the Akita and that's what this chapter is all about. Myra shares the magic:

"The Coal Miner was purchased from BJ Andrews as a ten-month-old puppy to become the foundation sire of Wishing Well Akitas. He became much more.

"Wondering how this big puppy would adjust coming from the relatively quiet life he spent in Bill and BJ's to a home with two children (ages nine and 11 years) plus numerous friends, I was a little tense. As with everything we have asked of this dog: he came, he saw, and he enjoyed.

"I have owned quite a few dogs in my life, most of these I raised from baby puppies, but there has never been a dog who has bonded and loved as much as The Coal Miner.

"The wins and admirers The Coal Miner collects at shows is making a place for Wishing Well in the competitive dog show world; but the true worth of a special dog

Ch. The WW Coal Miner O'BJ (Ch. O'BJ King's Ransom, ROMPX x Ch. The Dame's On Target O'BJ, ROMPX) owned by Myra Addington, Wishing Well Akitas. Multiple Group winner, Regional Specialty BB winner (over 400 Akitas) Miner is pictured at two years of age.

comes from inside—his heart, keen mind, and a true love of life, which he passes on to his puppies. This is what makes The Coal Miner our foundation, our rock, our hope when things go wrong.

"The Akita was bred as a Japanese treasure—a dog full of power, stability, devotion—The Coal Miner is that dog, THE COAL MINER IS AKITA!"

No trip through the South would be complete without a visit to Georgia in the spring. In addition to the glorious dogwoods, Georgia grows some of the nation's best Akitas! We'll visit with Robert Campbell, but right on the way is another group of famous dogs, so let's stop first and meet the **SHO-GO AKITAS** of **WARREN** and **DEBORAH SHIELDS.**

I've known some intensely competitive people in dogs and Warren Shields ranks right up there with the best of them. Proud and intent on presenting his dogs well, Warren isn't easy to "get by" in the show ring. When the ribbons have been hung, he's as pleasant and congenial as his lovely wife Deborah. Both are accomplished handlers and their dogs are always fit, clean, typy, and "right on"—a hard combination to beat.

Combining those "vital statistics" we all love to hear about with compellingly tender word pictures, the Shields introduce us to just a few of the many great dogs they have owned or bred.

Deborah is generous with her vast knowledge of canine health and shares personal experience in the field of homeopathic care with other interested breeders. With a daughter in vet school, the Shields family is very much "into" dogs. While it doesn't take the involvement of everyone in the family to be successful in a breeding program, we're all agreed, it sure helps!

In summing up the information provided by Warren and Deborah, it's very obvious they devote much of their time to the breed. In terms of returned love and satisfaction of having attained goals many people still regards as pipe dreams, we hail the following which we believe to be

valid records. Certainly they are enviable achievements and reflect the dedication of the Shields family.

Warren Shields is the only owner-breeder-handler to win an Akita National Specialty.

Sho-Go is the only kennel to have three generations of Akitas win Specialty honors in two different countries on the same day! This unbelievable happening involved Ch. Sho-Go's Rambo who was BISS and Ch. Sho-Go's Joboy Tuff-N-Stuff—Stud Dog winner and Award Of Merit. At the same time, Ch. Sho-Go's Magical Midnight was winning BOS at the Canadian National Specialty!

Sho-Go is one of perhaps only two kennels to have bred three Best In Show Akitas in three different countries and they were all *owner*-handled.

Warren and Debbie have the Number One Bitch in 1989—Ch. Sho-Go's Rock-

Multi-BIS/BISS Am/Can Ch. Sho-Go's Rambo (Ch. Sho-Go's Joboy Tuff-N-Stuff, ROM x Ch. Frerose's Dark Moon of Sho-Go, ROM)

N-Roxcie and the number One producer of 1988—Ch. Frerose's Dark Moon Of Sho-Go, ROM.

In addition, Debbie wonders if Multi-BIS Can. Ch. Sho-Go's Magical Midnight might be the only Akita to earn two Bests In Show all on one day, owner handled. She says he may also be the only Akita to get a CD and BIS all on the same day, owner-handled. I'd be willing to bet he will hold those records for a long, long time!

Multi-BIS Can. Ch. Sho-Go's Magical Midnight, C.D. (Multi BIS/BISS Ch. Sho-Go's Rambo x Frerose's Gem Genes of Sho-Go).

Ch. Sho-Go's Joboy Tuff-N-Stuff, ROM (Ch. Frerose's Shiraito x Ch. Frerose's Happy Star).

Ch. Sho-Go's Rock-N-Roxcie (Ch. Sho-Go's Joboy Tuff-N-Stuff x Ch. Frerose's Dark Moon of Sho-Go, ROM).

Ch. Frerose-Sho-Go's Yasashii (Multi BIS/BISS Ch. Sho-Go's Rambo x Frerose's Gem Genes of Sho-Go).

151

OKII YUBI AKITAS, established in 1968 by **ROBERT CAMPBELL**, breeder of nearly forty AKC Champion Akitas.

The list of great dogs produced by Bob reads like stepping stones through history and includes the number one sire and number two dam of all time. Bob was, if not the first, certainly the most successful in blending east and west coast lines. He used the big Kensha and Sakura dogs of the east with Haru Hime west-coast progeny and even shipped bitches (not so commonly done back then) to California to the great Ashibaya Kuma himself.

Bob tells us that "all I really tried to do was put together the movement and ring presence of Ashibaya Kuma with the big heads and chest of Haru Hime and the overall size, massive heads, and clean body lines of the Kensha and Sakura lines."

When he moved from coaching to administration, Bob studied dogs for three years before deciding which breed was right for him. He says, "I wanted a dog that was massive in size and appearance but at the same time, intelligent. It had to be an easycare coat and an athletic type of big dog. When I first saw the Shaffer's dogs, I knew right then that was the breed I wanted. Hazel and Rennie had imported their dogs from Japan and had about four Akitas at that time."

Okii Yubi means large and elegant and graceful. It was a fitting kennel name for the type of dog Bob set out to produce. Assem-

bling valid information was much more time-consuming back then, and developing a breeding program required a lot of studious decisions. A high school principal, Bob was well suited to the task, and his early work lives on in the pedigrees of many top kennels of the '90s.

Bob has been kind in sharing those early days with us. The winners of the 1969, 1970 and 1971 National Specialties are his priceless contribution to our breed.

Describing Okii Yubi as "a small kennel interested in the betterment of the breed," Bob kept his numbers small but the quality high. Recognizing superior sidegait in Mitsu Kuma's Splashdown, he saw the opportunity to combine both Splashdown and Ashibaya Kuma through Mikado. Of

Am/Mex. Ch. Fukumoto Ashibaya Kuma, ROM was a Go-Dan award winner owned by Bea Hunt, appreciated by Robert Campbell.

Mariko Bob says, "Mariko weighed over a hundred pounds and measured a good 26 inches. She excelled in size and substance and matched up great with Mikado."

By 1974, Okii Yubi was center-stage at the old Chicago International Amphitheater. Although the overall quality in the Chujitsu litter exceeded that of his litter to Mariko, Mikado was destined to become best known for his famous son Ch. Okii Yubi's Sachmo Of Makoto. The Chujitsu litter contained five champions, one of them being Ko-Tori Of Okii Yubi,

Yukan No Okii Yubi, ROMP (Am/Mex. Ch. Fukumoto's Ashibay Kuma x Toyo No Namesu Joo), owned by Robert Campbell, is the sire of the number two dam in breed history, Ch. Okii Yubis Dragon House Ko-Go, ROMXP.

the mother of Ch. Okii Yubi's Dragon House Ko-Go. That Bob saw Mikado's virtues and used him wisely is obvious for records show that Mikado's best work as a sire was under Bob Campbell's ownership.

One of the most noteworthy characteristics of the Okii Yubi dogs was their impeccable temperaments. Bob bred a red Haru Hime daughter to Ashibaya Kuma and that fortuitous breeding produced Yukan No Okii Yubi, a big red dog of perfect soundness and balance. Bob then bred Yukan to Sakura's Chujitsu and that produced Ch. Okii Yubi's Snow Jo, CDX, TD, member of a canine square-dance group, headliner of the Jacksonville drill team which performed at 1977 Westminster, 4-H Club "teacher," participant of the Golden Isles relay team, and featured weight puller. Oh, did I mention he finished his championship in less than six months and trained for his UD degree? Snow Jo was loved, owned, and trained by Mary Cordon Hanley.

Yukan became a dominant sire for Okii Yubi, producing bitches with unusual size and substance and stabilizing the attractive clear reds and apricots for the Okii Yubi line. His topskull was a wide as Bob's two hands.

At the 1969 Akita Club of America National, Am/Mex. Ch. Fukumoto's Ashibaya Kuma at two years of age winning Best in Show. Am/Mex. Ch. Kinsei Suna Nihon No Taishi Sho-Dan, CD at four years winning Best Stud Dog. Other winners include Sakusaku Tom Cat-Go and Mex. Ch. Imperial Rikimaru-Go. Photograph courtesy of Robert Campbell.

At the 1970 Akita Club of America National, Am/Mex. Ch. Fukumoto's Ashibaya Kuma repeating his Best in Show win and also winning Best Stud Dog. Best of Opposite was Nakkusu Ginko (right) and Winners Dog was Triple K. Tomo Go (center). Photograph courtesy of Robert Campbell.

At the 1971 ACA National, Am/Mex. Ch. Fukumoto's Ashibaya Kuma defends his titles and stands proudly with his winning get: Mex. Ch. Imperial Ginzan (RWD), Royals Aiko Sakura (WB) and Miyamoto Musashi No Kin Hozan (Best Puppy). Photograph courtesy of Robert Campbell.

At the 1974 Chicago Inernational, Mikado No Kin Hozan, ROM and his get: Ch. Shuso Saki Tumi of Okii Yubi, Ch. Kazoku Riki Maru of Okii Yubi, Ch. Kazoku Bofu of Okii Yubi and Okii Yubi Tora. Photograph courtesy of Robert Campbell.

I remember we actually measured! He was a big dog but without coarseness and had the tightest feet and best front one could ask for. He was Ko-Go's sire, a dog everyone loved, and could have been an easy champion were it not for a torn ear. He was a credit to the Okii Yubi name.

In addition to his administrative duties, Bob once again became active in coaching and is still a marathon runner. Every now and then, Bob managed to set aside family and professional obligations and enjoy showing his own dogs. He always depreciated his handling skills but actually was quite accomplished, and his dogs were always presented clean and well groomed.

Ko-Go's litter brother was Ch. Okii Yubi's Mr. Judge. Bob sold him as an adult to Sara Kletter and Fran Wasserman and when he went sterile, I helped Bob arrange Jud's retirement into the home of Doug Brooks. He didn't stay retired long! Still one of the best dogs of his day, Doug asked me to "just show him a couple times" and I couldn't refuse. "Judder" became a familiar force in Group rings of the Southeast. It was brief but it was fun.

It was no secret that Bob loved BigSon. E Oka's BigSon's Shadow was a fabulous youngster and looked as much like his sire as any dog could ever resemble another. I agreed to show Shad on the Florida circuit for my co-breeder Linda Henson. The climax of the eight-day circuit was the National Specialty, and, having helped select all three of the judges, I explained to Linda that I didn't think it proper to show

Ch. Okii Yubi Snow Jo, CDX, TD (Yukan No Okii Yubi, ROMP x Sakura's Chujitsu) was one of the most versatile of the Okii Yubi Akitas. He participated in a canine square dance group, a Florida drill team, a 4-H Club, a relay team, weight-pull competition...plus he gained the CDX obedience title and a Tracking Dog degree. Snow Jo was surely ahead of his time!

Ch. Okii Yubi Mr. Judge, ROMP (Yukan No Okii Yubi, ROMP x Toyo No Namesu Joo) shown placing in Group under all breed judge Melbourne Downing. "Jud" is pictured at seven years with "BJ" and his owner Doug Brooks.

under them. She was very disappointed because we both knew Bob Campbell would love Shad and so it was agreed that she would fly down from Chicago and show her own dog at the National.

I finished Shad with three five-point majors during the days preceding the Specialty, and speculation was high as to what Mr. Campbell would do with him in Sweeps. They needn't have wondered. Like the other two judges, Edward Stevenson and Virginia Hampton, Robert Campbell would judge the dogs, and nothing else! I knew that he would not deny Shad and I think it wouldn't have mattered to anyone at ringside whether I had shown the BigSon clone or not. They loved him! And so did Bob.

Bob enjoyed judging specialties and fun matches. He was a little nervous about

Ch. O'BJ Okii Yubi Miss Carolina, BigSon's litter sister. Owner handled by Robert Campbell, she was Group IV after winning BB over top Specials at only nine months.

Ch. Vindicator No Okii Yubi shown with his sire BigSon and owner-handler, Robert Campbell. Vindicator finished undefeated with five majors, including this win in one of the toughest puppy classes ever assembled.

doing Shar-Pei when we last visited down in Georgia but I'm sure he did a brilliant job. Once a dog man, always a dog man. The breed owes a lot to the small Okii Yubi kennel nestled among the dogwood and wild azaleas of Georgia. So do we.

In late 1994, Bob was fatally struck by a car while on his bicycle. A great loss to all who knew him or shared our love for the Okii Yubi dogs.

Bob Campbell awards Best In Sweeps at the 1985 National Specialty to future Ch. E Oka's BigSon's Shadow (Ch. O'BJ BigSon of Sachmo, ROMPX x Ch. O'BJ Kye Kye Go of E Oka, ROM). "Shad" was breeder-owner-handled by Linda Henson.

CH. OKII YUBI'S SACHMO OF MAKOTO, ROMXP

He came into our home that day,
his slanted eyes aglow
With all the wisdom of the ancients,
as though he seemed to know
Of greater dreams and prophe-
cies and secrets still untold;
Of snowcapped peaks and lotus
blooms and scrolls not yet
unrolled.
Our awkward efforts to invoke a
friendship yet uncertain,
Caused him to stubbornly with-
draw behind a silken curtain.
With studied patience, he just sat
and stared into the distance...
Till late that night a bowl of milk
broke down his young
resistance!
And so it was when we retired,
expecting plaintive cries,
We lifted him upon our bed—but
much to our surprise
He went back to his guarding-place
inside our bedroom door
And there he slept for all his years,
in comfort on the floor.
Demonstrative he never was and
yet we came to know
His footsteps treading in the night,
his rounds performed just so.
His savage snarl when danger
loomed, his patience with the
small;
His nose against my cheek. And
his loyalty to us all.
We took him to the largest shows
where he won with due acclaim.
A haughty showman, bold and
proud; a Champion of fame.

From coast to coast he conquered
all, but then he let us know
That there were more important
jobs and seeds he had to sow.
And so we brought him home to
stay for he had earned the
right
To be our friend throughout the
day ... and guard us in the
night.
His sons and daughters carried
on his torch to light the way
While the old man dozed beside
the fire, his muzzle growing
gray.
And then one day he came to me
with aged dignity.
Implored me with his misty eyes
and head against my knee.
For special time, to "go" again,
as always he would lead.
And so we walked, just he and I—
each in our great need.
We climbed the path where as a
pup he'd romped in joyful glee.
We paused for just a moment
beside his favorite tree.
And then we sat together up on
that wooded crest
Until I felt his grizzled head sag
heavy on my breast.
Now some of you have surely
known the joy a dog can bring;
The way a puppy's wagging tail
can cause the heart to sing.
And so you know my silent tears
were more than just goodbye.
Fare well my greatest friend, may
your Legend never die.

By Barbara J. Andrews

Ch. Okii Yubi's Sachmo of Makoto, ROMXP (Mikado Kin Hozan ROMP x Juho Mariko No Kin Hozan, ROMP) winning out of retirement at age seven, owner-handler Barbara Andrews.

Tamara Warren describes him as, "An original. Calvin Klein could not have designed an Akita that had such a changing and profound influence on a breed of dogs. Sachmo turned ordinary into magical excitement. Bill and I will always cherish our times with him. From the first minute we laid eyes on him, we were hooked in the fabric of Akitas. Simple joys of holding his lead, grooming, and just being near him will never be forgotten."

So much has been written about Sachmo that it's practically impossible to share anything new and different with you. The piece of poetry above is true—and painfully untrue. Would it have been better had we known of the tumor? Had some time there at the last? Surely I would have walked with him and we would have said a proper goodbye. The poem is only poetic license. A longing for the storybook ending, the way

Ch. Okii Yubi's Sachmo of Makoto, ROMXP (Mikado No Kin Hozan, ROMP x Juho Mariko No Kin Hozan, ROMP) pictured with his buddy Edward Finnegan who professionally handled Sachmo at several shows during 1980. Ed went on to become a familiar name in Akita rings, beautifully presenting many other top winners.

it might have been—if he were less than Sachmo.

He couldn't have gone without shattering our lives and if one is going to cut off an arm, it's better done quickly. His job was always to look after us. He wouldn't have wanted it the other way 'round. He would have died to protect us and in a strange way, he did. He died in his prime, not aged and weak.

It was a blood-filled tumor. There's a medical name for it but I've never discussed it enough to learn the pronunciation, much less how to spell it. Early that morning, Pam Glave and I bred him to Tarbaby and he was fine. As Pam was leaving, she called goodbye to him. He didn't get up.

We rushed him to the vet but by the time he set up for transfusion, the veins had collapsed. He died in my arms but he lives in the hearts and minds and memories and bloodlines of everyone who ever loved the Akita breed.

This isn't about records. He set them in the show ring; he set them among all-breed statistics. He stamped his kids like a branding iron—with fire and blood and his special mark. He touched the hearts of so many. Oddly, many newer judges of today know

him, including those who never actually had their hands on him but truly believe they actually judged him. One judge told me, "He had it the moment he walked into my ring. I don't know when I've seen a dog with so much presence, so much masculinity!"

Winnie Heckman discovered him as a youngster. He and I were bored, and Akitas never got looked at in Group anyway, so we played our "creep-mouse" game at the end of the line. He jumped back from the imaginary mouse and the lead slipped from my hand. I heard someone say "Oh hell, the Akita's loose!!!" and I was mortified. "Come here!" I whispered as he danced just beyond my reach. Here was a dog who rarely displayed his silly side and *never* in public—yet down went the front end, up went the butt, and he skittered sideways, laughing at me. The crowd giggled. "COME HERE!" in my "I-really-mean-it" voice brought him to me just as the judge turned around after examining the dog to be gaited. Did she know? When it came our time to be examined, she held his huge head between her hands for just a moment and looked into his eyes. It was mutual love at first glance.

There were a few other judges with whom he established an uncanny rapport: Roy Ayers, Ginny Hampton, Phil Marsh, Lou Harris.

During his first year in the ring, he often rumbled if the judges were too intimate or heavy handed. It wasn't a threat, it was a statement: "I don't like this indignity. Treat me with respect and get on with it!"

Most judges understood although I wonder how he would fare in today's rings. I was warned not to show him under Ed Bracy because he had just excused three dogs from the Akita ring for growling. Perhaps my nervousness made Sachmo a bit more testy and sure enough, he rumbled. Bracy never let on that he heard him. He put Sachmo second to a Sakura dog that never finished, but when I asked him later if it was because he growled, he said no, and then patiently explained to me that this was a guarding breed and I was too nervous. He thought Sachmo was new at this but knew that he was stable, and, no, he'd never fault a guarding breed for having protective instincts, etc., etc. Ed was a good dog man.

Sachmo loved grapes, the white seedless kind. They passed the time on long hauls back from California. He would roll the grape delicately in his mouth and then carefully spit the skin out, having swallowed the good part. His only toys were soft-drink bottles and cans, snatched up from a parking lot for a moment of exercise. He spent his first year in the cab of our truck and although he suffered some hardship and a decidedly unnatural development period, he seemed none the worse for it. He cut teeth (literally) on the steering wheel but as much as the gear shift fascinated him, he understood that it was forbidden. It wouldn't surprise me to learn that there are still fuel

Ch. Okii Yubi's Sachmo of Makoto, ROMXP (Mikado No Kin Hozan, ROMP x Juho Mariko No Kin Hozan, ROMP) was in the Top Five National rankings for 5 consecutive years, owner handled by Barbara Andrews.

boys and mechanics that know the "Peterbilt with the bear in it..." They learned not to tease him when they serviced our truck.

Back then, it was more common for loads to be hijacked and independent drivers carried sizable sums of cash. Someone tried to enter our cab twice; once while we slept and once while we showered. We know what happened the night someone opened the truck door—and met Sachmo. Only the bloody smears on the driver's window told the tale of what happened the night we were out. Many truckers carried a gun, we carried a dog.

He tolerated my daughter's Sheltie but refused to be herded. On a few occasions, he picked Donnie up by the ruff and pitched him out of the way. Donnie never seemed to get the message, and Sachmo usually just stepped over him, grumbling.

He hated German Shepherds. He had been "assaulted" by a pack of feral dogs in New Mexico, and most of them fled except two Shepherd-mix males, ugly enough to be littermates.

A year later, another pair of Shepherds, handsome neighborhood bullies, ran at my 11-year-old daughter when she was walking him after a bath. Athena was finally able to get the leash loop from around her wrist as Sachmo tried to clean the pavement with one dog while the other attacked him from behind. As I ran screaming down the hill, the two Shepherds took off with Sachmo in hot pursuit. A neighbor on his way home from work held the car door open and, after making sure my daughter was unharmed, we took off after the dogs.

We found Sachmo patrolling the porch where the two dogs lived. I peeked under the steps as I collected his dragging leash and sure enough, both dogs peered back at me. Laughing, we left them there and I called the owners that night. We never saw the dogs loose after that, but I doubt they would have ventured up the hill again anyway.

He loved my tiny Japanese Chin puppy and the youngster always ran straight to Sachmo when he felt threatened. We took

Ch. O'BJ Remus of Sachmo, inbred son of Ch. Sachmo out of his daughter, Ch. O'BJ Nikki No Nikki, ROMP. Shown winning BB just before succumbing to bloat, Remus was owner handled to this important win under Mrs. Peter Guntermann.

photos of him "cleaning" Sachmo's teeth as the big dog lay panting. He preferred to sleep on Sachmo's back and, dozing off, would gradually slide down the rib cage to lie nestled against his big buddy's belly. Sachmo seldom got up until the Chin awoke. He never stepped on the tiny dog although he got my sandaled toes more than once.

He was embarrassed by my Persians and their attempts to "kiss" noses with him. He would hold his head up high as they rubbed against his front legs with big hairy tails in the straight-up-perfectly-pleased position. If the tails brushed his nose, an explosive sneeze usually blew the cats away, but not for long.

Sachmo was a fascinating show-ring power; he was a legendary producer; but most of all, he was our family dog.

His greatest passion was also ours. Her name was **CH. OKII YUBI'S DRAGON HOUSE KO-GO, ROMXP.**

Ch. Okii Yubi's Dragon House Ko-Go, ROMXP with owner Bill Andrews. This casual snapshot was taken at age eleven. Her body rests just a few feet from where she stood in this photo but "Mama-Ko's" spirit is a constant influence over every breeding decision at O'BJ.

She finished her championship in six shows, defeated only once. As a Special, she was shown 11 times by Ed Finnegan, and she won BOB over nationally ranked male Specials nine times! In only those few shows, she became the number two bitch

and the number three Akita of 1979.

Ko-Go gave the breed 15 AKC Champions and just as important, she passed her loving character, her abundant good health, and her good looks on to all of her "pet" puppies. Ko-Go is one of only a handful of Top Producers that produced a Register Of Merit that produced a Register Of Merit.

Her glory was often overshadowed by Sachmo simply because we owned them both. Sachmo's presence initially overwhelmed visitors but a flirty wink from Ko-Go never failed to get attention. The smart thing would have been to continue breeding her to Sachmo, but that would have robbed her of the credit she deserved as a Top Producer on her own merit. There was once a rumor that she and Sachmo had produced some horrible fault which forced us to breed her out, but that was put to rest with her next Sachmo litter. She was a bitch to build on, and that's impossible unless one uses at least two different stud dogs.

We finally lost Ko-Go to cancer at 13 years. She made our lives immeasurably brighter and she lived a good life. For Ko-Go, every day was a good one.

Ch. Okii Yubi's Dragon House Ko-Go, ROMXP (Yukan No Okii Yubi x Ko-Tori No Okii Yubi) at six months winning Match Group IV with owner Barbara Andrews in April 1974. Ko-Go is the dam of 15 AKC Chs. and was ranked #3 Akita 1979.

about her: there is nothing we would have changed about Nikki No Nikki. Nothing.

Like her sire, she left us suddenly and she left us devastated. A blood clot to the brain caused her to seizure, and, although she lingered in intensive care for over 24 hours, we finally let her go. By then we had come to understand that God would be unbearably lonely with only people for company. Surely that is why He takes so many of our most precious friends to be with Him.

Nikki was bred back to her sire and following his death, we knew there wasn't another male dog anywhere that was her equal. You who own bitches of this caliber know exactly what I'm talking about. There was BigSon but we didn't want to double so close on his dam's side so we went to one of his outcrossed sons and that produced **CH. THE MAD HATTER O'BJ, ROMXP**. Hatter was born while I was in the

In writing about dogs which have had a profound impact on the Akita breed, it may seem that I am "hogging" the pages of this book. How can I apologize? If you would feel some sort of resentment, blame the dogs who, because of their genetic dominance, allowed us to own and breed so many great ones in spite of our muddling about!

We can't talk about the old ones without mentioning one girl who won't be found in the list of top showdogs or producers. She was our "beautiful blond," **CH. O'BJ NIKKI NO NIKKI, ROMP**. Thought by most breed authorities to be the best bitch ever produced by Sachmo, Nikki No Nikki was type personified, and she passed it on to her kids in generous amounts. Her temperament was unimpeachable; her movement was faultless and so it's pretty easy to tell you

hospital, and it was to be several months before I could do more than love her from a distance. There was never any question about keeping her for other than her head type and turn of stifle, she was definitely her mother's daughter: Same incredible coat, same jet black eyes, same faultless front and harmony to her outline.

Oh, there was this one little difference. By the time Hatter was two years old, she had earned the nickname "Piranha." She did like to eat ears or toes belonging to any Akita save her own daughters. The Akita is dominant. Some definitely more so than others! Once we learned to do it her way, she was never a problem in any way.

She was a natural showgirl and despite being a "mismark," she finished quickly with multiple Best Of Breed wins over ranked champions. She had never been sick a day in her life and never showed her age. We took her to a local show when she was seven years old and pregnant with her last litter. She wasn't entered of course but we had a good laugh because everyone was worried that she was! She was in full bloom, white as snow, and having the time of her life!

As for her litters, concerned about doubling up on the head and stifle faults we knew lurked in the background, we turned to the perfect solution playing with his "blue bear" in our living room. We bred her to The Widow-Maker. Perhaps we should have done with her as we did with Ko-Go and bred her out at least once, but we'd be fools to complain about the results of our repeated decision. To date, those matings have produced 16 American Champions, many of them Group placers and destined to become top producers like mom and dad. There are several more Hatter kids yet to be finished in the States. Hatter is also the mom of several international champions and top producers. To the success of the new number one dam of all time, we toast Sachmo and Nikki for it is their profound influence that made it possible.

If it seems in any way like Superman has been slighted here, let me set the record straight. In fact, let **CH. O'BJ BIGSON OF SACHMO, ROMXP** set the record straight. Still the youngest male to ever earn a Register Of Merit title. He became the top winning owner-handled Akita of all time and was ranked number eight Working Dog when he was retired due to my surgery. He probably still ranks as the all time number three owner-handled Akita. Number two sire until Widow-Maker edged by him, he will always be number one in Bill's heart. He was my husband's dog, literally from the moment of his birth.

His dam was Vi-Brook Tonya, a short stocky apricot bitch out of a litter by Ch. Dragon House Wri Of Sandhill (Yukan x Kami) and Dragon House Nikki No Kenicia, Ko-Go's three-quarter sister. I know I've lost you along about here because of the

Ch. O'BJ BigSon of Sachmo, ROMXP At 17 months, owner handled by Bill Andrews to BOS Senior Sweeps at the 1982 National Specialty under breeder-judge Jerry Hoskins, CJ Akitas. BigSon also made the final cut (equivalent to today's Award of Merit) in Special's Class.

kennel names. Wri and Nikki were registered under my second attempt at coming up with a name which wouldn't be similar to or confused with someone else's kennel name. After registering Sachmo, we had discarded "Makoto" for that reason and then ultimately, Dragon House was dropped in favor of O'BJ.

One never knows what path Fate will take. Brooks Smith was stationed in Iceland, and we were in Maryland when our co-owned litter was born. We took our pick pup, and the former Mrs. Smith sold the remainder of the litter. Several years later, Tonya was rescued from a puppymill in Kansas and we brought her home.

We called her "Miss No-Head" and we didn't like her coat either so we did the obvious. We bred her to Sachmo. Tonya had only four puppies: Ch. O'BJ Carolina Girl No Okii Yubi;

Ch. Voodoo Doll O'BJ (Ch. Kakwa's Orca, ROMPX x Ch. O'BJ Georgia Peach, ROMX) was RWB at the 1982 National Specialty. Even as a yearling, she demonstrates the class and style which typifies the O'BJ look.

a red female who was a National Specialty puppy class winner before being lost to bloat; a pet male; and BigSon.

The two females were born first. Naturally, Bill had already told everyone that *his* male would come from Tonya. We all thought he was crazy. Finally, a male was born and I called Bill into the study. He stood and looked down at the wiggly wet pup for a minute while I went on removing newspaper. Then he said, "That's my dog." Teasingly I remarked that he should at least wait until the rest of them were born before he made a final decision.... He just walked away, satisfied.

Isn't it funny how things happen, and, at the time, we are so unaware that something truly momentous or remarkable has just occurred? During the next few weeks, Bill never wavered as our friends cracked jokes about him choosing a puppy like that. It could have been a litter of ten male pups and BigSon would have still been Bill's dog. As the pup developed, people stopped laughing and started paying attention!

Oh, I trained him and showed him. I fed him, groomed him, and I loved him. But the two of them knew the score. BigSon was Bill's dog. He was Superman, he leaped off tall buildings, and, given half a chance, he would have walked through brick walls. He was a busybody and a clown and pulled like a draft horse and loved to mess me up in the Group ring, and no crate could hold him. He loved puppies and even in his last years, we always kept a buddy-baby next to him.

He hated cats with an undying passion, owing his second leg injury to a cat. His first goal in life was to be with Bill every minute, and his second was to kill every cat on the planet. Once he went over the five-foot chain link in the exercise paddock and we caught up with him down the mountain, racing around and around a furious male Chow which was fastened to a chain. My first thought was that BigSon had devised

Ch. The Real McCoy O'BJ (Ch. Okii Yubi's Sachmo of Makoto, ROMPX x O'BJ Miss Taken Tiger de Alicia) with breeder-owner Barbara Andrews. McCoy sired Widow-Maker and 4 other Champions from one litter before being exported to England.

some devilish new way of fighting, for the Chow was exhausted and overheated. Then I saw it. The cat. Obviously it belonged to the Chow household for it was skittering about under the Chow's hairy belly. BigSon darted in again and the Chow spun to face him, so

Superman made about three flying circles just outside the reach of the chain, and then, with me screaming hysterically, he tried to rush the dizzy dog from behind. Bill skidded to a stop behind me, having driven the truck to avoid the steep slope of Snob Knob.

"BIGSON." Doggone it, he didn't even have to yell. BigSon wheeled around, paused, looked back at the hissed-up cat and the teetering Chow—and then he went to Bill. I didn't know whether to cry or curse.

If I ever had doubts about the way Sachmo left us, watching BigSon age dispelled them. Old dogs are so wonderful, so wise, so *sensible*. And vulnerable. Having 12 years to prepare for the loss didn't make it any easier. I can share a few memories about Superman with you—Bill Andrews still can't talk about his friend.

There really isn't much to tell about our breeding program that hasn't already been written somewhere. In deference to those who have Akitas who come down from our line, we could hardly skip over our history, but I'll keep it short!

AKITAS O'BJ, BILL and BARBARA ANDREWS

The first Akita we met was at a show in Georgia long before AKC recognition. The owner said it was "a dog from Japan," and, although he was a big impressive-looking critter, I walked on with my Rottweiler bitch and promptly forgot the big odd-looking dog. Sorry, I wish the beginning could have been more exciting.

Ch. O'BJ Sachmo Ko-Son owned by Jorge Haddad and handled in the United States by James P. Taylor. In 1989 "Sonny" was the #1 dog all-breeds in Mexico and is shown here winning the Group at his first show in California.

called Sam Rivkin, then President of Silver State Kennel Club. I had sold Sam a Rottie pup and knew that he owned Akitas. By the time Sam and I finished talking, we had an Akita puppy on the way! She was Sabaku Kaze's Asgard Kami, bred by the Yelvertons.

Some of the year-end nationally ranked top-ten winners whom we owned or bred are as follows: Ch. Sachmo, Ch. Ko-Go, Ch. Orca, Ch. Zack, Ch. BigSon, Ch. Char-Ko, Ch. Storm Trooper, Ch. Abaddon, Ch. Cotton Ginny, BIS Ch. Widow-Maker, BIS Ch. Ransom, Ch. Kareem, BIS Ch. Chariots Of Fire, Ch. Razz M'Tazz, and Ch. Coal Miner.

Register Of Merit dogs bred by O'BJ have been recorded in those statistics, but the number of ROM descendants and top winners is incalculable.

People have said we've done a lot for Akitas. What most people miss is how much dogs, Akitas in particular, have done for us.

Living with, working with, talking about, sharing every facet of our lives with dogs have opened vistas most people only dream about. We've met people of all nationalities, different philosophies, and extraordinary talents. A love of dogs forces one to travel, whether it be to shows—or foreign lands. It keeps the mind busy, ever learning, ever exploring. It stimulates exercise when most people hang out in rocking chairs. It forces one to be humble. It lifts one to great accomplishments and drives the ego to exultant heights. It brings life into

I next noticed the Akita while browsing through a German magazine. My friend from Denmark was looking for a new breed and didn't want to strain our friendship by showing a Rottie. As we flipped past the head study of a big white dog, she stopped me. "What's that?" I thought a minute and then told her it had to be "that rare Japanese breed." She wanted to know more so we

Ch. Cotton Ginny O'BJ (Am/Can Ch. Kakwa's Orca, ROMPX X Ch. O'BJ Nikki No Nikki, ROMP) had several BOW awards, handled by breeder BJ Andrews. A multi-Group winner, Ginny made history by going Best of Breed at the AKC Centennial show.

our cupped hands and puts death at our doorstep on an all too regular basis. It helps us to understand both.

Being "in dogs" is a revelation in science, from the workings of DNA to the realization of how small is our place in the universe. Dogs bring out our best when we're with them, and our fierce love for them sometimes brings out the worst in all of us. They have challenged us and comforted us and made us laugh and weep. They have filled our days and filled our hearts. And, as so many have said in so many ways, they have shown us what unquestioning love and loyalty really are. Now I ask you, who has come out the winner in our long love affair with dogs?

The most famous of all the O'BJ dogs doesn't have a "call name." He's always been "The Widow-Maker," and, despite his

Ch. The Widow-Maker O'BJ, ROMXP in one of his best poses.... The Victory Dance. He loved the crowd and delighted in their approval of him. His unfettered, free-pose style appealed to both judges and ringside. Photo by Linda Henson.

see the big guy stretch out as he free-gaits across the yard in front of the other males is to know whence it came!

Not long ago we had visitors from another country and at the end of the day, we sat on the deck as Widow-Maker went about the business of re-marking his trees. Paulo shook his head and said, "We have seen your video and studied the pictures, and we have come to your specialty shows, but we never understood about the Akita until now." That is the highest compliment a breeder could hope for, and, as Widow-Maker trotted by, I knew our guest was sincere because I got goose-bumps too!

His size and bone are ex-traordinary, but there have been other Akitas with the same assets. Maybe they didn't carry their bulk around a ring as well as The Widow-Maker. So I've been told. The shaded black and bold white markings are eye-catching, but there have always been flashy Akitas. His symmetry speaks to the eye of the artist, but other dogs have good balance. His clean strong head and jet black eyes are nothing new to our line. His stallion-like bearing and attitude are pretty much typical of the Akita breed. The soundness he displays is, thank goodness, becoming more common in the Akita ring. His ability to free pose is a bit more unique, but because my back was worn out by horses many years ago, we've always tried to produce dogs sound enough to show free style. So I guess you'd say there isn't any one thing that remarkable about The Widow-Maker, except maybe that all these virtues are found in the same dog....

fearsome name, he's the big black dog that carries his favorite blue bear to bed...

CH. THE WIDOW-MAKER O'BJ, ROMPX became the number two sire of all time before he turned eight. His flash and style and tremendous sidegait captured the hearts of Akita people and judges from coast to coast, and to see these virtues passed on to his progeny is every breeder's dream. We're proud and gratified by the knowledge that our line has helped so many others realize their dreams. To

BIS Ch. The Widow-Maker O'BJ, ROMXP (Ch. The Real McCoy O'BJ x Ch. The Same Dame O'BJ, ROMP) winning the Group under Specialty and Multi-Group judge, Mr. Louis Harris. Breeder-owner-handled by Barbara Andrews, Widow-Maker is one of the three most consistent Winners in Breed History and also the #1 Owner Handled Akita All Time.

People used to ask us if we were ever "gonna breed another Sachmo," and then they used to say "there will never be another BigSon," and now they say "Do you think you'll ever have another one like The Widow-Maker?" The answers are simple.

No, we never bred another Sachmo. Never tried to. BigSon had many of the best features of Sachmo, but he was his own dog. We'll never have another Widow-Maker. Who would want to duplicate their children? To what end? Each is unique, each is an individual, each has enriched our lives. That's all we ask of our dogs.

Leaving the mountains of North Carolina, let's journey down to the flatlands and visit with **INAKA AKITAS** of **BILL and TAMARA WARREN.** When Bill Warren first contacted us, it was to purchase a pet male. A professional investigator, Bill had applied his skills to sorting out breeders and bloodlines. He not only knew where his Akita was going to come from, he knew exactly what he wanted. Or so he thought.

When we moved to North Carolina, the Warrens came to visit. It just so happened that I had bought back a pet puppy from a divorce situation and was thrilled to discover that she had blossomed into a show puppy. Only Bill Warren can say if it was love at first sight, but I can tell you that instead of waiting for a pet male, Bill Warren left carrying a fifty-pound armful of female, show-quality puppy! She became the famous Ch. O'BJ Michiko Of Wri, ROM, thus the Warrens became a part of several footnotes in Akita history.

Tamara became an accomplished owner-handler and Michiko finished easily. Ring-side loved the beautiful blonde and her beautiful dogs and the Warrens were "hooked."

We had planned to breed Michiko back to her grandsire, Sachmo. Tragically, he died before she was old enough to mate and so we bred her to a ten-months-old pup who had yet to prove himself as anything other than a puppy sensation. He had defeated several of the country's top-ranked Specials, completing his title at nine months. But could he produce? Could he even sire? We didn't know.

BigSon delivered an emphatic "Yes!" to both questions, and so it was that the baby dog destined to become the number two top sire of all time, sired his first litter to a young bitch destined to make history as the dam of an all-champion litter of five puppies!

Tamara kept two from that litter and finished them in record time. Literally. She's far too modest in stating, "Ch. Jake finished his championship at age 14 months in three consecutive days of showing. He is a multi-

Ch. Inaka's Shiroi Oboko (Ch. O'BJ BigSon's Jake x Village's Tasmanian) Bred and owned by Bill and Tamara Warren, photo by Bill Warren.

BOB winner and is out of an all-champion litter of five. He is the sire of four champions and top obedience Akitas."

Tamara had been waiting for a Sachmo son. There was a special tenderness between Tamara and Sachmo and when he died, it seemed only fitting that she should have something from his last litter. There was this one male, a little runt of a dog. Too perfectly constructed and too proud and regal to ever be a pet, but possibly too small to be much of a show dog. We hadn't done much to save him. I occasionally guided him to a nipple when his bigger, stronger siblings shoved him aside in the first moments of jockeying for position at the milk bar. After that, he never gave up his spot! He was small but he was all Akita.

We gave the little one to Tamara knowing that he would develop under her nurturing care. When we saw him at about seven

Ch. O'BJ Michiko of Wri, ROM, (Ch. O'BJ Little Bear of Wri x Bar K's Delilah De Alicia) bred by BJ Andrews, owned by Bill & Tamara Warren, Inaka Akitas. Photo by Bill Warren.

months, we were astounded. He was absolutely magnificent! His genes had won out over a difficult beginning in life. Tamara is too modest in describing Remus and her part in his development: "Ch. Remus fin-

Ch. O'BJ BigSon's Jake (Ch. O'BJ BigSon of Sachmo, ROMXP x Ch. O'BJ Michiko of Wri, ROM) Breeder Bill Warren and BJ Andrews, Owner Bill and Tamara Warren, Inaka Akitas. Photo by Bill Warren.

Ch. Beoth's Three Toes Griz (Sleuh's Shoko x Ch. Bear of Thors Ninno, ROM) shown in Group competition with handler Roy Murray. Griz was a top ranked winner two years for owner Lee Ana Dorsett.

also received a Group second and a Group fourth. She finished her championship the next show at the age of nine months. She is the dam of two multi-BOB bitches, one a champion and the other needs just one point. She is also the dam of the number one obedience bitch for 1990."

It's refreshing to see young people come into the breed and, through judicious purchases and breedings, quickly gain the respect of their peers. Well, sayings become sayings because they are true and indeed, "Cream rises to the top."

The average life span of a breeding program is five to seven years. Thankfully, many Akita lovers are founding solid breeding programs today which will go far beyond the dropout period, providing good beginnings for breeders of the future.

Obviously, space prevents listing all of the bright young people coming up in the ranks,

ished his championship, owner handled, at 12 months of age. Multi-BOB winner from puppy class and multi-BOB and Group placer as an adult. Inbred son of two of the greatest Akitas who ever lived. Producer of several champions."

Remus was lost to bloat at only four years of age. In dutifully notating the photo information, Tamara states his sire, dam, breeder, owner... and then "Home: Bill and Tamara Warrens' hearts forever, greatly missed."

In the opinion of many, the lovely bitch "Oboko" was one of the best to come from the Inaka Kennels.

Tamara Warren tells us, "Ch. Oboko was 1987's number one bitch, Group Systems, *Akita World*. She was the youngest bitch to date to receive a Group first win, at eight months of age. In the same weekend, she

but I love Texas so let's mosey on down to Austin and visit with **DAVE and LEE ANA DORSETT** and their **CLASSIC AKITAS**. A Baylor graduate, Lee Ana is the epitome of a no-nonsense Texas lady. One can imagine her riding the range with her handsome husband a hundred years ago but today she and Dave settle for riding herd on three young sons, multiple business interests, and a "passel" of well-bred Akitas.

Like so many of the new generation, the Dorsetts are using computer technology to its fullest advantage in compiling pedigrees, tracking show records, and in sorting and defining genetic information.

Their first nationally ranked dog was multi-Group winner **CH. BEOTH'S THREE TOES GRIZ,** bred by Patti Lamb. His sire, Sleuh's Shoko, was a red-brown Sachmo son out of a Sachmo/Ko-Go granddaughter. Often owner-handled by Lee Ana Dorsett, Griz was pro-handled by Roy Murray to number six in Breed points and number seven in Group points 1988 and 1989. He is a rich red with black edging around his clear white markings. His owner says, "He is prepotent for short backs, color, tight cat-like feet, high set tightly curled tails, and thick luxurious coats. He also is dominant for his absolutely lovely temperament."

None of us know whether the babysitting stories of Japanese legend are true. This one is. It involves **CH. O'BJ KO-TAUSHAMO OF WESTWIND, ROMXP,** a

the child's mother. "It's okay," he called out, "seems my dog has found a new friend." The woman hurried across the yard but was reassured by Dick's affable greeting and the gray-muzzled old dog.

She explained that the children were collecting for the March of Dimes. Dick's suggestion to allow the child and Tausha to go collecting together was no better thought through than was the mother's agreement, but if he had been more cautious, there would have been no story to tell. Dick retrieved Tausha's heavy leather lead, the length of which was almost double the little girl's height. Laughing at the child's clumsi-

"Captain Bear and Cody Bare" Cindy Smith's pet Akita and her son Cody in a tender moment.

big red Sachmo and Ko-Go daughter we retired to every dog's dream home, Dick and Addie O'Neil in Florida.

Addie was out playing golf and Dick was watching television with Tausha when their quiet afternoon was interrupted by a tiny little knock at the door. Momentarily blinded by the bright sunlight as he stepped to the screen door, Dick didn't see the diminutive figure until he reached down to stop Tausha from pushing through the door.

"Oh, what a big dog!" chirped the little girl as Tausha sniffed her up and down, tail signaling her pleasure. Oblivious to Dick, the little girl giggled, "Ooo, stop that, your whiskers tickle." Tausha's tail wagged faster. Dick heard a car door slam and, looking up, realized that the woman at the curb must be

ness in hanging onto the dog, the leash, and the collection box, the mother returned to her car and slowly followed them down the street.

The way Dick tells it, that little girl took in twice as much money as anyone else in her Scout troop. He's sure it was Tasha's presence because he watched the neighborhood Scrooge dig deep into his billfold, laughing at the child and her huge bodyguard!

OK, this episode is like the stunts you see on television, and carries the same warning. Don't do it. Although Tausha was not accustomed to children, she was a very mature show bitch, wise in the ways of the world and accustomed to making up for deficiencies in judgment on the part of her human friends. Even so, it's amazing that several of the doors they knocked on belonged to barking, challenging, feisty little dogs and as s a couple of neighbors reported to Dick, Tausha seemed to be taking her job as guide for the little girl very seriously. She ignored the neighborhood dogs as she and her new little friend made their rounds. Knowing Tausha and her impeccable character and intuitive intelligence, we never doubted the story nor its outcome as Dick began to tell us about it. Still, I caution all owners of any large breed known to be dominant-aggressive, especially with neighborhood dogs who may have teased them from behind the safety of a fence. This is not an especially wise thing for two adults to do. The responsible party here was obviously the dog!

If we leave the sunny south and go way up the continent of North America, we would arrive at the home of **KAWAKAMI AKITAS and BEVERLY WILKINSON.**

The Kawakami Kennels of Michael and Beverly have contributed several important Akitas to both American and Canadian breeding programs. Based in Duncan, British Columbia, the Canadian kennel is perhaps best known for their two famous sires, Can. Ch. Matsutake's Cody Bearpaw, ROM, and their subsequent import, Am/Can. Ch. O'BJ High N Mighty No Goshen, ROM.

We are told that "Cody Bearpaw is the sire of many Canadian Champions and also has to his credit, the number one Akita in Canada in 1989 and 1990. Sired by Cody Bearpaw, Am/Can/Bda. Ch. Wesaka's White Lightning has achieved more points than any other Akita in breed history in Canada. Cody Bearpaw is the sire of several Specialty winners in Canada and also in the U.S.A."

Quick to seize an opportunity, the Wilkinsons were able to acquire the top producing American Champion O'BJ High N High Mighty, known as "Uriah." A litter brother of the famous Ch. Widow-Maker, Uriah was bred by Barbara Andrews and purchased by Goshen Kennels at eight weeks old. He was owner-handled to his AKC championship and sired many multiple-champion litters for Goshen before he was sold.

Am/Can. Ch. O'BJ High N Mighty No Goshen, ROMX (Ch. The Real McCoy O'BJ x Ch. The Same Dame O'BJ, ROMP) is shown completing his Canadian Championship with a BB win under judge Mr. John Perfect from New Zealand.

Kawakami fell in love with Uriah, and Bev owner-handled him to his Canadian championship *undefeated* at six years of age. He is co-owned by Mikata Akitas and Shibas, Garth and Linda Wald of Alberta, Canada.

OVERHILL KENNELS of MEG PURNELL-CARPENTER

Although not the first to exhibit Akitas in the United Kingdom, Meg Purnell-Carpenter bred the first Akita litter to be registered in the U.K., was the first to win national year quarantine in to be in England and after much consideration, Overhill Kennels, proprietess Meg Purnell-Carpenter, was selected. Meg was then a well-known breeder of German Shepherd Dogs and a very highly respected dog person. The London Police had bought dogs from Overhill and, indeed, many of her top youngsters are still serving in law enforcement in Europe and even in Australia! All reports of the Overhill Kennels were filled with praise and

Am. Ch. O'BJ Sachette No Okii Yubi (by Sachmo x Ch. Okii Yubi's Southern Bell) owned by Meg Carpenter, Overhill Kennels, Pensford, England. She was the first American Champion in England, and the first of several O'BJ Foundation dogs sold to England and Australia.

acclaim for the breed, and still ranks as England's premier breeder. A highly respected championship show judge, Meg is now considered one of Europe's foremost authorities on the Akita.

I had agreed to sell two puppies to Ken Taylor in Australia, the first Akitas to be imported from the United States. Back then, dogs were required to quarantine elsewhere before going on to Australia. It was a hard decision to agree to the sale, and we insisted on holding them until five months of age. Actually, we needn't have worried.

Arrangements were made for the one-

so, away went two of my prize puppies to a foreign kennel, en route to a mysterious land.

It was those two Akitas which caused Meg's life to take a new direction and which ultimately brought her worldwide recognition. Dreading the prospect of parting with the two pups she had come to love, Meg asked for a foundation bitch for herself. During the months of quarantine, I had gained a friend and without hesitation, we agreed to sell her one of our very best bitches. But here, let Meg tell you herself:

"One of the most exceptional Akita bitches

I have been privileged to live with is the Am. Ch. O'BJ Sachette No Okii Yubi. Sachette was whelped on September 16, 1980 and was bred by Robert Campbell and Quinon Coggins. Her sire was the immortal Am. Ch. Okii Yubi's Sachmo of Makoto and her dam, Am. Ch. Okii Yubi's Southern Bell. She was sold to us by Bill and BJ Andrews as our kennel foundation for the breed in this country. She is fawn with a black mask.

"Her first litter—the first to be bred in the U. K.—was by the Am/Can. Ch. Kakwa's Orca son, O'BJ Aces High. These offspring were extremely successful and helped to establish the breed in this country with top-winning progeny, not only from this, but later litters. Bill and BJ warned us that Sachette was a character. It was not unknown for her to steal every dog's toy from their run by hooking them out with her feet and dragging

Overhill's Kita Mouri (O'BJ Aces High x Am. Ch. O'BJ Sachette No Okii Yubi) a top bitch in England, breeder-owner-handled by Meg Purnell-Carpenter.

them under the fence. At nearly 11 years old, she has not changed and still constantly helps herself to anything that belongs to others, this includes bedding, bones and toys, to name but a few items. She is overall 'in charge' of the kennels and makes it clearly understood to any fellow Akita that threatens to take her throne that she is not yet ready to abdicate!

"Her teeth are worn down and her wonderful face is now silver gray with age, but, at 11 years, she is still very fit, active, and as sound in movement as she was as a youngster. We owe so much to Sachette for her contribution to our breed, not only in our kennel but in this country. She has passed down her soundness and type through several generations. Many of the top-winning Akitas in England today are directly descended from her. Her sire may be immortal—but to us, so is she."

I later exported a big rawboned Orca son out of an old Krug bitch. He was sound as could be and, fortunately, his sire had "typed" him nicely. He has been a good influence on the breed in Australia, but he also left an important contribution behind in England. Being a very astute lady, Meg was quick to recognize the advantage of using O'BJ Aces High.

Mindful of her stature as a judge (she has judged at Crufts Dog Show and is a member of The Kennel Club), Meg is not one to glorify or exaggerate the quality of a dog, particularly one of her own. I try to refrain from that boring trait too, but I must tell you that Kit would make them all sit up and take notice in AKC rings today. Her movement is effortless but not without drive. Although she is a stocky bitch, she has class and elegance, and her lovely clear markings and rich dark coat are the finishing touches on a first-rate bitch. Meg keeps it simple but you can be sure, Kit earned new respect for the breed in the U.K. and her daughter Lite Fut would be a multi-Group winner in this country just on her size, presence, and spectacular movement! Of these two, Meg says,

"Kit is a black and white pinto bitch born on October 23, 1983. Her sire is O'BJ Aces High, a son of Am/Can. Ch. Kakwa's Orca. Her dam is the Sachmo daughter, Am. Ch.

O'BJ Sachette No Okii Yubi. Kit was one of the puppies from the first English-bred litters. She was shown in the early days of Akitas in this country, when we had very few breed classes. She had a great deal of success, if beaten, it was only by her litter sister. When Kit reached breeding age, there was very little selection of stud dogs, so she was shipped to the U.S. to be mated to the top dog, Am. Ch. The Widow-Maker O'BJ. The result of this mating was four pups, two dogs and two bitches. These, the two bitches, have been extremely successful, particularly Overhills Cherokee Litefut, who was top-winning Akita puppy in 1987, top-winning bitch 1988 and 1989, and has already acquired one Challenge Certificate and three Reserve Challenge Certificates.

Australian Ch. O'BJ Piece of The Rock (Ch. Okii Yubi's Sachmo of Makoto, ROMPX x Ch. O'BJ Nikki No Nikki, ROMP) at 15 months. Photographed with Meg Carpenter, (Proprietress of Overhill Quarentine Station) just prior to the final leg of his long journey to Australia. "Rocky" became a Best In Show winner for owner Ken Taylor.

"Kit was not mated for two years and then was mated in 1988 and 1989 to the same dog, Vormund Hot Shot at Fantasa, whelping two puppies in the first litter and five in the second. Of these, one is a New Zealand champion and BIS winner, one an Australian champion with several others on their way to titles. Kit was top Akita and top rare breed brood bitch in 1989. She is much loved by everyone. She has a gorgeous head, lots of substance, bone, and a true Akita temperament."

Kita Mouri only produced 12 puppies in total including these two English champions. Other champion offspring of hers are Australian Ch. Overhills Mac the Knife, New Zealand Champion and Best In Show all-breed winner Overhills The Lodge Master, and Jamaican Champion Overhills Chinook. Other top winners from Kita include Overhills the Freemason and Overhills Fatal Attraction.

The first importation of an Akita to Overhill Kennels in the UK was the all white bitch O'BJ White Hope, imported from Bill and BJ Andrews. She was bred by BJ Andrews and Susan Oswald. Her sire is Am/Can. Ch. Kakwas Orca and her dam Am. Ch. O'BJ Yoki Bara of Omisto.

Hope was exhibited at her first championship show in April 1983, having to compete in the Any Variety Not Separately Classified (the equivalent of AKC Miscellaneous classes). At the West of England Ladies Kennel Society's Championship Show, her debut, the competition was extremely strong from other breeds in this category, as there was an entry of over 80 dogs and bitches.

The judge was one of the country's top all 'rounders, Mrs. Anne Davies (now Mrs. Anne Arch), who appreciated Hope's qualities enough to reward her not only Best Bitch but Best Any Variety Not Separately Classified at this show on the day. This was just the first of many top show awards in Hope's career.

The next import to Overhill was Am. Ch. O'BJ Sachette No Okii Yubi, a daughter of the immortal Sachmo and her dam was Am. Ch. Okii Yubis Southern

Bell. This bitch was to become one of the most influential bitches in the foundation of not only the Overhill Kennel but the U.K.

Imported by Meg Purnell-Carpenter and Shella Gonzalez-Camino, Sachette was the first champion to be imported. Her first litter was by a son of Am/Can. Ch. Kakwas Orca x O'BJ Aces High who was en route for Australia to Ken and Thelma Taylor of the Kyooma Kennels. The litter born on October 23,

a great impact on the British show ring. Lizzies Girl's great Best Any Variety Not Separately Classified win at Crufts in 1985 handled by BJ Andrews from the O'BJ Kennels was a highlight.

Other imports to the Overhill Kennel have been the male Katokaze Krusher of Katai, a Sachmo grandson. His dam was Nagas Red Dawn of Makoto. Krusher sired among others the first Junior Warrant Male winner.

The next import bitch was Pinelake

Ch. Overhill's Cherokee Lite Fut (Widow-Maker x Kita Mouri) breeder-owner-handled by Ms. Meg Purnell-Carpenter, demonstrates correct movement made possible by good breeding, careful rearing, and superb conditioning.

1993 was the first British-bred litter and comprised of four bitches and three dogs.

Well-known top winners and producers from this litter were Overhills Kita Mouri, Overhills Marlows Miracle, Overhills Lizzies Girl and Overhills Hichiko Taipan. Long before championship status was granted to the Akita in the U.K., these littermates, among other Akitas at this time, made

Parka bred by Messrs. Powell Boyter and Simons. Her sire was Am. Ch. BigSon of Sachmo and her dam Am. Ch. O'BJ Cody of Spotted Bear.

Overhill was then fortunate enough to purchase Widow Maker's dam Am. Ch. The Same Dame O'BJ who has been a great influence on much of the present-day stock in England.

Overhill, having gained so much from the O'BJ Kennels, have been able to

English Import, Overhill's Pacer (Rediviva Chiyon Fuji At Overhill x O'BJ White Hope at Overhill) bred by Meg Carpenter, owned by Barbara Andrews.

work in furthering the breed in the U.K. by breeding dogs of correct Akita type and soundness.

Overhill bred the bitch, Overhills Pacer, whose sire was Rediviva Chiyon Fuji of Overhill (a pure Japanese dog) x O'BJ White Hope of Overhill. Pacer was sent out to Bill and BJ at O'BJ and is added to the U.S. gene pool. Mated to Am. Ch. The Widow-Maker O'BJ, she produced Am. Ch. Mighty Maverick. One of his sisters, The Humming Bird of Overhill returned to England with the Overhill Akitas.

A recent star in the Overhill Kennel is the male Overhills Non Imported. This black and white pinto combines all the blood of the imported stock plus Japanese bloodlines. At this point in time, although still very young he is unbeaten in Breed classes and has already gained a Reserve Challenge Certificate. His future looks bright but, undoubtedly without the excellent stock that was sent to us at the very beginning, we would not have been able to breed and have the quality of stock that we now have. All of the dogs at Overhill hold current eye certificates and are x-rayed."

In 1987 B. J. Andrews was invited to England to give a breed seminar, or as they call it there, a Teach-In. While there, a teenage bitch caught my eye. It didn't surprise me to learn that her sire was Rediviva Chiyon Fuji at Overhill.

On a previous judging trip, I had suggested to Meg Carpenter that the very masculine, very Oriental young dog she was boarding could work with the two big girls she had purchased from us. Chiyon Fuji, "Chico," as he was called, was a dog of stature—not a big dog, mind you, but one which commanded attention, standing high on the ground as though he owned it. Having seen Chico, I understand why some Japanese standards referred to the feet as "grips."

Meg agreed and quickly managed to purchase Chico. She used him very successfully with O'BJ White Hope at Overhill, a daughter of Am/Can. Ch. Kakwa's Orca, ROMX and Ch. O'BJ Yoki Bara of Omisto. Hope represented a strong double up on Sachmo and Mikado and was therefore an excellent choice to put to Chico. The brindle youngster I had spotted was from that breeding. She was **OVERHILL'S PACER**. Meg and I discussed the possibility of bringing her to the States. How difficult it all was back then! Just the fact that JKC registration numbers appeared on Pacer's certified pedigree was enough to send the AKC registration department into orbit. It took attorneys to sort out the AKC and in the end, Pacer was enrolled "for breeding purpose only." This meant we couldn't show her. To my knowledge, she and Tashi are the only Akitas ever registered this way by AKC.

Pacer is unique in many ways. She represents the perfect combination of Japanese type beautifully blended with American type. She has bone, substance, and size from the O'BJ side of the pedigree. She has the elements of type and the endearingly frustrating personality of her Japanese heritage!

She is not completely domesticated. Perfectly self-sufficient, an instinctive and competent hunter, she could do quite well without our loving care. She laughs and tosses her head and charms every man she meets!

Failing the opportunity to fulfill her role as huntress, she nonetheless performs the instinctive capture ballet of the wild canine. Pretending to spot a mouse-creature in the grass, she leaps into the air bringing all four feet together in a point, then plummets to earth, trapping the imaginary mouse beneath her feet. With a quick snuffing motion, she grabs the make-believe mouse

and throws it in the air, then gives a victorious shake of the head before laughing and bounding away. She plays this game, not to amuse me, but for the benefit of her puppies. Admittedly, her puppies usually ignore this display but by their seventh week, they will sit "front row center" and attentively absorb the lesson. We have no doubt that Pacer's offspring would survive in the wild. They may forget their housetraining; they may forget how to pose in the show ring; they may (like their mother) forget their name when you call them to come inside; but they will never forget how to catch a mouse!

She uses the same graceful light-as-air movements in playing with her puppies. Mimicking the above-ground-airs of the Lippizaner stallions, she leaps among her babies. It never fails to cause bystanders to gasp with fear that she'll trample a puppy, but she always lands harmlessly.

She's an easy keeper, requiring minimal sustenance. This could be from her primitive genes or perhaps from her ancestors having adapted to minimal food availability during postwar years. Unquestionably, she could subsist quite well on fish and rice, but because of the dense nutritive content of our American diet, she limits herself to about a cup and a half dry measure food per day, plus of course, her extra fresh goodies. For the first two years of her Americanization, she resisted eating more. She finally adopted the American penchant for lots of food and, like most of our girls, she is now on a perpetual diet.

Her coat is immense with a thick wooly undercoat and harsh protective guard coat which does what it's supposed to do! Consequently, she never gets dirty, seldom needs grooming, and requires bathing only after whelping or when she is blowing coat.

The differences which are so apparent in Pacer and her children (and even her grandchildren) have sustained our belief that the Akita and the Shiba retain many of the undiluted instincts of their ancient forebearers. Although Pacer is more likely to pounce on an imaginary mouse than she is to brace a bear, let there be no doubt, she would bring a bear to bay and drive him mad in utter frustration as he would never get his paws on her!

And therein lies the practical reason for the Akita's size to be coupled with exceptional agility. Certainly the massive, heavy-boned, show specimens invoke human awe, but, if lacking the agility of the hunting canine, they would be laughed at by a bear or a wild boar! While none of us expect the modern Akita to be confronted with any opponent, human or otherwise, the breed purist will insist on an Akita with the physical ability and courage necessary to make a bear "make tracks."

Meanwhile, the Akita was gaining in popularity in England. The breed was attracting the notice of avid dog fanciers such as **PATRICIA NEIL** of **SANJOSHA KENNELS.**

Sanjosha Kennels of Somerset, England was founded in 1986 by Mrs. Patricia Neil. Pat purchased a Sachmo daughter from us. Without the wide availability of top stud dogs available to breeders in the States, Mrs. Neil was nonetheless able to breed Hoshi wisely and successfully.

Top Sanjosha winners are Sanjosha's Kotaishi, Junior Warrant-titled in May of 1989; Sanjosha's Shiroi Tasaka, Top Akita Puppy 1990; and Sanjosha's Shiroi Ninkimono, unbeaten in puppy class during 1990 also Best Akita Puppy at the Crufts Dog Show 1991.

It's noteworthy that Crufts is England's equivalent to our Westminster Show, but with far larger entries, averaging 20,000 dogs of all breeds over four days.

Pat says, "Ninki was only beaten in 1990 by his brothers. Kotaisha was unfortunately run over by a car on his second birthday and died from back injuries. His owner was understandably heartbroken.

"It's strange, actually, that although 'Hoshi' wasn't the most fantastic bitch in the world, she's passed on so many attributes to her offspring, in particular a lovely, bouncing, willing temperament, good character and coat, and good angulation."

Sanjosha's Shiroi Ninkimondo (Freestead's Ci The Promethean x Sanjosha's Tora No Yona) competing for Best Puppy at the Crufts Dog Show in 1991, a class she did indeed win. Breeder, Pat Neil of Somerset, England.

Sanjosha's Shiroi Tasaka (Freestead's Ci The Promethean x Sanjosha's Tora No Yona) was the top Akita puppy in 1990 in England. Breeder, Pat Neil.

The Akita Breed Standard

THE AKC STANDARD

Dog breeders might presume to bake a chocolate cake without a recipe, but you can bet they'd never attempt to create a great dog without a recipe—the breed standard. To omit any of the basic ingredients (temperament, structure, movement) is to wind up with something other than a cake...or an Akita. To continue the analogy, a chocolate cake with no icing may be tasty to some people, but the gourmet will want lots of scrumptious icing. Type is the icing on the cake. If you skimp on the icing, you may have an Akita, but it will be boringly plain!

Tiare Caudill Arndt explained it best in a feature article for the 1984 *Akita Reference.* "Terry" was then and is now the chairperson of the ACA standards Revision Committee.

In "Goings On ... With The Akita Standard," Terry writes, "What serves as a guide for the breeder? Who helps direct them towards proper selection of mates for the next generation? Whether haphazardly or with definite purpose, a motivating goal for breeders is SUCCESS. Success to mean: for the profit-minded, bigger puppy sales; for the devoted breeder, a step closer to the ideal dog. The ideal dog is able to prove his merit by achievements in the show ring and in the breeding circle. Whatever the motivation and definition of success, the desire for its achievement is universal.

"A measuring stick of successful dog breeding can be gauged somewhat, though not exclusively, in the show ring. The AKC judging system and judges are largely responsible for the perpetuation of the breed's conformation. Dog show judging as well as fad breeding have been known to be detrimental to a breed. Vigilance and education for both parties would prove beneficial in avoiding this unfortunate happening.

"Thus far, we have in the chain of a breed's perpetuation: breeder, success, show ring,

BIS Ch. The Widow-Maker O'BJ, ROMXP winning one of his ten Bests in Show with the author handling. Widow-Maker is truly as close to the standard as an Akita can come, and as James P. Taylor eloquently states in the "Preface" of this book, this incomparable dog shows the "new generation" the pure essence of the Akita in America.

Am/Can. Ch. Ashmen's Bronco Bill of Bruin (Ch. Koma-Inu Bronze Bruin, ROM x Ch. Windom's Kaki Kisa No Ashmen) bred and owned by Judy Ashmen.

judges. The missing link to complete the circle: *the breed standard. T*he standard, the "guide." If a standard appears well stated, interpretations will still vary. For this reason, we would do well to examine each part of our standard to see whether this verbiage is as accurately presented as possible."

Just as Terry's words aptly explain the need for a breed standard, there could be no more fitting introduction to the Akita standard than the one in the official publication of the Akita Club Of America. *The Akita, A Guide* was first published in June 1974 and is still in use today.

"If it were necessary to describe the Akita in one word, 'dignity' would suffice. For it is this concept that the breed embodies. Whether in proud stance or no-nonsense movement, the breed's dignified presence is its most distinct quality. Each element described in the standard is designed to contribute to this impression.

There is an emphasis in Akita standards on the head. The overall broad and triangular head shape is brought to extraordinary impressiveness by the harmonizing triangular shape of the eyes and ears. The product is an alert and fearless expression.

As a balancing agent, there is a large, full tail. It cannot trail behind or up in the air but must curl around to meet the dog's back or rest against his flank.

The Akita is in the bottom range of the large-size breed category. His size and obvious strength leave a lasting impression on all who see him. At the same time, there is no harshness in his appearance. For the short, thick and lustrous double coat softens the rugged outline of muscle and bone.

In his driving movement, the Akita combines great power with a precision and smoothness which make it seem as natural to be moving as to be standing still. Every step is a purposeful expression of the dog's own will.

The breed character is reserved, silent and dominant over other canines. Although the Akita is unruffled by minor irritations, he is alert toward other dogs, and any serious challenge is met with swift retaliation.

With man, the Akita is a delightful companion. He gives in devotion and protection more than he could ever take in food and shelter. Friendly strangers are treated with respect, but trespassers find the door barred by an awesome figure."

THE OFFICIAL STANDARD

GENERAL APPEARANCE — Large, powerful, alert, with much substance and heavy bone. The broad head, forming a blunt triangle, with deep muzzle, small eyes and erect ears carried forward in line with back of neck, is characteristic of the breed. The large, curled tail, balancing the broad head, is also characteristic of the breed.

HEAD—Massive but in balance with body; free of wrinkle when at ease. Skull flat between ears and broad; jaws square and powerful with minimal dewlap. Head forms a blunt triangle when viewed from above. *Fault*—Narrow or snipy head. **Muzzle**—Broad and full. Distance from nose to stop is to distance from stop to occiput as 2 is to 3. **Stop**—Well defined, but not too abrupt. A shallow furrow extends well up forehead. **Nose**—Broad and black. Liver permitted on white Akitas, but black always preferred. *Disqualification*—Butterfly nose or total lack of pigmentation on nose. **Ears**—The ears of the Akita are characteristic of the breed. They are strongly erect and small in relation to rest of head. If ear is folded forward for measuring length, tip will touch upper eye rim. Ears are triangular, slightly rounded at tip, wide at base, set wide on head but not too low, and carried slightly forward over eyes in line with back of neck. *Disqualification*—Drop or broken ears. **Eyes**—Dark brown, small, deep-set and triangular in shape. Eye rims black and tight. **Lips and Tongue**—Lips black and not pendulous; tongue pink. **Teeth**—Strong with scissors bite preferred, but level bite acceptable. *Disqualification*—Noticeably undershot or overshot.

NECK AND BODY—**Neck**—Thick and muscular; comparatively short, widening gradually toward shoulders. A pronounced crest blends in with base of skull. **Body**—Longer than high, as 10 is to 9 in males; 11 to 9 in bitches. Chest wide and deep; depth of chest is one-half height of dog at shoulder. Ribs well sprung, brisket well developed. Level back with firmly muscled loin and moderate tuck-up. Skin pliant but not loose. *Serious Faults*—Light bone, rangy body.

TAIL—Large and full, set high and carried over back or against flank in a three-quarter, full, or double curl, always dipping to or below level of back. On a three-quarter curl, tip drops well down flank. Root large and strong. Tail bone reaches hock when let down. Hair coarse, straight and full, with no appearance of a plume. *Disqualification*—Sickle or uncurled tail.

FOREQUARTERS AND HINDQUARTERS— **Forequarters**—Shoulders strong and powerful with moderate layback. Forelegs heavy-boned and straight as viewed from front. Angle of pastern 15 degrees forward from vertical. *Faults*—Elbows in or out, loose shoulders. **Hindquarters**—Width, muscular development and comparable to forequarters. Upper thighs well developed. Stifle moderately bent and hocks well let down, turning neither in nor out. **Dewclaws**—On front legs generally not removed; dewclaws on hind legs generally removed. **Feet**—Cat feet, well knuckled up with thick pads. Feet straight ahead.

COAT—Double-coated. Undercoat thick, soft, dense and shorter than outer coat. Outer coat straight, harsh and standing somewhat off body. Hair on head, legs and ears short. Length of hair at withers and rump approximately two inches, which is slightly longer than on rest of body, except tail, where coat is longest and most profuse. *Fault*—Any indication of ruff or feathering.

COLOR—Any color including white; brindle; or pinto. Colors are brilliant and clear and markings are well balanced, with or without mask or blaze. White Akitas have no mask. Pinto has a white background with large, evenly placed patches covering head and more than one-third of body. Undercoat may be a different color from outer coat.

GAIT—Brisk and powerful with strides of moderate length. Back remains strong, firm and level. Rear legs move in line with front legs.

SIZE—Males 26 to 28 inches at the withers; bitches 24 to 26 inches. *Disqualification*—Dogs under 25 inches; bitches under 23 inches.

TEMPERAMENT—Alert and responsive, dignified and courageous. Aggressive toward other dogs.

DISQUALIFICATIONS

Butterfly nose or total lack of pigmentation on nose.

Drop or broken ears.

Noticeably undershot or overshot.

Sickle or uncurled tail.

Dogs under 25 inches; bitches under 23 inches.

Approved by the American Kennel Club April 4, 1973.

NOTE: You might wish to place a large paper clip or bookmark at this point so that you can easily refer back to the standard as we continue our discussion.

A COMPARATIVE ANALYSIS

Unlike many AKC purebreds, the history and development of the Akita is still recent and pertinent. Many people do not understand how our present breed standard evolved and the important differences between the American Akita and the Japanese Akita of today.

There are several Japanese standards, just as there were earlier versions of the American standard. We now have only one AKC standard so we shall refer to the others only to compare wording, intent, and descriptive terms, and to take historical note of portions which were omitted or changed.

You'll remember that the AKC was adamantly opposed to the continued importation of dogs from Japan and even to the mating of dogs which represented "import" characteristics. Not being privy to all of the decision-making process in 1970–71, we can only surmise why salient parts of the Japanese standards were deleted from the approved AKC version but the fact that they were led to the development of a very different "type" of dog.

There are several registries in Japan. This may be one of the reasons the AKC initially refused to recognize any one association but I was told by the AKC that they (AKC) did not accept the integrity of the Japanese stud books. And with good reason.

To refresh your memory, Nippo was established in May 1923, Akiho in 1924, and Akikyo in 1943. Therefore, the Nippo standard is the oldest and, to many people, the most prestigious. Each of the other standards were modeled after the Nippo standard. To further confuse the issue, there is also the dominant Japanese Kennel Club which registers and oversees all breeds. In 1991 the JKC was successful in persuading the Fédération Cynologique Internationale (FCI) to ban or withhold awards from all "American type" Akitas.

The first American standard was published in 1956 by the Akita Kennel Club so it's only natural that much of the wording is directly from the Japanese standards. Rather than reprint each standard, much of which would be redundant, we'll mention only the important differences between the first American standard, the Japanese standards, and our current AKC standard.

The 1956 standard used a scale of points which was later dropped. By late 1960, the newly formed Akita Club Of America was involved in rewriting the standard and there were several revisions, including one which restored and specified white as an allowable color.

Naturally, everyone had their own idea of what was correct. Thankfully, the breed was represented by a few good dog people who kept a level head. Interesting examples of differing personal perceptions are found under descriptions of the breed's purposes. One American version described him as a "sled dog" but fortunately, the '50s' Akita was also defined as "a guard dog, child's companion and all around family dog," a multi-purpose role which he fills admirably.

The official AKC standard is the only formula by which all breeders should measure their stock and by which all judges must evaluate exhibits. In the very first sentence, we're told this breed has "much substance and heavy bone." The requirement for size and power is stressed again and again throughout the standards for the Akita. For anyone still not quite sure how big is "big," size is once and for all dealt with under "Size."

In order to emphasize that the breed is "tough" without directly stating that the Akita should be able to whip his weight in wildcats, there are subtle reminders. The standard says he's courageous, has powerful jaws, small ears and deep-set eyes (less vulnerable to injury), a comparatively short, thick muscular neck (difficult to grasp); he's moderately angulated (as are all fighting breeds); and finally sums up what it has been hinting at all along by stating, "Aggressive toward other dogs." These descriptive terms are most often combined in the terrier standards. Whether you judge, breed, or are considering first-time ownership, please don't overlook the significance.

Even the description of the tail says this is a proud, dominant, no-nonsense kind of dog. "Tightly wound," "proudly carried," and "high set" are terms which exactly describe the tail position of the dominant canine. Naturalists identify the pack's dominant wolves by their tail carriage. It's an unfailing sign of rank, and of momentary displays of dominance or challenge.

The standard fails to stipulate that the Akita was used for hunting bear and boar—not quail. There is a 1992 ACA proposal which would add the sentence "a dog used for hunting large game in the mountainous regions of Northern Japan." For obvious reasons, our standard doesn't mention the dark days of fighting Akitas. Only historical records deal with this important background information, enabling us to better understand the physical and physiological makeup of the breed.

One word, one visual image, will keep cropping up as we explore the Akita's physique: "Thick." It's used over and over again. From thick ear leather to thick neck to thick pads to thick tail root, it's helpful to program ourselves to "think thick" when assessing an Akita. There's nothing thin or delicate about any part of this breed.

General Appearance:

The 1956 standard stated, "belongs to the Spitz-type or Husky family." That simple sentence typified the breed for judges, as well as for the general public. It's unfortunate that it was removed.

Ch. Tschumi's Flash owned by Pam Glave, Imarii Akitas. This head study clearly demonstrates small forward set ears, the distinctive furrow (which runs from between the eyes to well up the forehead), pleasingly almond shaped eyes, and the overall triangular appearance of a magnificent Akita head.

It described the breed as "massive, muscular, with well-knit frame." As with the Japanese standards, which also require agility and nimbleness, there is a consistent demand for power and proper attitude. One such perfectly descriptive phrase states, "standing firm on the ground to reveal his power." The Akita doesn't just occupy space—he has the physical ability to control it!

The Japanese standards ask for a clear differentiation between the sexes and a proposed ACA revision states, "The male dog should express masculinity by his build, facial expression, and presentation. The female dog, in contrast, should express femininity without weakness of structure."

Head:

Like the Collie or Bulldog, the Akita is referred to as a "head breed." Having assessed the overall balance and outline, the most important anatomical part to be considered is the head.

"Massive" does not mean a Saint Bernard or Mastiff head. The 1956 standard stipulated that "there should not be too much dewlap or loose skin about the throat." That the words "too much" were in deference to the loose-skinned, heavy-jowled Dewa-type dogs, which were still popular in Japan, is obvious. Conversely, the Japanese standards recognized the problem and all versions reflected a determined effort to correct type by demanding tight skin and specifically faulting loose lips.

Finally recognizing our slackness (no pun intended), a revision to the 1956 American standard required the head to be "free from wrinkle" but, unfortunately, certain factions were accommodated when the official standard was rewritten. Much controversy still abounds over the addition of the phrase "when at ease" and there is a current proposal to delete those three words which so subtly corrupt the proper facial expression and type.

The Akita head should be "dry," a term which not only describes tight skin with no wrinkles and flews but also suggests a tight mouth which does not drool! Like all other canines, the Akita perspires through his tongue but he doesn't froth, slobber, or drool.

In comparing the exaggerated heads of domesticated dogs with those of the wolf or coyote, we can see that the wild canines are strong in jaw muscle, capable of cracking the bones of their natural prey. The "cheeks" are wide and well developed but the muzzle is not so broad or deep as to create the eye, occlusion, or breathing problems often present in drastically altered breeds. The perfect Akita head is not exaggerated although there is strong development of the backskull. When viewed from above, the occipital bridge is comprised of dense, thick bone and is surprisingly broad.

A symphony of triangles: O'BJ Back To The Future owned by Barbara Fay. "Tucker" is a black masked, clear golden fawn with an exceptional headpiece.

Joan Linderman put it beautifully when she described the Akita head as a "symphony of triangles." From just about any angle, the head, as well as the muzzle, ears, and eyes; all form a slightly elongated triangle, each part in perfect harmony with the overall effect of triangle on triangle.

Muzzle:

"Broad and full" does not equate to a blocky head. The numerical proportions for length are clear. Remembering the Akita to be of spitz-Arctic type will help to define correct skull width.

The AKC video example of an "over-done" head which describes the stop as being "too abrupt" is not so clear. The stop should be strong and "well defined," so that the muzzle is visibly differentiated from the backskull. A ski-slope not only is wrong but it denotes weakness and oddly enough, when the stop recedes, the characteristic furrow (down the center of the skull and to the bridge of the muzzle) becomes more filled in.

One fault described under "Head" might better have been dealt with under "Muzzle."

Bearing in mind that the Akita is a natural breed, muzzle proportions which hint of the Chow Chow are much too much for the Akita.

Nose:

One Japanese standard plainly states the nose shall be "pink" on a white Akita. The decision to use the term "liver" was unfortunate. The genetic liver coloration common to some sporting breeds is not found in the Akita. "Liver permitted" is our misworded attempt to make the proper allowances for the white dog.

That isn't to say that black pigmentation can't be found on a white dog. It exists, but when it truly belongs to the dog (not to the hand of an artistic cosmetologist), the eye rims and portions of the lips and gums will almost always be black.

What is usually seen on the white Akita (outside of the show ring) is a grayish, sort of charcoal-smutty nose. The edges of the nose leather may be darker with the center portion shading to a light brownish gray; the perfectly natural result of nature's own paint job—gray pigment over pink flesh color.

The ACA video provides a perfect example of this shading and also of a "Butterfly" nose. According to *The Complete Dog Book,* an official AKC publication, a butterfly nose is a bright pink (unpigmented) pattern on an otherwise dark nose. According to Dr. Spira, a pink spotted nose is often encountered in youngsters (such as the Great Dane in his illustration) and may take a year or more to completely fill in. Slow pigment may occur in white Akitas or even in those with a black mask if there is a white half mask or muzzle marking.

Although not mentioned on the video, a grayish or brownish nose with a smattering of black spots is not terribly uncommon in whites. Darker pigment over lighter pigment is visibly (and genetically) not the same as unpigmented areas, ergo, a butterfly nose. Although seldom seen in the show ring, if one is brave enough to show a white dog with nose au naturel, then judges should accept it as such. If it isn't "butterfly" and it isn't totally lacking in pigment, then it's preferable to the deception so often encountered.

In summary, a nose with brownish or charcoal nose pigment, even if unevenly shaded, is not, repeat, *is not,* lacking in pigmentation. While

Ch. Okii Yubi's Sachmo of Makoto, ROMXP (Mikado No Kin Hozan, ROMP x Juho Mariko No Kin Hozan, ROMP) is the #2 Sire of All Working Breeds. Bred by Robert Campbell, owned by Bill and Barbara Andrews.

we would all prefer naturally black nose leather which puts no one on the interpretive spot, a nose which has no bright *pink* unpigmented areas is an acceptable nose.

Ears:

Let's just say that translation errors may have led someone plagued with ear problems to believe that the ear must reach to the eye rim. Actually, the ear should not extend beyond the eye rim. The standard says the tip will touch, not "reach" the eye rim. Photographic evidence is clear, as is the spitz background. Miss Keller's beloved pet (with one flopped ear) or the much revered

Hachi-ko only prove that some dogs in Japan had faulty ears, just as some dogs here have faulty ears. We should just adhere to the standard, and chastise those who would attempt to twist it into something which is in direct contradiction to all versions of all standards, American or Japanese.

Astute dog people are quick to realize that a long ear may be in perfect proportion to a long head. It may indeed reach only "to" the eye rim when anchored on a backskull more befitting a Collie! That does not make it correct. It's but a classic example of two wrongs not making a right! The ears must be small in proportion to an otherwise correct head. "Small" is small. The standard doesn't qualify the requirement by saying something like "relatively" small.

We shouldn't have to measure. The figurative example wasn't meant to be executed any more than we are expected to use a slide rule to compare the distance from stop to occiput. For those exacting people who prefer to measure, the method is so straightforward that instructions would normally have seemed patently condescending. Not so since the release of the ACA Akita video.

Therefore, you will forgive me for explaining that the ear is to be folded FLAT to the skull, not raised up over the thickness of

several fingers! The ridiculous demonstration on the ACA video serves no educational purpose other than to show how to manipulate overly long ears so that they do not extend beyond the eye rim. If an ear of correct length were to be measured in this way, of course, the tip would fall far short of the eye rim....

The Akita is a very functional dog and the ears reflect his utilitarian development. The small, thick ear leather doesn't tear as easily in a fight, no matter the opponent. Equally important, it's less prone to frostbite in the frigid climate of Northern Japan. Very few Samoyeds actually pull sleds across the tundra, but the standard still demands those small "Arctic dog" ears. Our standard calls for even smaller ears, actually, *Chow-*sized ears. If you would doubt, please refer to and compare the referenced standards.

The ears and tail are two of the distinguishing features of Akita type, with the ears being the more distinctive. Other breeds, such as the Chow, have a curled tail and short, thick ears, but the forward slant of the Akita ear is unique. A proposed addition to the standard would add "*Fault*—ears vertically erect in profile."

Ch. O'BJ Kudos For Kolor, (BIS Ch. The Widow-Maker O'BJ, ROMXP x Ch. The Mad Hatter O'BJ, ROMXP) at six months. The split mask is enhanced by the dark goggles around her eyes, creating a stunning effect on an outstanding head.

Eyes:

Round or protuberant eyes are totally

wrong. Not only does the shape and size of the eye determine expression, practicality reminds us that the small, deep-set eye is less vulnerable to fang and claw.

Eye size and shape corresponds to personality types in all breeds, and beyond that, the placement of the eye is so important that it defines a species as either predator or prey. Cocker Spaniel expression and personality would be as dreadfully incorrect on an Akita as would a Bull Terrier eye and personality on a Great Pyrenees! For this reason, tightness of the rim, size, shape, oblique placement; all are vital to complete the "inscrutable" image of an Oriental guarding dog.

An Akita face that looks like it might be anything else is just not an Akita. The triangular shape is somewhat different than the wolf-slant of other northern breeds. The upward slant should be noticeable, but not so much so as in the Shiba.

Never should the "triangular shape" be formed by loose skin. The odd tucks, niches, and gathers one occasionally comes across in the show ring are not natural. Entropion and ectropion can be and often are surgically corrected. Tight eye rims are demanded in order to minimize the mastiff-type influence which still plagued breeders of the 1950s. It was important enough to warrant a cautionary reminder then—and it still is.

The size of the eye is "small," like the ears. The correct eye does not lead to "eye problems." PRA, lens luxation, and other such problems are more often found in dramatically altered breeds, not in the spitz-type dogs. The proper Akita eye is a healthy, non-tearing, sparkling, distinctively shaped window to the soul of a primitive beast bound by love to his human friend.

No allowance is made for lighter eye rims in white dogs—it's simply understood. You will occasionally see dark shading, sort of an outline around the eye, which, for want of a better term, I've dubbed "eye liner." Women know exactly what I mean. Only visible on lighter colored dogs, the eye liner often extends beyond and "lifts" the outer corner, thus emphasizing the Oriental expression. Certainly not a required feature; eye liner is like the decorative writing on that chocolate icing!

Lips and Tongue:

The Hozankai standard (Japanese) and the American standard of 1956 both faulted (minor fault) black spots on the tongue, perhaps considered reflective of the Chinese Chow. The spots persist even today but are almost never present in dogs which show the GSD or Mastiff influence.

Although no allowance is made for lip color in the white Akita, it's "understood" to be primarily pink, as are the gums. It's taken for granted that lips and gums will be primarily black in a dark dog, although some pink mottling is often present and, as it's not faulted, must be accepted.

It is not taken for granted that the lips will be tight enough, therefore, as with the eye rims, we are reminded.

Teeth:

There's a current proposal to drop the confusing word "noticeably" and this might resolve one of the gray areas of our breed standard.

The standard does not specify tooth size but being a somewhat primitive breed, the teeth should be large for the mouth, thus appearing "strong" and capable of seizing and holding large game.

Neck:

The Akita should be capable of handling big game or another powerful dog. A well-muscled neck provides the leverage needed to maintain grip, and a thick neck is difficult for another animal to grasp.

"Comparatively short" doesn't mean a stump between head and shoulders, but given the purpose of the breed, a stump would be preferable to a swan neck.

There's an understandable tendency toward an "elegant" dog with a long, graceful neck. Breeders must be prudent lest faults become "virtues" when popular winners are widely used at stud. Showy and pretty in the show ring is not always correct for a breed. The end result is usually a change in the standard to accommodate the fault...

A good rule of thumb, if the neck is long enough to have a "pronounced crest," it's long enough—and if it looks "elegant," it's too long!

Body:

The Japanese standards, analysis, and discussions stress harmony and balance. Following the Japanese penchant for numerical comparisons, our standard states the proportions "as 10 is to 9 in males; 11 to 9 in bitches." The Japanese standard says "90/100 in dogs and 90/110 in bitches" and it clearly stipulates "measured from the foremost part of the brisket to the farmost part of the hip." We adopted the same numerical ratio and the exact same methods of measurement.

There's an easy trick to assessing body proportions. In one Japanese standard, the experts on balance explain it this way; the actual back (from behind the shoulder blade through the loin) should be one-third the total length of the body. The shoulder assembly, viewed from the side, should be one-third of the total body length, i.e., equal the breadth of

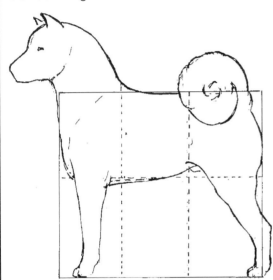

Horizontal line indicates actual depth of brisket rather than the outline which is affected by thickness of coat or the mammary development/loose skin usually present in the brood bitch.

Drawings by the author.

"Longer than high, as 10 is to 9 in males; 11 to 9 in bitches. ...depth of chest is one-half height of dog at shoulder."

A slight difference in head carriage and crest of neck between the male and female is portrayed, as is the slightly higher tailset of the male and proportionately thicker bone. A female of the same height as a male should weigh more due to extra body length and more body fat. She may have slightly more angulation and more turn of stifle, in keeping with her longer frame.'

Body length proportions of one-third to one-third to one-third and height ratio of leg length equal to body depth should remain the same for both sexes.

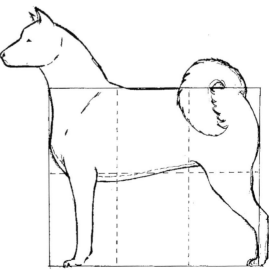

the rear quarters. Mentally dividing the profile into thirds enables us to easily determine correct balance.

In the early 1970s, most breed enthusiasts could quote the Japanese standards "chapter and verse." Many breed standards don't specify the measuring points but in retrospect, ours should have spelled out the measuring instructions from the Japanese standard right along with the stated ratios. We didn't bother because (like measuring height or ears) it was assumed everyone knew how. No one suspected that some 20 years later, an attempt would be made to change that which had always been!

Thankfully, history can not be changed, including the drawing on page 13 of *The Akita—A Guide,* the official publication of the Akita Club Of America. That excellent graphic was patterned after the very precise Japanese drawings. Given a "given," it seems inconceivable that anyone would attempt to promote a new way of measuring but the AKC/ACA video does just that!

Although the video is an excellent production, there are some problems. We must remember, the only official reference is the AKC breed standard. Even the AKC does not have the power to change it without the consent of the majority of the membership of the parent club. The video is one of many educational sources available to the student breeder or judge but it is no more official than this book! A small minority (in power at the time) decided that the body length should be measured from point of shoulder to buttocks rather than from sternum to buttocks. I'm unable to provide you with a reason why anyone would attempt to corrupt 40 years of recorded history in less than 40 seconds of video tape.

For those who wisely want to know the why of things, allow me to, once and for all, put this issue to rest. The difference between the sternum and the point of shoulder is roughly 2 inches in an adult male. A difference which would create a dramatic change in outline and balance. A 27-inch male would not be 30 inches long—he might actually be 33 inches long!

As a comparison, the Rottweiler standard specifies body proportions "as 10 is to 9." It too asks that depth of body and length of leg be equal. Even so, judges and breeders will agree, the Akita presents a slightly higher stationed profile than the Rottweiler. But wait, the Rottie standard specifies that the dog is measured "from the breast bone (sternum) to the rear edge of the pelvis," not from the point of the shoulder. Therefore, the Akita would actually be much *longer and lower* to the ground than the Rottweiler if measured from the point of the shoulder! If bred to the body proportions as given on the ACA video, the Akita profile would look more like the Siberian Husky or—are you ready?—The German Shepherd Dog. Akita breeders in all countries have diligently worked to overcome the influence of the GSD, as well as other breeds. Dark saddle markings are still seen but of more consequence, the long back is often accompanied by other atypical conformation characteristics such as an exaggerated turn of stifle, sloping pasterns, sloping croup, and low tail set.

The ACA membership knew nothing of what was on the video until it was released, but one has to wonder how something so obviously incorrect slipped by AKC? Actually, the AKC did recall the video due to another misrepresentation, but all the mistakes were not edited out. Unless and until the AKC sees fit to redo the entire program, we must live with serious errors in a work which should have been a wonderful educational tool.

A steep rear will elevate the rear quarters, thus causing a dog to be "high in rear." Just as faulty is excessive rear angulation wherein the hocks must be positioned too far back in order to be properly perpendicular to the ground. This creates a sloping topline. As the back should be level, correct angulation becomes more than just a movement-related requirement.

Loose skin is faulted yet again in this section. The Japanese standards are a bit more loquacious, calling for a tight body and tight skin, and faulting loose skin or "sloppy body."

Ch. Okii Yubi's Sachmo of Makoto, ROMXP taking his first of many owner-handled Group Placements. He was only a gangly youngster, but Mrs. Winifred Heckman was well known for her uncanny ability to discover the great dogs of the future. Certainly, this award was prophetic.

The AKC standard doesn't describe the shape of the rib cage which the Japanese refer to as "boat shaped." A more familiar description (in this modern world of giant ocean liners) would be to say the rib cage should resemble an egg standing on its small end.

The *only* serious faults are listed here: light bone and rangy body. It's surprising how many people can readily associate light bone with a competitor's dog; and yet, when asked what else is a serious fault, can not for the life of them, remember "rangy body." The opposite of rangy body? Remember, "think thick." Short back. Substance.

Tail:

The standard is so well written one would not think this could be a debatable matter and yet, tails have always been a serious subject of discussion.

The following is excerpted from "Tattle Tale Tails," Spring 1976 *The Akita Handbook:*

"When the tail is completely down, it usually indicates faulty temperament rather than a structural fault. While I realize that we have no disqualification for shyness, we *do* have a disqualification for bad tails; and a bad tail is a bad tail, regardless of the reason. I personally feel poor tail carriage due to shyness is a far more serious fault than a structurally bad tail. You can live with and love an ugly dog, but an unstable dog is a joy to no one.

"Consider the standard and the very precise wording regarding tails. Large and full, set high and carried over back in a three-quarter full or double curl, *always* dipping to or below level of back." (Emphasis mine.)

First of all, a three-quarter curl is *not* a curve, nor is it a gay tail, and while some would say this allows for the curved tail waving gaily over the back and occasionally brushing the loin, the second sentence of the standard dispels that idea once and for all: "On a three-quarter curl, tip drops well down flank."

"So either a tail is fully or double curled, or it must drop well down the flank. Pretty plain English. Therefore, the only tail which would be acceptable as just touching the back but *not* dipping below the level of the back would be the tightly curled tail which by virtue of its tightness does not slide off to one side, thus extending below the level of the back."

"If we allow dogs with structurally bad tails to compete and finish, we are defeating our purpose. If we allow dogs with bad tails due to bad temperament to finish, we are in even worse trouble. I've heard all the excuses: 'He's just a little uncertain' (means shy); 'He doesn't like the mats...or the grass...or the concrete...or whatever' (what *does* he walk on?); 'He hasn't been out before.' (Shouldn't matter unless he's been shut in a closet); 'He isn't feeling too well today' (Then let's hope he isn't contagious);

'His tail got stepped on' (You've got to be kidding—it should have been curled up out of the way!)...and the list goes on and on.

"As long as we allow handlers to prop tails in order to conceal a *disqualifying* fault, the tail will tell the tale in the whelping box." (Excerpt from *The Akita Handbook* by the author.)

Nearly 20 years later, there are still judges who ignore the breed standard rather than disqualify. Breeders must be sure they understand the standard, present only correct dogs, and then insist that judges uphold the disqualifications.

Once more, there are only three acceptable degrees of curl: three-quarter, full, and double. Only the full and double curl may dip to or rest on a level with the back. The three-quarter curl must "drop well down the flank." It can not just rest on the back.

The set on, carriage, and the degree of curl have always been of paramount importance. Japanese standards are notably brief and to the point, lavishly supplemented with detailed drawings. The tail is succinctly described in both the old Akikyo standard (1949) and the revised (1954) version as "thick and coiled, powerful, the tip of the tail reaching the hocks." The verbal imagery is excellent. "Coiled" is a wonderful word. "Powerful" may throw the reader for a moment until one realizes that the tail is so indicative of temperament and overall structure. Oh,

BIS/BISS Ch. Running Bear's Sunburst (Ch. Big D's Akanboo Akai Palaccort x Am/Mx Ch. Kuma Yama's Palace Court Dani) has excellent height-length proportion and striking color and markings. He's owned by Bob & Judy Gresham, handled to this Group win under judge Robert Matchett by handler Keith Pautz.

and there's that word again: "thick." Meaning both in boning and in the fullness of the hair.

It must be thick and bushy to balance the proper head. The standard reminds us that the hair must be coarse, straight, and full. Ideally, it should look something like a big bottle brush when the dog is in good coat. Even when blowing coat, we should never settle for a thinly or sparsely furred tail, either of which signifies an unhealthy dog or one with a basically faulty coat type. There should be thick undercoat on the tail, just as on the body. Lacking undercoat, the longer hair of the tail will separate or droop, creating a plumed effect.

There has been some debate regarding the stipulation that the tail bone reach the hock. Experienced dog people understand that a short tail can easily reach a long hock. They also know that just as in measuring ears, two wrongs do not make a right. It might be easier to visualize the tail as being about two-thirds the height of the dog, regardless of hock length.

Although not shown at full extension, this bitch demonstrates moderate angulation and level topline. Her head carriage is a bit high because she is not fully extended. When the Akita moves with purpose, the head lowers as the forequarters reach to pull in more ground. She is So. Am. Ch. The One To Keep O'BJ, owned by Maurizio Moretto.

"Has wonderful angulation," "really laid back shoulders," "great turn of stifle" are terms often used by people who don't realize they are innocently praising a clearly described fault. Moderate is moderate. It is not as upright as the Chow Chow and not as angulated as the Doberman.

"Strong and powerful" applies to bitches too. Stringy, flat musculature is incorrect in either sex and heavy bone is required to support a relatively heavy body. It also does not break so easily. A good horseman will know exactly the right bone—round, dense. Elliptical-shaped bone almost always occurs in conjunction with thin, ropey pasterns and loose feet. Faults usually accompany faults.

Elbows should be tight to the body without being pinched. In a tightly constructed, hard-bodied, athletic dog, the shoulders will usually be held in good position by well-developed muscles.

Forequarters:

We must curb the tendency to award and breed for overly angulated dogs. The requirement for moderate angulation is repeated again under "Hindquarters" and under "Gait."

Hindquarters:

Originating in rocky mountainous terrain, the Akita has a lower thigh that should have good length, and the bone must be strong right to the ground. In many Akitas, the bone becomes noticeably thinner below the hock joint. This is especially bothersome in a breed which must depend on strong rear quarters to provide push to the rest of the body, whether scrambling over treacherous terrain, or instantly out-maneuvering the swipe of a bear's paw! Thin bone, out of proportion to the rest of the skeletal structure, puts a fighting-hunting dog at a serious disadvantage.

Once again, the requirement for angulation is "moderate," essential to maintain agility while still affording stability in a physical confrontation. In order to squat low on the rear quarters in a close situation, the hocks need to be short (well let down) and well under the dog.

The Japanese standards emphasize prominent tendons and joints. Although the Akita is almost cat-like in terms of suppleness and flexibility, he should not be loose-jointed. The stifle and hock tendons should be thumb-thick and well defined.

In striving for a large dog with heavy bone, we tend to forget that the tremendous growth rate and early weight gain may outpace developing tendons and ligaments. As we add excessive bone, we are in danger of losing the tight skin, hard muscle, and tight-knit body; ergo, the Akita loses the ability to do the work nature and man intended for him.

It may be that the Japanese mention of prominent joints was a result of a problem with overly flexible joints and loose tendons as breeders struggled to eliminate the influence of other breeds. Perhaps the word picture was only meant to typify the structure. By honing in on one small part of the anatomy, a well-rounded dog person may visualize the overall type and function of the breed. One does not see steel sinew and large "knotty" joints on breeds of softer construction. While accidents happen to the most resilient of athletes, poor musculature and weak joints will increase the odds of injury. We must be aware of these basics of construction, especially as we are now seeing a disproportionate number of cruciate ligament injuries.

Dewclaws:

Front dewclaws are tight to the leg, and not overly large. They are seldom removed. Rear dewclaws are rare but it's wiser to check

newborns than to wait and notice them when the pup is several weeks old.

Feet:

Japanese descriptions frequently refer to the feet as "grips," such as "the paws are thick and have a tight grip." This delightful terminology describes not only the physical shape of the feet but also the "in command" temperament of the male Akita. Indeed, he should stand on the ground as though he owns it and has no intention of letting it go!

The Akita has fully webbed feet and swims on the surface like an otter, using both front and rear feet as opposed to the typical "dog paddle" of most breeds. Accomplished swimmer that he is, still, he'd rather just cool off in shallow water unless motivated to enter deep water.

Coat:

Considering the near-Arctic climate of Akita Prefecture, the correct coat must be thick, waterproof, triple layered, with a big off-standing functional guard coat and a dense wooly undercoat. Short, thin, wavy, or soft coats were not uncommon in the late 1940s and early '50s while the breed was being slowly and painfully rebuilt. Photos from the '60s show an overall improvement and by the '70s, Japanese winners consistently sported massive coats with abundant guard hair clearly exceeding 4 inches. By the mid-80s, Japanese breeders had succeeded in eradicating the skimpy coats caused by the introduction of foreign breeds and crossbreeding with the Tosa.

None of the Japanese standards gives any measurement for the length of coat. We again call upon the lecture of Mr. Hiraizumi some 25 years ago. One of two active members of Akiho who had firsthand knowledge of the breed in the pre-war period, Mr. Hiraizumi was Officer and Chief Judge of Akiho when he addressed west-coast breeders during the 1970 Nisei Week Akita Show. Questioned about coat length, he responded "There is no specific length in terms of centimeters or inches. The overall appearance of the coat is of more importance than actual length. The coat of an Akita-inu comes in three layers. There is a wooly undercoat, a medium length middle coat, and a coarse outer coat...If the coat is in proper condition there should be a general appearance of a bristled, yet, soft quality or fluffiness. It is this fluffy quality which gives the coat its look of fullness and is not only desirable but also sought after. If, on the other hand, the wooly coat was not dense enough, then the outer coat would not stand nor bristle in the desired manner."

In America, faulty coats are often excused due to climatic factors. Although a dog in the North Pole would surely have a heavier coat than one indigenous to Florida, it's the genes (and health) that control coat quality.

When asked about the weather's influence on coat length, Mr. Hiraizumi said that was not to be considered, pointing out that many parts of Japan are much hotter than our southern or coastal states. He stated that many of the profusely coated Japanese winners on the slides were in fact from those very warm areas in Japan. He observed that some American dogs appeared to have a short coat because it laid flat on the body and he felt this was tied in with too rich a diet.

The Japanese standards specifically fault a coat "too short" just as they do excessive or moku coat. It's unfortunate that those who drafted the AKC breed standard guessed at the length of coat on the withers

"Morgan" is a longcoat with excellent coat texture with thick undercoat. Coats of any length may be too soft or lack undercoat, either of which causes the hair to appear limp and lifeless or to lay flat instead of bristling and standing off from the body as required under the breed Standard. Therefore, a coat of proper length which is soft, thin, or flat, is as incorrect as a long coat.

and rump rather than plucking a hair from that area and laying it to a ruler. Or, perhaps they did just that but were confounded since so many of our dogs of the early '70s were still haunted by the influence of the short-coated breeds. Mr. Hiraizumi and other Japanese judges politely but unfailingly disparaged the lack of coat quality in most American dogs. Mr. Hiraizumi summed up his impression of coat problems by stating that the coats were "too short" and then elaborated, explaining that they were also "too thin" and "too scarce." American dogs would be ever so much "better dressed" had those who drafted the final version of our standard heeded Mr. Hiraizumi's admonition "when speaking of the length of coat, appearance rather than the measured length is taken into consideration. A coat that has a bristled, full or fluffy, and hence 'long' appearance being desirable."

This discussion by the most noted authority of the 1960s and '70s is not to be interpreted as a plug for "long coat" any more than it is meant to say that the Japanese have the first and final word on breed type. It's an explanation of how the basic look of the breed in America was forever altered because we attempted to accommodate current faults rather than describe the ideal. As with the allowance for wrinkles and other such seemingly small changes,

American coat type suffered from the editorialized version. The efforts of the JKC to ban American-type dogs could have also stressed the differences in coat length and fullness as well as color. This is not to say that our dogs are inferior to the Japanese dogs, only that they are different in areas which are not necessarily beneficial to the dogs.

On the matter of coat, the AKC/ACA video is no help at all. The top winning lines in every country are those with big full Arctic or spitz-type coats. Nonetheless, the video challenges the wording of the AKC standard by emphatically stating a coat "longer than 2 inches on withers and rump is undesirable." The standard does not say that. It doesn't even imply that a coat longer than 2 inches is faulty. Given the logic of where the breed originated, a coat longer than 2 inches would surely be more correct than one shorter than 2 inches! What the official standard actually says is that the body coat is "approximately two inches." Not a few dogs have coats shorter than 2 inches. If we are to read things into the standard which aren't there, surely these dogs are as faulty as longcoats.

Many have found such departures from the standard difficult to accept. An interesting comparison has been drawn between the fact that the video skims over the only *serious* fault listed in the standard yet it harangues on coat length, something which is not accorded much importance in the standard other than to fault any indication of ruff or feathering. Within the context of another sentence, the video casually mentions that the example has a "rangy body" but the narrator incorrectly

A self-masked Akita, this lovely bitch is Great Rivers Lady In Red (Ch. Brookstaten's Maxwell Smart x Ch. Great Rivers Delta of Snowcrest) co-owned by Terry Fried and Nadine Fontano.

states it to be an "undesirable characteristic." A rangy body, thankfully, is not characteristic of the Akita. The previously consistent format which displayed the exact wording of disqualifications or faults against a blue screen with a voice-over for emphasis is inexplicably not used for the only *serious* faults mentioned in the standard.

Instead, the printed format is once again used to emphasize the words "any indication of a ruff on the neck or feathering elsewhere on the body is also faulty. Body coat should not be trimmed." The implication is that hair longer than two inches is a much more serious fault than a rangy body or fine bone! As for trimming, there has never, ever, been any prior reference to trimming of body coat. Is the video implying that someone might trim a longcoat and show it? If so, it would be legal according to the breed standard, whether trimmed or not! In fact, some Akita fanciers were so outraged over this flagrant misrepresentation that they exhibited longcoats just to make a point. The longcoats didn't win, but some received ribbons based on overall faults and virtues.

Even those who shiver at the thought of someone showing a longcoat are deeply offended by these subversive attempts to change the standard without changing the standard. Once again, a few individuals have added to and taken away from the official standard, thus creating confusion rather than clarification.

Color:

In our early (1956) standard, white dogs were disallowed although they were pre-

Perfect "moderate" front and rear angulation, including turn of stifle and "hocks well let down." The neck is "comparatively short". Although he has a "level back with firmly-muscled loin and moderate tuck-up", Ch. O'BJ BigSon of Sachmo could be improved by adding one inch of leg length, thereby equalling the depth of brisket ("chest is one-half height of dog") and bringing the height to body length ratio closer to square. His double curled tail is "set high" but according to Japanese judge and breed authority Hideo Ito, it is faulty because the last curl reverses. It is also somewhat short.

ferred by many Japanese. The colors mentioned are "fawn, red, dim-brindle (cat-striped), all grays and silvers." The markings were precisely described as "white muzzle, white blaze up face, white chest, white feet and white tip of stern —black shading on foreface and ears and at the end of tail. Light tan and cream shading on legs and tail." The omission of any reference to pinto or spotted coats and to solid white dogs was corrected when the "standard of perfection" was revised in 1963.

Incredibly, there was a disqualification for "white markings on neck" which would have disqualified many of Japan's current winners as well as our own! This is but another sad example of someone's personal agenda creeping into the standard.

The 1970 standard changed the color descriptions once again by adding, "No more than one-third of the coat may be white and the white may appear only on the muzzle as a blaze, on the chest or forelegs, as a collar, or on the hind paws and tip of tail." This ridiculously worded sentence was rewritten and condensed into its present form.

Color was still a hot topic during Mr. Hiraizumi's Nisei Week talk in August 1970. Asked why the kurogoma coloring was undesirable, he responded, "Dogs of the kurogoma coloring, which began with Kongo, are generally found to display the undesirable traits of loose skin, wrinkles, and poor coat

Three month old puppy, O'BJ Kudos For Kolor, is a white dog with head markings, not a white dog with a mask. There should be no confusion regarding the statement "whites shall have no mask." Head markings and facial masks are two entirely different gentic factors, head markings being common in several otherwise white breeds such as Pyrenees and Bull Terriers.

condition as depicted in Kongo. In contrast, dogs with the brindle coloring generally have a tighter skin, a good coat condition, and a better overall structure."

The Akikyo standard provides as a list of acceptable colors: "black, fox red, sesame (goma), black brindle, fox (yellow red), white." There is no mention of pinto or spotted patterns much less the stipulation that spots must cover a certain portion of the body. Much to the consternation of some breeders, it does mention colors which are "not becoming to an Akita dog, but resembling those of different breeds." Examples given are "red brindle, dark brown, chestnut red, or dogs with a black back," meaning a German Shepherd Dog-type of saddle. So to those of us who love the bright, beautiful reds, including red brindles, this comes as somewhat of a shock and for obvious reasons, it's downplayed in

American works on the breed.

The important thing is that we do not breed by nor judge by the Japanese standards. My references to them and to our own early breed standards are presented only to help us understand how our present standard evolved.

Most people love the reds, all shades, from the lighter clear reds with white masks to the rich chestnuts and sables. Most breeders still avoid the saddle markings because of the other faults associated with it, not because it is in itself unattractive. Today's breeders prize a pretty white collar, and yet, conversely, a controversy has arisen over pinto and parti-color. Even more confusing, black has fallen from favor in some countries due to a misunderstanding of current Japanese position on the color. Black was once a very popular color and would be today were it not often associated with certain other type faults which are abhorred by Japanese breeders.

The white dog has its own problems. Spring 1976 *The Akita Handbook* featured a guest editorial by Carol Foti entitled: "The White Akita ... Its American Future." Ms. Foti deals adroitly with the prejudice linking white to albinism and then goes on to say, "Many white Akitas have noses that contain some 'liver' or rose-coloring along with the black pigment. Herein we run into trouble with American judging.

"Keeping in mind that most judges never see a white dog exhibited with other colors, and since they are basically programmed by other breeds to frown upon that color, the white Akita is having a difficult time competing. Many are being disqualified from the show ring on their nose pigment." She then goes on with an eloquent plea to adjust the standard to prevent "the reverse prejudice of our times."

Ms. Foti was right, the future of the white dog was in serious jeopardy during the '70s and is still far from secure. In addition to the troublesome nose, a white must also have a really good head piece in order to overcome the association with a white GSD.

Many breeders and judges are put off by freckles and blotches on the legs. There's no mention of freckles in the standard although many people argue that "brilliant and clear" also applies to the white markings. The highly respected Japanese judge Hideo Ito suggests that an infusion of Dalmatian blood is responsible for freckling and he made it clear that freckling is most undesirable. Whether freckles or blotches can be traced back to the Dalmatian or some other influence such as the harlequin Great Dane is a moot question; it is distinctly untypical of the spitz-type dog.

Although rarely seen, the black Akita may have light tan or rust "Doberman" markings. Like freckles, this is a foreign characteristic but as it's not mentioned in the standard, the pattern must be accepted in the ring.

The description of pinto could have been taken from the standard for the pinto horse. It's a pattern unto itself and does not pertain to freckled, spotted, patched, parti-colored or white dogs with head markings. The video uses the term "undermarked pinto" which is a fair enough term for a dog who doesn't have enough color to qualify for the universally accepted definition of pinto. Most people refer to a dog with less than one third body marking as a "mismark." The author pleads guilty to initiating that term. And how I regret my poor choice of words.

Under the breed standard, there is no such thing as a "mismark." The Akita doesn't have to have a third of its body marked any more than it *has* to be "white, brindle or pinto." Thankfully, most judges have a broad familiarity with other breed standards and, therefore, are not concerned with whether we call the non-pintos mismarks, undermarked, hooded, white-with-head markings, parti-colored, or piebald.

Gait:

The Japanese describe movement as nimble, with the ability to quickly change direction. Although the demand for superior

Ch. The Widow-Maker O'BJ, ROMXP demonstrates the level topline, extension, and controlled drive without "kick" which is correct for the Akita. The Akita should not prance. There should be little daylight between ground and pad; the thrust should be forward, achieving just enough height to clear the pads from the ground but not so much as to create the "floating" gait desired in some breeds. The rear feet should step into the paw print left by the front pads with no over-reaching or side-winding. The shoulder should open fully to accommodate a brisk stride of moderate length. Head carriage is not that of a sight hound or Sporting breed—the Akita is a Working breed with a destination and a determination to get there!

agility is clear, the breed isn't judged on movement. Perhaps that accounts for some of the structural faults associated with "import" type. The odd thing is that very few dogs outside of Japan could "run 12 to 16 kilometers in 45 minutes" on a daily basis. A kilometer being .6 miles, even allowing that the dog is not actually worked at a hard run, this represents pretty intensive road work, considered the ideal by many Japanese owners.

Regarding "reach," there's a simple equation: if front and rear angulation is correct, the stride will be of moderate length. A dog with a long-reaching stride will be off balance, unable to quickly change direction, unable to race through heavy forest and across treacherously rocky terrain. He should, as has been aptly put by one Japanese authority, be "able to maneuver as he pleases."

Our 1956 standard did not deal specifically with gait, yet made an interesting (and true) observation, "At full run the back legs move together to permit ready spring when hunting."

The Akita gallops with the rear legs wide apart, providing excellent center of balance, even at speed. When he slows to a trot, the legs tend to come closer together as a wider center of balance is not necessary. It's as difficult for a wide, powerfully built Akita to single track as it is for a Malamute, but neither should the Akita have to roll like the Bulldog in order to accommodate an excessively broad chest and short legs.

Size:

Many people believe the Japanese dogs are much smaller than our dogs. Prior to the restoration and the use of small native breeds, the Akita was massive, with many specimens described as well over 28 inches.

The Nippo standard (the earliest Japanese registry) calls for the males at 25.2 to 27.6 inches with females at 22.8 to 25.2 inches. Again, written record of Mr. Hiraizumi's speech in Los Angeles provides interesting background. Asked if we were at a low point in size, he said, "In the beginning (dog fighting era), the Akitas were large, and size was sacrificed in order to improve its quality. The

small size detracts from the basic qualities that have been refined and emphasis is now being placed on producing a sturdier dog. In answer to your question, yes, the trend will probably swing not so much towards a larger dog, but towards a sturdier one...The important point to be taken into consideration lies in bone structure. A small-boned dog will give an impression of being weaker and smaller compared to a large-boned dog."

Worth remembering too is that dogs that are very cobby and compact will appear smaller (and weigh less) than a dog of comparable height that has a longer body.

In 1965 there was a proposed addition to the American standard which would have stipulated "males—90 to 140 pounds generally; bitches—70 to 100 pounds generally." Although size was a great issue then just as it is today, the weight range proposal did not meet with agreement. The argument being that the Japanese standards did not specify weight, only that there be balance between height and weight.

I have never had anyone call wanting to buy a small Akita. We should never disregard the importance of size while at the same time, we must admit that breeders will often exaggerate size to cinch the sale or the stud fee. The sentence, "the weight is to be in proportion with the height and length" was deleted from the official standard. Perhaps it should have been left in because new admirers of the breed find it difficult to relate weight to height, especially when breeders quote such ridiculous weights for their animals. The average weight range for females is 70 to 80 pounds and for males, 95 to 105 pounds. Dogs which actually weigh the magical "140 pounds" may exist, but are rarely seen in the show ring and are even more unlikely to be seen in the winner's circle.

A compromise regarding the previous size requirements of $25^{1}/_2$ to $27^{1}/_2$ inches for males and $22^{1}/_2$ to $24^{1}/_2$ inches for bitches was reached, and the official standard resolved once and for all the minimum height requirements. Size greater than 28 inches is not faulted.

For this reason, height too is often exaggerated. Most males fall right in the average, 27 inches. Most females measure slightly below average, under 25 inches.

The important thing to remember is that height can be gained or lost during measurement. Even when officially measured, a dog can change his height by an inch depending on whether he's "up" for the bait, has been well trained for the measuring process, or, as is more often the case, he is relaxed or drawing down from the wicket.

The Akita was not ever to be confused with the Shiba or the other small Japanese breeds... if soundness and type are equal, the large dog is to be preferred over the small dog.

Temperament:

The Akikyo standard lists as the first and therefore, presumably the most important requirement for the breed, "character presentation." Temperament is last in the AKC standard but that is no excuse for breeding from or awarding specimens which are of faulty personality and character. This is the only portion of the AKC standard which you will find this author in disagreement with—not in the wording, but to the lack of importance accorded the subject.

The ACA video is somewhat misleading. Perhaps in an effort to downplay the aggressiveness (or as I prefer to characterize it, "dominance"), the opening and closing footage portrays the Akita as a sled dog. Although the Akita is of Arctic type in physical appearance, he should never be represented as a sled dog! One occasionally sees members of endurance sled teams which resemble Akitas, and a tiny handful of very capable and determined owners have successfully worked Akitas in harness, but

the breed is not a reasonable choice for those interested in developing a sled team.

Temperament is described in the 1956 standard as having, "a combination of good nature and courage, alertness and docility." Guarding instinct is well described as "dependability and readiness to protect anyone or anything put in his care is foremost." The section also describes the dog as an "intrepid hunter of deer, bear and wild boar." An interesting reference to aggression is found under expression. There it states "dignity, power and fight if aroused."

The sentence in our current standard, "Aggressive toward other dogs" is blunt and utterly correct. It's there for a reason and, should an unscrupulous breeder try to mislead a buyer, that phrase should alert him into asking more questions. If the prospective owner wants a family pet that will fit into a multi-dog household or one in which the

Ch. Chereed's Quantum Leap (Ch. O'BJ King's Ransom x Chereed's Quintessence), winning B.O.S. under judge Ric Chashoudian. She's bred by Reed and Cher Keffer, owned by Barbara Sikkink and Robert Pinney.

children bring their friend's dogs over to play, he should choose another breed.

The video script also says "any aggression in the show ring toward dogs or people can not be tolerated." We agree, no unprovoked aggression towards people can be tolerated at any time, guard breed or not.

But aggression toward dogs? Why contradict the standard? Failure to deal with reality is grossly unfair to the potential owner and, ultimately, to the dog. Any hint of a physical confrontation must be corrected and avoided, but an Akita should not be faulted for being an Akita any more than a Scottie should be discarded for being ready to spar or a Basset Hound penalized for wanting to sniff the mats.

No owner or judge should tolerate a physical display or the thought of "sparring" as is done in Japan and in AKC terrier rings. Even so, we shouldn't attempt to alter the dominant nature of the breed. Wouldn't it be a dull sport if all dogs looked and acted exactly the same? It is the different personalities, as much as the wide range of physical characteristics, which attract people to ownership of a particular breed.

An Akita is not aggressive towards other dogs in the same sense as many of the terrier breeds; he isn't looking for a scrap. He simply is at the top of the pecking order and expects other dogs to concede the fact. If they do not, and if they are of a size to be considered worthy of a response (the Akita often ignores a small, yappy dog), they'll be reminded that they have met an Akita. Eye contact from an aroused Akita and perhaps a low rumble are almost always sufficient to convince the challenger that he has made a serious error in judgement. The Akita is not a bully and as soon as the other dog breaks eye contact, the confrontation is ended.

In the ring, the quiet dignity and superior attitude should be considered a virtue. There has been some discussion on changing the word "aggressive" to "dominant." Many breeders object on the basis that we have a duty to present the Akita as he really is, not as a more saleable product!

The Claim Jumper O'BJ, owned by Renwick and Leslie Thompson has a "dropped ear," common in puppies of this age but a disqualifying fault in the adult dog.

It might have been appropriate to mention in this portion of the standard that the Akita is a relatively silent breed. This is but one more reason he is an excellent choice as a family protector. When an Akita barks, it is rarely a false alarm.

Despite its placement in the order of things covered in the standard, the section on "Temperament" is succinctly and perfectly worded. The Akita is *alert* to any sign of intrusion or trespass. If he suspects something is out of order, he will *respond.* He will approach an intruder with an air of undeniable *dignity* and, given reason to challenge, he will do so with *courage* unsurpassed by any breed!

Disqualifications:

The five disqualifications are pretty straightforward. Butterfly nose is defined by AKC. Ears that are not strongly upright all the way to the tip are to be disqualified. If one notices that the occlusion deviates from a scissors or level bite, the dog is to be disqualified. If the tail doesn't make a full circle and rest on the back, it must drop well down the flank or it's a disqualification.

And lastly, if in doubt about size—measure!

JUDGING THE AKITA

This is not an attempt to instruct on the art of judging dogs. Most breeds have idiosyncracies, a knowledge and understanding of which will enable a judge to do a much better job with that breed. Attempting to judge all dogs by the same yardstick is something no sensible dog person would do and yet, it's a common enough reaction when confronted with a large entry or a close decision.

Before getting all bogged down with individual features of type, make sure the silhouette is correct. One of our most distinguished judges, Mr. Frank Sabella, advises his colleagues to first pull out the dogs which present the proper outline for the breed. He suggests (well, actually, Frank seldom suggests...) they be put at the head of the line but in no particular order. Then judge those dogs on individual features of type. Then move them to confirm what you already know regarding structure.

Ch. Raiden of Jo-Uba, ROMXP (Ch. Okii Yubi's Sachmo of Makoto, ROMXP x Dragon House Nikki No Kenicia) bred by BJ Andrews and Brooks Smith. Raiden was BOS at the largest show ever held in America, the AKC Centennial Show. World-renowned judge Thelma Von Thaden made a profound statement on type by awarding Best Opposite Sex to Raiden and Best of Breed to Ch. Cotton Ginny O'BJ. Raiden's litter sister is Ch. O'BJ Nikki No Nikki, ROMP and she is the dam of Ch. Cotton Ginny O'BJ. Raiden was handled by Sidney Lamont for owner Brooks Smith.

Judges occasionally resort to selection based on the familiar: soundness and showmanship. Let's deal with soundness first. There's the age-old debate, which I personally don't consider worthy of debate except as it applies to a very small number of breeds, in which soundness is stressed as being of primary importance.

There's a simple rule which might help the rookie judge through those first few assignments. Soundness may be the *deciding* factor; it should never be the criteria!

To me, that is basic to the art of judging. But in addition, there's the complexity of what is sound in one breed being not at all correct in another. Therefore, the judge that truly knows and understands type will be confident in sorting them out and will not have to fall back on "the other dog moved better today" or "he showed better than your dog."

Showmanship. That wonderful, animated, difficult to define, extra something which draws the eye to a dog. It can be a plus or a minus, depending on whether it's correct for that breed. For example, the

Akita is alert and inquisitive and anything but dull, but he's a guardian and in public he should be rather serious. He should project a confident, calm, dignified air of authority. He should not sparkle like a Min-Pin nor smile like a Sammy.

The young female Akita may wag and prance and delight in charming onlookers and, indeed, this is showy. The mature male is more likely to consider that his mere presence should be sufficient. While he may be trained to arch his neck and maintain some degree of interest in an enticing bit of food, he bores easily and a seasoned campaigner will often show his disregard for show-ring routine.

He quickly learned not to respond to a "Who do ya think ya are...?" muttered by the dog behind him. He's figured out that attractive females will not be allowed to accept his advances. He knows the bait will keep coming whether he wants it or not. He is quite aware of his superiority among the other dogs and wonders why in the world his handler keeps trying to prove it! Trotting around in a little circle by himself doesn't interest him. He knows he's only going to turn around and come back to stand in front of someone who will make noises he's heard a hundred times before.

While he will try to perform out of respect or love for his handler, the Akita is an honest breed, and it's difficult for him to pretend excitement he does not feel. He will usually be more animated in the Group ring. First, it gives him a chance to stretch out and move; something he couldn't do in the confines of the small breed ring. And secondly, he may become quite interested in the possibility of catching the dog in front of him! Here, his strong desire to "be first" and his instinct to dominate other dogs can transform a bored Akita into an awesome sight as he powers around the ring.

There's no question that a dog's virtues will be far more apparent when he is on tiptoe, quivering with excitement. And let's face it, his faults will be ever so much more noticeable when he's bored, hot, or tired. But make and shape, coat quality, ear set, head shape, bone density, size and substance all remain constant whether a dog is hanging from a high wire or asleep in the stands!

Akitas do not tolerate heat as well as most other spitz breeds. The Malamute may be woo-wooing and the Siberian still dancing but the Akita is likely to be looking for a cool place to put his underbelly! This is especially true of dark-colored dogs, which absorb the sun's rays and quickly overheat. A dog who is uncharacteristically animated in the ring, particularly when the rest of his peers are struggling to stay awake or keep cool, is suspect. He may have faulty breed temperament or he may be under the influence of something other than expert handling.

A dog who is poorly conditioned or not in tip-top physical health will feel the effects of heat, humidity, and travel stress much more than a dog who is at his peak. Judges must strive to balance the natural desire to award flash and showmanship with a demand for correct breed type. It doesn't matter how long we stare at a lineup, the dogs will not change. The one with the dippy back will not get better and the long ears on the one with the good front will not get shorter. The stallion of a dog which is so correct standing will not move better, no matter how many times you send him around the ring. The ability to discriminate between superficial virtues and those which are lasting and important to that particular breed is the hallmark of a great judge.

One of the more common mistakes made by new Akita judges is prolonged eye contact. The Akita is one of only a few breeds which will maintain direct eye contact with a human. Not only will he hold that contact, but the mature male may interpret it as a challenge from a stranger. Judges should not prolong eye-to-eye communication with a strange male; he's apt to misread your signals. Also disconcerting to judges who don't understand this phenomenon is the dog who refuses eye contact. While this may mean the dog is ill, or it could indicate faulty temperament, you shouldn't underestimate the seasoned campaigner. He knows you don't mean to be rude or to challenge him and so he politely makes up for your lack of understanding by looking away!

Other common insults to a dominant breed with latent fighting instincts are: grasping the dog by his cheeks, picking up the feet, pushing on or bending over the shoulders in the dominant position.

Holding the dog by the cheeks in order to examine the head is first of all, unnecessary, and secondly, it's a stimulating sensation for any dog in whose veins runs the blood of fighting ancestors. Even the bitches will not appreciate this familiarity.

The well-schooled dog is quite tolerant of the examination, including having his teeth and testicles looked at by strangers. What he is not accustomed to is having a stranger grab him by the foot! Akitas hate having their feet touched. This has nothing to do with nail clipping, they just hate it for reasons known only to them. While most are so well mannered they will accept it, it's still risky business and a wise judge will not attempt it.

The same may be said of bending over the dog's shoulders. Many judges think nothing of reaching across to position the offside leg during examination but placing the head or body over a dog's shoulders is a sign of dominance. Likewise, bouncing the shoulders or shoving and rocking the dog from side-to-side is downright foolhardy with any large guarding breed. Both of these actions represent exactly the same sort of dominance-jockeying maneuvers engaged in by two strange dogs—just before the fight erupts. The mature Akita, male or female, is not likely to welcome this symbolic display from a stranger.

There's a tendency to reward over-angulated dogs. The Akita was not designed for pulling power. He was not meant to cover long distances at a tireless trot, which would leave his human hunting companions far behind. He doesn't need the well-turned stifle of the herding breeds and he rarely wants to get there fast enough to resort to a gallop. The young dog will run and leap and chase imaginary game and even a mature dog will break into a gallop when overcome with joy, or if he spots real game. Otherwise? No. At best he will trot, confident that the world will wait for him.

Judges must accept responsibility for enforcing proper proportion because, generally speaking, breeders have shown an inability or unwillingness to be bothered with balance. While we've done a good job improving heads, ears, and tails, we seem to have lost the dog... That delicate balance of one-third shoulder, one-third midsection, and one-third rear quarters, is in danger of being lost, very possibly forever. It is therefore extremely important that the judging community understand and demand the correct outline.

When the trained eye takes in the profile, noting narrow hams and rear, or upright shoulders set too far forward, it's easy to see that the correct ratio of 9 to 10 can be achieved due to an excessively long middle piece. This is *not* balance.

Ear size, set, and thickness are functional requirements which must not be overlooked in the show ring. The forward slant and the well-cupped bell are unique to the Akita. A good handler can make upright ears appear to slant forward by clever use of the bait so if you're in doubt, assess the angle with the dog in a relaxed pose. The Akita does not "use" his ears in the same way other breeds do. They're carried erect and forward unless the dog is showing extreme submission, pleased and utter relaxation, or bored resentment, in which case, the ears are laid back. The laid-back position is not one you should see in the show ring.

Runny eyes may be caused by allergies or entropion. Take a close look. Eyes with those funny-looking "tucks" in the eyelids are not to be tolerated. Eyes may be surgically corrected for health reasons but no judge should permit such faults to be perpetuated by a "champion" dog. More unusual is the hound expression and sagging eyelids, but you won't be likely to consider this dog due to the other faults associated with its type.

Some judges insist on a full mouth exam. Not only is this not in accordance with the breed standard (which makes no mention of the number of teeth required), but unlike Dobes and Rotties, most Akitas have not been trained to accommodate a search for back molars. Youngsters become confused and adults may resent it. In either case, a wrestling match usually ensues, causing unneeded upset to all parties.

A judge once asked if I thought he was wrong in disqualifying a dog which had a couple of teeth out of alignment. He said the lower front incisors were slightly forward of the upper incisors in an otherwise level bite. I said "How much out of alignment?" He replied, "Enough that I noticed it...." and even as he said it, we both nodded. Of course he should have disqualified the dog. We then acknowledged that he might not have noticed the angle of those middle incisors, therefore, the handsome dog could have taken major points towards its championship. As it turned out, the dog did take points the following day and that win completed his title. Obviously, the second judge failed to notice the bite.

Remember that tail shape, curl, and carriage are the second most important type characteristic and also a good indicator of breed character. It must be proudly carried, tightly wound, signifying a dominant, brave, bold individual. This is no less true of the adult non-estrus female. The sweetest bitch in the world will crank her tail a notch tighter as she struts by a strange female!

Females in season and young puppies may be forgiven for holding the tail down during examination or when being posed. A very hot adult may stand with its tail relaxed. In any case, the tail must curl *on* the back or come up high enough to flip down the flank when you ask the dog to move. If it doesn't, the dog is either extremely faulty in temperament or structure, or it's near collapse. Depending on your assessment, it should be disregarded, allowed to leave the ring, or disqualified.

As many judges have remarked, the Akita is a very unique kind of dog which doesn't fit into any one slot. It makes him a bit more difficult to judge, but a very interesting dog to own!

For the record, I would like to emphasize that the exceptions taken to the content or wording of the AKC/ACA video are only in those areas in which the video conflicts with the official standard. As a breeder, I couldn't do justice to those who seek knowledge of the Akita if I failed to point out some of the more serious misrepresentations. May I remind you, I am not the self-appointed keeper of the standard. We all are, each and every one of us!

PRESERVING TYPE

The preservation of basic breed characteristics should be foremost in any breeding program if the public is to distinguish the Akita from "look-alike" dogs, be they mongrel or purebred. Unfortunately, those less glamorous "essence of breed type" points tend to get lost in the quest for "prettier" or more stylish dogs who can win more or who are more appealing to the buying public.

We've discussed the individual features of type: headpiece (including ear set), tail, coat, and of course, the variety of colors and patterns shared only by the Siberian within the Working Dog Group. But with the exception of ears, none of these physical characteristics really identify the Akita. An Akita with the proper make and shape can be forgiven for imperfections in ears, head, tail, or coat because you'll still know him as an Akita. Most good dog people understand this and yet I'm frequently asked what is the very first thing I look at, even before considering individual features. The answer is simple. Silhouette.

Imagine an ink blot. Do the Rorschach test in your mind. If you had only a black silhouette, could you identify the breed? You could if it were a Doberman, a Greyhound, a Corgi, or a Collie. You should be able to distinguish between a Malamute and a Siberian. But, now the crucial test, could you tell the difference between a small Akita and an Elkhound or Siberian? Is it a large Akita or a Malamute? Is it a short-coated Akita or a Canaan Dog? Oh dear, perhaps it's a longcoated Akita, or a Samoyed, or maybe it's a tall Chow Chow?

This is not just a silly exercise for if you stopped reading, closed your eyes, and did the mental imagery, you realized how many Akitas you see in the ring which, on a dark night, could easily be confused with one of the above purebreds!

Every breed has what's called a drag, meaning a tendency to return to the averages set by nature. It's the genetic influence of all the ancestors which make up that breed. In the Bull Terrier, for instance, it's a constant tendency for a noticeable stop to creep back into the smooth egg-shaped profile of the head. Breeders must constantly work to preserve the imposing size and stature which make the Wolfhound or Mastiff a dog of great proportions. The more that man dramatically changes the natural appearance of the wild canine, the more we must work to retain the distinguishing features of type.

Most varieties of European and forest wolves are somewhat low-stationed and nature seems to take exception to the up-standing appearance of breeds which man has succeeded in modifying for his own needs. Breeders strive to retain the desired balance in the Dane, the Fox Terrier, the Doberman, or the Borzoi. The Akita is very possibly the descendant of the higher stationed Arctic wolf and might not be so much affected by this "drag" were it not for the recent (historically speaking) genetic influence of the German Shepherd Dog and other European breeds.

The Akita should be upstanding with a level topline, neck length in *natural* balance with a fairly short back, and he should be of moderate angulation, standing well over his feet. We know he isn't an Elkhound because of the ear size and set and the less square profile. He has more leg, shorter back, and tighter tail than the Siberian. Ditto for the Malamute, unless of course the Akita is a bit hairy and has a sickle tail, in which case, he should leave the ring. Faulty Akita structure can be similar to a Canaan Dog, but even before we reject the look-alike for its light bone and rangy body, we know it isn't a Canaan Dog because of the Akita head, coat, and tight tail. Distinguishing a longcoat Akita from the Samoyed or Chow Chow may be a bit trickier, but the excessive coat would create too heavy an outline for a proper Akita. And of course, even with the tails cut off, the long sloping topline of the GSD would immediately tell us it's not just a short-legged Akita.

When the profile is right, then you can work on the individual features of type which help to account for that correct silhouette. Only then do they become important. An Akita ear on a Tervuren outline would be meaningless. The proper Akita tail is often found on a Chow Chow but that doesn't make the dog an Akita any more than the interesting assortment of colors make it a Greyhound or a Siberian.

Once we have a firm idea of type for a given breed, preserving it against the encroachments of personal preference becomes another matter. Fashion plays a

English Import, Overhill's Pacer is sired by a Japanese dog out of an O'BJ bitch exported to Overhill Kennels in England. Very traditional in color, coat, balance, ear size and set, she also exhibits the bone, substance, front quarters, and overall size of the American half of her pedigree.

large part in the development of all man-made breeds. There is however, a difference between a fashion of the time and changing the basic look which typifies the breed. Constants such as the size and slant of the ear or body proportion or the curled tail must be protected. We must not impose personal hangups or preferences on our fellow breeders.

For example, we look for exaggerated bone on junior pups. If the legs don't look "like tree trunks" at that age, it's doubtful the mature dog will have adequate bone. But bone can be too heavy in the adult. A dog with legs like a St. Bernard will be of the same personality profile; in fact, the excessive bone is probably a throwback to the St. Bernard which was used during the dog-fighting era. Thus a personal preference for excessive bone, which in fact became a national agenda, would have the effect of changing the basic personality and type of the Akita.

Suppose I prefer a chestnut-red dog over a brown dog. There are those who (referring to the Japanese standards) would argue that I am wrong. Perhaps. Perhaps not. If its my preference and the AKC standard does not fault bright red, I'm entitled to breed for bright red dogs. If I'm successful and my red dogs are otherwise outstanding, chestnut or red sable could well become a fashionable color. But if the standard faults these colors and I persevere against the breed standard to the point that I'm able to impose my personal preferences on all Akita fanciers by changing the standard, I have done a terrible disservice to the breed.

Fads change. Pintos (mismarked or otherwise) are very much in fashion now. In the '50s, they were not. Considered "pure" in Japan, whites were actually excluded from one American standard. Brindles are still universally favored. Reds, both self and white masked, are currently in vogue in both countries but were at one time heavily criticized in Japan as lacking in character.

"Import" type was considered second rate for nearly 20 years until suddenly the pendulum swung in the other direction. The current Japanese dog has much to offer but we must remember that being Japanese does not make one omnipotent. Japanese authorities (usually given that title by an American who would like to be considered an authority) are still inclined to state what they wish the breed to be, or what they personally would like to see winning, rather than the accomplished fact.

So it is that within the limits of the standard, we each have our concept of ideal type. Each person interprets the written word differently and sometimes even the spoken word is heard through already convinced ears. No doubt, ten different people came away with ten different ideas about what I said when I gave a breed seminar in England. Even when doing judge's workshops here, it's amazing what people later think they heard!

Different interpretations. Slight variations in winning bloodlines and the opinions of those who judge them. All of these small diversities make our sport interesting and exciting. Breeding fine animals—and judging them—is not an exact science. If it were so, there would be no challenge. So we are free to express our individual priorities and preferences but only so long as they are in accordance with the official AKC standard.

An increasingly popular color, this shaded black youngster is Chilean Group and BIS winner, The Black Magic Ace. Bred by Maurizio Moretto, he's by Widow-Maker grandson, Seisan's Ultimate Warrior x The One To Keep O'BJ, themselves top winning show dogs in South America.

Following in his BIS dad's pawprints, BIS, BISS Am/Can. Ch. The Joker Is Wild O'BJ (BIS Ch. The Widow-Maker O'BJ, ROMXP x Ch. The Mad Hatter O'BJ, ROMPX) won his first Best in Show under Eleanor Evers in 1996. His handler Papoose has racked up dozens of Group firsts and enough Bests of Breed to make Joker hit number one. Former owners, Roger and Jan Kaplan; current owners, Lillian Kletter and Laura Payton. Bred by the author.

Proving Grounds

WHY SHOW?

Quoting from a feature article published in the 1984 *Akita Reference,* Tiare Caudill Arndt, Chairperson of the ACA Standard Revision Committee, has this to say about the need for structured shows:

"In 1973, the Akita joined the ranks of the Working Group. A dog bred in Japan, the large-sized Natural Monument, with ties to royal households, utilized for hunting, guarding, and where space allowed, family pet. A

"Good hands" are second only to good care when evaluating a professional handler. The way in which a puppy is touched during training and presentation will determine its attitude toward the show ring and shape its adult character. Like many well known handlers and judges, James Taylor is a second generation dog man. Is that special skill with animals one which is acquired or inherited?? Either way, be sure you are dealing with a true professional when it comes to your best friend's care and training.

dog fierce and powerful, loyal and playful, the Akita can take on many roles. In the U.S. the Akita is enjoyed primarily as a friend and companion, a protector, and a show dog.

"As with a majority of AKC breeds, the latter usage, 'show dog,' rings with prominent sounds. Why this importance? Why dog shows? To ensure and promote the continuance of a breed for present and future enjoyment to man, and to safeguard for posterity a small representative with its definite role in the total picture of living things."

Good reasons all. Terry sums it up perfectly, now let's explore some of those reasons in detail.

In all our years in dogs, we have never met anyone who proclaimed he was not trying to breed good dogs. We have met a few who excused breeding from non-champions by claiming that dog shows are all "fixed" and that it doesn't prove a thing, or that it's a waste of time, etc., etc. Such are the mutterings of a loser, unable or unwilling to show a quality dog properly. Makes as much sense as someone entering the Indy 500 with the family car and then complaining that the flagman didn't give him a fair start.

Remember that any dog which has no disqualifying fault under the breed standard is "show quality." Any car that runs will get you to Indianapolis—but it won't get you on the track. Most of us started out trying to show a dog which wasn't really capable of winning, and we learned many valuable lessons with that first dog. If we liked the sport, we eventually purchased a winnable dog. Perhaps we purchased a show puppy but were willing to sacrifice a few losses in order to become skilled as owner-handlers. Some of us "made it," and these are the people you will meet at show after show,

Ch. O'BJ BigSon of Sachmo, ROMXP wins Group Two (behind 1983's #1 dog all breeds) under eminent all breed judge and recognized Akita authority, Mr. Roy Ayers.

winning some days, losing on others, but always enjoying the competition and the camaraderie of shows.

Many fanciers become involved by accident, not design. They buy a nice pet, breed her, raise a litter, pet them all out, and in the process, discover there are places where other dog lovers congregate and show off their dogs. Perhaps their first exposure to "shows" is through a local obedience class or they happen to stumble over a fun match.

Honorable people quickly come to grips with a simple economic fact. If one is going to bring seven or eight puppies into this world, one had better be prepared to ensure good loving homes for those innocent creatures. They either decide not to breed or they make sure that what they produce will be in demand. Less ethical people may dump unsold puppies and breed the dam again.

The good news is that public education is working. Even families which are not interested in showing or breeding have become more aware of the practical value of a good pedigree. Today's owner is more likely to realize that a puppy from a careful breeding program, which exemplifies attention to genetic details of health and temperament, is a more prudent purchase. Such a puppy is much less likely to need ongoing vet care, behavioral counseling, or expensive training. It comes well loved and socialized and is therefore more likely to fulfill the family's expectations.

Certainly the person looking for a show-

215

quality puppy will want to buy from some- one who is winning in the ring and breeding from proven show dogs. How else can one expect to produce winners? Anything else is simply illogical. The public is becoming much more aware that a meaningful pedigree is exemplified by the champion or obedience titles it contains. A buyer will look askance at the litter owner who purports to sell a "show- quality" puppy but who in fact doesn't even own a show dog!

The show ring provides a stage for the breeder's best efforts and a gathering

genetics and the possible problems represented in every conceivable pedigree, then how can that person be willing to expend the time, money, or effort required to select the right stud dog and properly rear a litter of puppies?

Indeed, there are countless reasons why the show structure is vital to all who would take on the responsibility of adding to the canine population. While all AKC judges are not equally knowledgeable, the fact is, the best dogs win most of the time. Equally important is the coming together of breeders, handlers, and

Two great bitches, Ch. Cotton Ginny O'BJ (Multi-Group Winner) and Ch. O'BJ Cody of Spotted Bear (inbred Sachmo daughter) winning BOS and WB under breed authority Eleanor Evers.

place where he may assess his peers' breeding programs. Anyone who produces more than one litter should be actively exhibiting. How else can the litter owner know if his bitch is truly worthy of reproducing the breed? The fact that she's sweet and "everyone says" she's beautiful does not qualify her to make cute puppies in today's overcrowded world. Even experienced breeders must continue to show, else they fall behind and become "kennel blind."

If a person isn't willing to meet the challenge, seize the opportunity to study many other Akitas, meet other breeders and exchange information, learn about

owners of various breeds. The show atmosphere provides for healthy interchange of ideas, catching up on all the news, veterinary advances, improvements in food products, and so on. It's an important social event for several hundred thousand people who share a common interest and look forward to meeting on a regular basis. Dog shows are sort of like weekly medical-sales- political-educational-scientific conventions all rolled into one!

And what of the dogs? Well, first of all, if they're considerately handled and cared for, healthy dogs will eagerly look forward to show time. Handlers will tell you that the dog who just lazes around during the week becomes active and excited as the weekend draws near. Show dogs are known to have itchy feet. Like the sled team at harnessing time, show dogs are eager to go!

Considerate owners make sure that their dog has a pleasant trip with lots of love and attention. He should be kept as cool as possible and must have plenty of clean cool water, preferably brought from home. Remember, Akitas drink a lot of water, particularly in warm weather. Five-gallon plastic containers with spouts are great and a big cooler will hold drinks for the family and ice for the dog!

If you make it fun for the dog and if you don't become too discouraged or caught up in petty jealousies, I promise you that dog shows offer exhilarating excitement and immensely fulfilling recreation for both dog and owner.

Most of us begin to take shows too seriously and every once in awhile our Akita reminds us that shows are supposed to be fun. Bored with an unusually long judging procedure (back when the Working and today's Herding Groups were one group), BigSon had exhausted his bag of tricks and, for once, was standing quietly. That should have warned me.... As the long line advanced "one dog up," he suddenly leaped up on a table which had been set aside from the Toy Group. One moment he was at my side and the next, he was sitting up on the table like a king surveying his domain! Ringside loved it, and, of course, that inspired him.

A few minutes later, unimpressed by my whispered threats to re-arrange his head type, he turned to face the center of the ring as a St. Bernard made an agonizingly slow "down and back" the whole length of the oversized ring. Ringside fidgeted and even the judge became impatient, but finally they were almost back to the judge. Just as the sloth-dog and his elderly owner passed by BigSon, he performed the Akita bow. His deep, chest-to-the-floor salute

Ch. W. W. Dreamsycle Design winning at 14 months under Judge R. Stephen Shaw. Breeder/ Owner Myra Addington, Wishing Well Akitas.

seemed to offer respect to the white-haired handler, or tongue-in-cheek congratulations on completing the trip, depending on one's interpretation! Ringside tittered but then, typical of good dog people, they warmly applauded the giant dog and his beaming owner.

Judging resumed and relaxing a bit, I chatted with someone at ringside. Suddenly, there was a blur of movement as BigSon mounted the male Giant Schnauzer standing placidly in front of him! My delinquent dog made a couple of distinct mating motions, the crowd went wild, and the Schnauzer surely turned red under his black whiskers! I peeled BigSon off the disgraced dog, whose handler was in such a convulsion of silent laughter that she was momentarily incapable of soothing his wounded dignity. It all happened so quickly that when the judge turned to see what the uproarious laughter was about, she saw only an (innocent) Akita standing on tiptoe, head up, eyes twinkling and every muscle taunt with mock challenge towards the still-embarrassed Schnauzer. I let him stand. The judge was impressed. As she turned her attention back to the next dog in line, I reeled BigSon in and gave him an obligatory lecture. He just looked up at me with those devilish black eyes and yawned. He knew I didn't mean it. Ten minutes later when the judge pointed to him, he smugly led me to the Group One position as though he'd planne the whole thing!

That story becomes a story only because it's so unusual. As exhibitors (and breeders), we must remember that the Akita is a Working dog, not a circus dog. It's difficult to convince the male Akita that trotting around a show ring and looking "showy" over a piece of food is the equivalent of having a real job. If it's hot, or the dog must stand in direct sun, the best we can expect is that his innate priue will come through at the right time and that he will move well enough to convince the judge that he could handle anything from bears to burglars! Even on a long hot day.

The Coco Chanel O'BJ (Widow-Maker x Overhill's Pacer) winning in Group her very first show weekend. She is owned by Bob and Kim Ottenbrite, Nova Scotia Canada.

GROOMING AND CONDITIONING

We judge people by many yardsticks, one of which is their manner of dress. It's what we notice first. A bum in ragged, dirty clothes puts us on the defensive whereas an approach from a tastefully attired stranger is usually welcome. Our initial opinion may change but first impressions are inclined to linger. So it is in the show ring. A judge may find that front or rear movement isn't what he had hoped for, but he still retains the image of a well-presented, attractive dog.

The term "well groomed" as applied to people refers not only to cleanliness but to good manners and an overall well-kept, stylish appearance. It is usually so in dogs too. A scruffy-looking dog is rarely well behaved and therefore is not nearly as socially acceptable as is an immaculately groomed Toy Poodle. Who will "ooooh and ahhh" over a flea-bag? Not your neighbors. Not your vet. And not your friends and family. So remember, we are judged not only by our clothes, our home, and our car but by the pets we keep and how we keep them!

Everyone who sees your dog for the first time should marvel over his coat. People seldom fail to comment on a glorious Akita coat and the longcoats are no exception. A gleaming vibrant coat is especially dramatic in a dog the size of an Akita.

In the show ring, the judge has only a moment or two to assess the lineup before he begins individual examinations. He doesn't have his hands on the dogs, he isn't observing expression, he's not looking at movement. His trained eye isn't searching so much for faults as it is for balance, symmetry, outline, condition, and, in the Akita ring, a proud, noble animal which he would trust to protect his own family. That critical first evaluation will be stored in his subconscious until confirmed or refuted during the individual examination.

The coat determines quality and health. While color and markings may define symmetry, a gleaming coat, along with style and charisma, will draw the eye back to a dog again and again. Let's assume your dog is properly built and really fills the standard. You have him beautifully posed, attentive, neck arched. But his coat is flat, lifeless,

Hasu's Stardom In Action (Ch. Northstar's Mad Maxx x Ch. Hasu Nikko of Skylake) winning a 3 point Major at her first show at 6 months of age under Judge R. A. Stein, handled by Patti Rhoades for breeder-owner Sue Lopez.

dull. His tail looks sparse because you didn't have time to groom it when you took him out of the crate, and his neck appears weak for the same reasons. Remnants of his undercoat are peeking through his outer coat, giving him an overall straggly appearance. Worse yet, he's at the beginning of his

Ch. Goshen's Chariots of Fire (Ch. O'BJ King's Ransom, ROMPX x Ch. The Dame's On Target O'BJ, ROMPX) pictured at nine months, "Hoss" became a Multi-Best In Show winner. Breeder BJ Andrews, owner Goshen Kennels.

blow, and his naked legs belong to some other dog, not the one with the full body coat. Is this balance? Hardly. Perhaps you don't even notice his stained bare elbows anymore. You're used to seeing them that way, along with those calluses on his hocks.

Compare your dog with the first-place winner who has a sagging topline but whose coat has been brushed (or moussed) to stand up to hide the dip in the back. The tail, which is rather loose and flat coated, has been blow dried to appear its very fullest.

The second-place dog is blowing coat too but was prepared by an artful groomer who carefully blended and smoothed the line of demarcation between naked legs and well-coated body. The skimpy undercoat has been separated and fluffed from the skin upwards and the entire coat then smoothed, eliminating the ragged appearance of a dog between coats. His coat has been topped with a dressing designed

Ch. Noji's Ivy of Crown Royal, R.W.B. at the 1989 National Specialty, (Ch. O'BJ Kings Ransom, ROMXP x Ch. Daijobu's Vampirella O'BJ, ROMX) is owned by Ingrid Linerud and Bill Erwin, bred by Bill and Marcia Erwin.

to reflect the light, giving a glossy, healthy appearance, even though you saw him in the exercise pen and know darn well it's in that dull "between-coats" stage.

Third place is lacking in bone but the leg coat has been filled and lifted, and any hint of stain has been erased with a good cleaning agent. You know your dog has a better, stronger neck, but the other dog was groomed to exaggerate a lovely crest and arch.

If you can see these differences in grooming, then you can help your dog when his coat is "off," and you won't leave ringside swearing you've been cheated out of a deserved win! You may have the better dog, but the other dogs were better presented and, in all fairness, the judge didn't have an opportunity to see them before they were groomed. He can only judge on what he observes during a scant few minutes of evaluation.

The same applies to the actual stacking and gaiting of the dogs.

Ch. Frakari's Rockets Red Glare set a record by winning three consecutive Sweepstakes before going on to Hawaii to join his proud owners, Henry and Nancy Kapali at Napali Akitas. "Cappy" is by Ch. Tobe's Return of The Jedai, ROM x Ch. Date Tensha Pot Luck, ROMX bred by Ira Winkleman.

Professional handlers are usually better than owner handlers. That's OK; if you practice and have good timing and coordination, you can become equally adept at showing off the good points and concealing your dog's faults.

Learning to groom properly will be easier than mastering your skills inside the ring. Don't take shortcuts. Make no mistake, there's a fine line between good grooming and illegal enhancement. Artificial coloration is forbidden as is the presence of any foreign substance left on the dog's coat when it enters the ring. Hopefully, your dog's color will be clear and rich and you will never be tempted to resort to dyes, rinses, or grooming sprays which add false color. To add gloss to the coat is permissible but a freshly bathed Akita in full healthy coat will have a shine that comes from within, from good health and good breeding.

To be well conditioned, a dog must be physically fit and mentally sharp. The dog who lazes around the kennel or yard all week with nothing to do and nowhere to go is not a fit dog. Make it a point to take him out for a jog or, if you're not up to jogging with him, cheat a little—try a bike. With someone to help, you can even jog him from a car but beware of exhaust fumes, engine heat, traffic, and turns. Regardless of your method of roadwork, be sure to

Ch. The W. W. Coal Miner O'BJ (Ch. O'BJ King's Ransom, ROMXP x Ch. The Dame's On Target O'BJ, ROMXP) at 18 months with handler Vicki Fillinger. Owned by Myra Addington, Wishing Well Akitas, the huge dog is a multiple Group and Specialty winner.

select a safe route where you will not be challenged by other dogs.

Swimming is great although pool water will be hard on the coat. Be sure to rinse your dog after a swim, even in seemingly unpolluted lakes and streams. Remember, his coat will hold chemicals which rinse easily from our bodies.

Frisbee and ball games are not so well suited to a large heavy dog but one which is very fit can often be encouraged to play such games when it's cool outside.

Keep him mentally fit by giving him a job. It doesn't matter whether it's fetching the paper, basic obedience, patrolling your premises, or helping you in the garden. Make him feel important and useful. It will pay off in the ring...and the living room.

OK, back to the crowning glory for a dog that is in top form. He is genetically programmed for a big full standoff coat. Grooming skills, emotional and physical health, and optimum nutrition all perfectly combined can't create a lush coat if someone didn't breed for it! You've heard the saying about making a silk purse out of a sow's ear? Right. It can't be done.

One often hears excuses made for short, skimpy coats, but Mr. Hiraizumi, Akiho's head judge, in response to a question regarding the influence of weather on coat length, responded very succinctly, "No, I don't think weather had any influence on the length of coat since many parts of Japan are much hotter than it is here." By here, he meant California. The same can be said of dogs bred in Florida; many have coats equal in texture and quality to dogs bred in Michigan or Minnesota. Mr. Hiraizumi went on to say, "One reason why dogs appear to have short coats is because of the tendency to lay flat on the body, a result of the diet being too rich. When speaking of the length of coat, appearance rather than the measured length is taken into consideration. A coat with a bristled, full or fluffy, and hence 'long' appearance being desirable."

A good Akita coat will have bounce and body. Each hair will be distinctly gleaming. It will not be short. It will not be thin. It will not lack top coat. A velvety, pile-like coat without bristling guard coat is about as appealing as single-layered mink stole.

If your dog is blessed with correct coat, it can still be no better than his health. Coat condition is a dead giveaway for a dog which is stressed, wormy, suffering or recovering from chronic disease, or one which has been deprived of adequate nutrition. Great nutrition will bring your dog into full bloom condition!

The final key to opening the door where Trickster Fate has hidden the perfect show coat is in daily attention to the hair itself. You cannot bathe the dog, grab a brush, and instantly correct weeks of neglect the day before the important show. This doesn't mean he must be groomed every day, although it does give the two of you some special, private, just-relaxing time together.

Who can resist running the fingers through a clean healthy coat? Do it! It will keep the natural oils distributed and remove loose hair. The next best thing to a chamois for polishing the top coat is hand stroking. For down-to-the-skin stimulation of the follicles, rub your spread fingers against the lay of the coat, thus lifting, separating and ruffling the hair.

Dogs which are housed indoors will show the effects of artificial heating and cooling. Everyone knows that forced air heat dries the coat and skin but how many realize that air conditioning also pulls moisture from the coat? A simple solution is to put a spray bottle with plain water in the refrigerator. When he's in the kitchen watching you prepare a meal, give him a spritz with the cold water instead of a treat! Much better for his health and it'll work wonders for his coat!

Avoid the use of artificial conditioners, rinses, coat enhancers, polishes, texturizers, etc. They are designed to be used on a coat which is not in great condition. Alcohol-based products set up a Catch-22 situation as regular use dries and strips the coat of natural oils. Others may leave a slightly oily residue which attracts dust and dirt which in turn, abrades and gums up the coat. There's nothing external which can improve an Akita coat in peak condition. It will have sheen and shimmer and a vibrant life of its own which no grooming product can match.

So, you have to *breed* a good coat, then *feed* a good coat. If you missed out on the genetic part, there's nothing you can do about it except try to make the coat appear fuller and richer by skillful grooming for the show ring.

Fighting the basic changes which occur with the blowing of the coat is futile. Metabolism slows down when a dog blows coat, much as occurs when a bird molts or a snake sheds its skin. The perfectly natural process usually results in a diminished appetite and a general sluggishness. You can try to work through it, or you can do what may be best for you and the dog—take a short vacation from shows. If the dog is fighting it out for final rankings, you'll want to keep going, but, remember, he's not at his best in ways other than coat quality.

Many owners make the mistake of trying to "hold" a molting coat. While you might get by for a week or so with this tactic, the shedding process, once begun, is inevitable. The best defense is a good offense! Get it out! The sooner the old stuff is gone, the sooner new hair will take its place. If your dog hasn't been wormed lately, it's time to do so and also have a good overall health checkup. Shedding is a reminder to update shots and eradicate parasites and a good indicator that females will be in season very soon. It's also a good time to take care of anything requiring anesthesia as that will cause an unscheduled blow.

Do not rake against the growth as this will break off and damage the guardcoat. You'll notice that the guardcoat never sheds to the same degree as the two layers underneath. The guardcoat can, however, lose vitality and, acting as a barometer of health, it may lose pigment or become very harsh and brittle in an unhealthy dog.

So, using the undercoat rake and starting behind the ears, move slowly and carefully through the coat, ending with the tail. Be very gentle with the tail. Akitas do not like to have

Jade-Shogun's Beni Hana, sired by Am./Can. Ch. Dune's Duncan Idaho x Shogun's Yukitama of Jade, bred by Jade-Shogun Akitas. Kotaishi is owned by Phil and Wendy Reed, Beni Hana is owned by Jade-Shogun Akitas. Breeder Terry Arndt points out "excellent bear heads and little ears from Duncan, along with the sweetest disposition coming through Kuma Ryoshi's granddaughter."

If you do not have a professional grooming table (which is a wise investment and will last the lifetime of the dog), you can make do with an outside picnic table or some other steady table. Do not try to make your dog stand on something which is shaky. It will frighten him and make the entire experience unpleasant for you both.

The first step in a thorough grooming is careful use of an undercoat rake, a tool which can be purchased from a wholesale catalog but not usually found at the local supply. It looks like a fixed-prong garden rake with a short handle and teeth which are slightly barbed to gently pull the loose middle coat and packed undercoat free. Use the undercoat rake in the same direction as the hair grows.

the hair pulled there. Do not use the rake on the legs or face. When you have most of the dead undercoat out, then change to a pin brush.

A pin brush looks something like a wig brush. It's made of very smooth stainless steel pins about two inches in length set into a rubber backing glued to a wooden handle. (The rubber backing often pulls loose in cheaper quality brushes, so get a good one to start with.) Now work the coat in strips, starting on the cheeks and brushing each section of hair forward against the natural lay of the coat with the exception of the croup (the area of the back just in front of the tail root) which should be smoothed flat so that he doesn't appear high in rear. You may use the pin

Ch. O'BJ The Maker's Rebel Yell (Ch. The Widow-Maker O'BJ, ROMXP x Ch. O'BJ Ko-Tausha Tuc, ROM) pictured finishing his title with owner handler Katie Asling, Hoka-Hey Akitas.

present, the dog should be seen by a veterinarian. This is an indication of infection or ear mites for which he will need medication.

You should also check the mouth for any sign of abscessed teeth or irritated gums. Yes, dogs do get toothaches and suffer in silent agony with something you have forgotten to notice. There are tooth scalers available for dogs and most Akitas will tolerate this attention.

During the preliminary brushing, as well as during the washing and the final blow drying, you should feel for any lumps, sores, or suspicious areas which might otherwise go unnoticed. Pay particular attention to the male dog's sheath and testicles and the female's mammary glands, being sure to palpate well up into the armpit and groin area.

Humans have a different pH so people shampoos and conditioners are not ideal for dogs. While they won't seriously harm the coat or skin, there is risk of an itchy reaction or drying out of coat which you are hoping to restore. If the coat is very soiled or has become kennel stained, liquid laundry detergent will whiten the whites and dish washing liquid will remove all traces of body oil. The second shampooing should then be with a good-quality dog shampoo.

Getting an Akita wet to the skin is not easy! If the coat is of proper thickness and texture, it's almost impervious to water. You may have noticed that your Akita can go swimming, come out of the water, give a good shake, and on a sunny day he's pretty dry in a half hour. Nature's protection for Arctic animals can be frustrating to us humans when it's bath time.

Squeeze the water through the coat, making sure that it has penetrated to the skin. The water, by the way, should be only

brush on the legs and don't forget the back of the ears, armpits, and the groin area.

When you have the last of the loose hair out, use a stainless steel "greyhound" comb to continue to lift and separate the hair. The comb will discover missed places where the undercoat is still packed and thick. If it's loose, go ahead and lift it out with the comb. You may use the comb on the face, legs, and feet to gently loosen and pull free the very short, close undercoat.

By now you and the dog will both be ready for a break, so let him down from the table and give him an opportunity to shake and run around the yard and eliminate while you make sure you have all the bathing essentials assembled.

Before wetting the dog, clip toenails and clean ears with a cottonball moistened with alcohol. Do not probe down into the ear. If a thick dark brown or reddish waxy buildup is

EXPOSICION CANINA
JUEZ SR.
RAMON PODESTA
SAN FELIPE

MEJOR RAZA

FCI

So. Am. Ch. Seisan's Ultimate Warrior, a top show dog with many Best In Show and Group wins, was bred by William and Judith Furlong, M.D. "Spike", a Widow-Maker grandson, is owned by Maurizio Moretto of Santiago, Chile.

lukewarm, never hot. Test it on your wrist. You should feel only the slightest sensation of warmth. The second sudsing (always lather twice) can be a little warmer to help open the pores and speed the shedding process if the dog is blowing coat. The final rinsing should be slightly cooler than body temperature to help close the pores unless you want to stimulate shedding.

The best place to bathe? Outside. On a warm sunny pleasant day. Set up the grooming table, run an extension cord for your dryer, and hook the hose to the "Y" connector behind your washing machine so that you can adjust water temperature. Don't allow the electric cord to touch the wet ground. If you must bathe inside, put your bathing suit on and be sure to prepare a path so as to get a dripping dog to the grooming table with as little water damage as possible.

It's helpful to put a drop of mineral oil in the corner of each eye, just in case the tearless soap gets into the eyes. A cottonball inserted in each ear will keep the ears dry,

and the dog will not be so likely to shake during the bath.

Suds him up, not neglecting under the throat, down the chest, in the groin and vaginal folds. Then rinse, starting at the back of the head behind the ears, and holding the hose or shower attachment close to the dog's body to avoid splattering and to assure through penetration to the skin. Squeeze and squeeze and squeeze the water through the coat. Then work up a second lather over the body and lastly, using tearless shampoo, on the face and head. Then rinse, rinse, rinse. Be especially thorough in removing all traces of detergent from the genital area, between the toes, groin, armpits and under the jaw and throat.

If you are going to use a conditioner or oil treatment, do so now. Otherwise, you may elect to make a solution of 4 tbsp. white vinegar to a gallon of tepid water as a final rinse. The vinegar will remove the last traces of detergent, finish off any half-drowned fleas, and leave the coat sparkling clean.

In a pinch, we sometimes use one of the

225

better quality human hot oil treatments. While shampooing the dog, put the oil tube in a bowl of hot water. After rinsing, squeeze the oil into a pitcher of hot water, pouring it over the coat and working it through. Allow it to stay on the coat as per directions and then rinse thoroughly.

Before even reaching for a towel, squeegee as much water as possible from his coat. You'll be amazed at the amount of water, and hand-squeegeeing will tremendously speed drying time. Be careful to prevent a premature departure from the grooming table which could result in a slip on the wet surface. Attach the leash and help him down from the table...and stand back. Encourage him to shake as you trot him around and let him empty his bladder.

When his top coat is pretty dry, it's time for a brisk towel rub, followed by blow drying. It will be easier with the dog up on a table. Do be careful about plugging in the blow dryer if you are standing on a wet surface. After all, you wouldn't want to leave your Akita before you've had a chance to admire your handiwork.....

Using the pin brush and again, working in sections, lift the coat while directing a warm flow of air through it as you brush. This will take some time although the process can be hastened by purchasing one of the high-powered blowers sold at shows or in professional mail-order catalogs. The air is heated only slightly by the motor but is forced through a hose nozzle under great pressure and actually blows the water from the coat. They are much gentler on the coat (and your hands) and will dramatically cut the time spent finishing up with a regular dryer.

Make sure that you get the dog dry to the skin, particularly in troublesome spots which are likely to become hot spots. The croup is a tricky area. Even when you think it's dry, the contact of the tail resting against the body will seal in moisture which can easily become a "hot spot." The same is true of the warm areas of the body such as the groin and armpits. Don't forget those hard-to-get-to areas under the throat and brisket.

This process can take some time, and you may want to give the dog (and yourself!) a short break between sessions. If your pup is chilled, do not take a break until the warm areas where the blood runs closest to the skin are dry. These areas left damp can chill the blood, especially as his skin is not used to being wet in those protected places.

Show grooming is not much different than the thorough weekly grooming you've been doing all along. The Akita coat is not supposed to be scissored or clipped. Clipping whiskers gives the dog's face a neater, more professionally groomed appearance but is a matter of personal preference and you may like your dog with whiskers intact. It's permissible to tidy up the longer hairs around the feet and between the pads. Trimming the feet will make the foot look tighter and thicker, and clipping the hair between the toes and the pads will help cut down on the amount of mud a house dog tracks inside in bad weather.

Mink oil or any type of oily grooming product will overly soften the correct Akita coat. Leaving the face and head until last, start with a pin brush. Lift and separate the coat a section at a time, misting the coat to prevent breakage. You may use plain water or, if you must, a coat conditioner or bodifier. If the dog is between coats, then use something which adds body and sheen. If using clear water, you may leave the coat quite damp. It will dry by the time you get to the ring.

Working the coat up and towards the head, brush the chest, neck and shoulders. Shoulders should be brushed upwards from the elbow, then flattened just behind the shoulder itself so that the dog does not appear to be elbowing out as he comes toward the judge. The top of the withers should be brushed up and then carefully smoothed so that there is a nice blended line from neck to back. If the dog is soft in topline, you may wish to leave the top coat standing up as much as possible to conceal the sagging back. If the back is firm and hard, then you may smooth the guardcoat so that it is very lustrous across the back. This is quite attractive as the judge bends to go over your dog. His hands will tell the truth, but careful shaping with a brush can make a favorable first impression. From the hip bones back to the tail set, brush the coat absolutely flat. The tail has a tendency to ruffle the coat up so you must smooth it so that the dog doesn't look high in the rear when viewed in profile. Thoroughly comb the sides, the belly, and the upper thighs, areas indicative of careless grooming.

The going-away view is very important. The hair on the buttocks will be somewhat flattened from being constantly sat on. Use a cornstarch to those areas and let it sit while you finish the rest of the grooming. A light coat of chalk will whiten but remember, before going into the ring, all traces of chalk or cornstarch must be removed.

The tail and head should be done last. Using a pin brush and beginning at the base of tail, fluff the hair up so that it stands out like a big bottle brush. Don't forget to mist the coat as you work it. Then, just before going to

Ch. O'BJ Kotausha Tuc, ROM (Ch. O'BJ BigSon of Sachmo, ROMXP x Ch. O'BJ Ko-tausha Mo of Westwind, ROMXP) breeder-owner-handler Barbara Andrews.

comb here to lift and separate and, when you have finished, comb or brush in a horizontal direction. Make sure the anus is clean and, in a bitch, make sure the genital area is also clean and tidy. If she is in season, you'll want to give her a last minute cleaning before going to the ring.

You are now ready to do the feet and legs. Here we advise using the fine end of a "greyhound" comb or a slicker brush. A slicker brush is a small wooden-backed brush with hundreds of tiny, thin stainless steel bristles. Use it to carefully lift the leg coat and the thick hair on the feet.

If the elbows or hocks are stained, apply ringside, wipe any dust, particularly chalk dust, from the face. Make sure the eyes are clean and not running from grooming spray or other substances. Fluff up the cheek and face hair. If the nose leather is dry, a tiny smidgen of petroleum jelly will not only soothe it but add gloss.

Okay, jump him down from the table and stand back and admire your handiwork as he shakes himself and struts his stuff!

RING PRESENTATION

First of all, give some thought to the color of your dog and the clothes you should wear. Don't wear orange with a red dog or beige

Ch. Frakari D's Akambo No Barnaby, (Ch. Hot's Mo's Barnaby Jones, ROMX x Ch. Date Tensha's Pot Luck) breeder Ira Winkelman. This B.I.S winner is handled by Lyn Martin St. Michael for owner Lois Harris and is pictured winning under Mrs. Roxanne P. Mahan.

"well groomed." That means the handler too. Clean, tidy clothes with no smudges. Skirts of decent length, not so full as to interfere with the dog when gaiting and not so tight as to . . . restrict your stride. Men, get rid of the jangling change and keys in your pockets. Button your sports coat. Flapping coattails are distracting to the judge and the dog. Wear sensible, skid-proof shoes and if the ring surface is tricky, use tacky-paw on the dog's feet. Girls, save the dangly jewelry for evening wear; it gets in the way of a dog show.

Leave your brush outside the ring. You are showing an Akita: a naturally presented breed. He doesn't need constant brushing and combing. Pay attention to the judge, not to adjusting every wayward hair.

The popular snake chain collars are beautiful on a smooth-coated breed but are highly impractical for a coated dog. The metal chain-type choke collars also tend to wear and damage the Akita coat. It is quite permissible to use a thin nylon choke collar for the breed ring as well as the obedience ring. A good nylon collar is almost unbreakable and will withstand far more pressure when needed in an emergency than will the chain portion of a choke-chain. It is the round ring which the collar passes

with a fawn dog. Don't wear a black skirt with a black dog. In fact, while I've often worn black myself, it's not a good choice for an Akita as it shows every little frizzy bit of undercoat which the dog decided to let go of that day. The dog should stand out against the background of your slacks or skirt so choose a color that compliments him.

And remember what we said about being

Ch. O'BJ Kaala Skylake, (Ch. O'BJ BigSon of Sachmo, ROMXP x Ch. O'BJ Kotausha-Mo of Westwind, ROMXP) handled by Dixie Perry for owner Susan Charpentier. Bred by Susan and BJ Andrews, Kaala is the dam of top ranked multiple Group winners, Ch. O'BJ Striped Kareem Skylake and Ch. Hasu Nikko of Skylake.

through which is most likely to break and the slight give of the nylon helps prevent the abrupt snap which is likely to pop the ring. Because it is lightweight, a nylon choke will generally stay high on the neck, giving optimum control; and if the right color is used, it's practically invisible on a properly coated Akita. Personally, I feel the Akita does not need gaudy jewelry to be fashionable nor to command attention. The proud, alert breed specimen in glorious condition, standing free posed and seemingly untethered, is an awe-inspiring sight.

If it's cool, crate or sit with your dog close enough to the ring that he can see what's happening. Allowing your dog to observe the performance of an advanced dog works just as well in conformation as it does in obedience. Dogs learn by watching. That's how mama dog teaches them, remember? Even a well-started dog should benefit from the occasional opportunity to watch other dogs go through their paces.

One of the most common handling mistakes is that of constantly fussing over the dog—stacking, restacking, fixing that crooked foot, grooming, fiddling with the tail, etc. If all the judge sees when he looks at your dog is a flurry of hands and movement or your body

Ch. Zinja of Tetsu-Hito, a Top Ten Akita of 1988 - 1989, he gained Championship titles in Puerto Rico, So. American, and Peru and is Ch. of the Incas, Americas, and the World. Owned by Phil Grey.

bending over the dog while you set up the offside leg, he can hardly be expected to evaluate your dog and, therefore, is unlikely to consider it for a placement.

Don't shove bait at your dog just as the judge approaches to examine the mouth. If you use bait, it's fine to give him a nibble as the judge moves on to examine the rear quarters and testicles. Never throw bait in the ring. Don't distract other dogs with squeaky toys or funny noises.

Never allow your dog to crowd another one. Keep plenty of room between dogs, especially when moving. Don't let yourself get crowded into a corner or forced to stack behind a tent pole.

Learn how to stack and pose the dog before taking it into the ring. Practice at a shopping center where you can see your reflection in a plate glass window. Practice quickly posing the dog so his virtues are shown to best advantage as

Ch. Noji's Demons Begone, (Ch. O'BJ King's Ransom, ROMXP x Ch. Daijobu's Vampirella O'BJ, ROMX) was Best of Winners and Sweepstakes Winner at the 1988 National Specialty in Denver.

Ch. To No Koichi, a Champion in America, Canada, Bermuda, Puerto Rico, South America, and Santo Domingo, he was ranked #3 in AKC ratings from January to May 1985. Owned by Phil Gray, pictured with Judge Sam Pizzino, handled by Rusty Short.

Ch. The Cat In The Hat O'BJ, (The Widow-Maker x Hatter) shown as a yearling under National Specialty judge Sam Pizzino, handled by Carol Laubscher.

Ch. Sea Breeze Sea Fare'in Sarah (Ch. O'BJ BigSon of Sachmo, ROMPX x Ch. Alii's Storm Warning, ROM) as a young "new Champion" going BOS. Bred by Linn Greene, owned by Kim Poulin.

Ch. Tasha Karma San, a beautiful white bitch owned by Phil Gray who says she was his first bitch and best friend.

reflected in the mirror, just as the judge will see it.

The same is true for those win photos. It's terribly frustrating for the show photographer and a weary judge who may be running behind schedule when an exhibitor spends several minutes setting up the dog only to have it move again just as the photographer is about to take the picture. Practice setting up as previously described and then work at having the dog hold the pose long enough to get a photograph. That means have someone create distractions, drop a chair, throw a piece of bait under his nose, or whatever it takes to teach him to stand motionless when you give him that special command.

Know your dog's best angle, and be insistent about having him photographed that way. You are not at the mercy of the show photographer. You are the one paying the bill, and, although you must respect what the photographer sees from the camera's angle, you know what you want in the finished photo. You will only have one opportunity to take that photo with that judge, commemorating that win. So, do it right, and do it quickly before the dog, the photographer, and the judge all lose patience with the whole procedure.

Some photographers pay no attention to things like a sagging tail or saw-horse pose. The handler is intent on setting the front, getting the arch in the neck, and hasn't noticed that the tail has come uncurled. Many photographs intended for advertisement have been lost to such a moment's distraction or a show photographer's ignorance of each breed's requirements or impatience on everyone's part. If you think the dog's tail might have become relaxed or that he shifted weight and stance, have the photographer take another shot.

Don't use photo time to talk the judge's ear off. He might actually remember you or the dog and not be nearly so willing to award you next time if he has to put up with your chitchat. Thank him for the win, get the photo, and let everyone go on about the business of running a dog show.

And if you didn't receive an award, leave the ring gracefully, thanking the judge for his consideration as you accept whatever ribbon he hands you. If you receive no ribbon, just leave quietly and mannerly after having congratulated the winner. And praise your dog once you are through the gate. Chances are that he performed well and will be confused if you act angry. Not only that, hugging your dog will make you feel a thousand percent better!

RING POLITICS

Charges of corruption abound in any sport, from baseball to hockey. Ours is no different. Dog shows are no different than any other

Ch. The Mad Hatter O'BJ, ROMPX (Ch. Daijobu's Joto x Ch. O'BJ Nikki No Nikki, ROMP) won her regular class under Anthony Hodges and then Sweeps under breeder-judge Reed Keffer, Chereed Akitas. A top show dog, "Hatter" also went on to become the #1 Dam of All Time.

Ch. The Midnight Torch O'BJ (BIS Ch. The Widow-Maker O'BJ, ROMXP x Ch. The Mad Hatter O'BJ, ROMXP) winning BOB from puppy class, breeder-owner-handler Barbara Andrews.

society. The proficient handler who could finish the most miserable specimen; or the breeder who managed to acquire a top dog from some other breeder but was unable to breed a great one; the socialite who employed a top handler to promote the purchased great one; well, many of these people have gone on to judge dogs without ever grasping the basics of evaluating dogs. No one will argue that.

The other end of the spectrum represents the talented handlers who could spot a great dog in a rough, ungroomed, untrained puppy, shown three rings away by a novice owner. It is their capable hands, training, and conditioning which shaped many such youngsters into legendary winners. There are the breeder judges who themselves became legends within their respective breeds and who will never fail to award excellence, regardless of who handles the dog. Such judges have treasures of knowledge to offer from the center of the ring, and the smart exhibitor will study

sport, or for that matter, the business world. Not every coach is a winner and not every business is profitable. Not every aspiring executive can become CEO. You will soon catch on that it's usually the losers who yell "fix" the loudest. Those who enjoy success on a given day certainly don't want that moment of achievement spoiled by some poor sport who says the winner had drinks with the judge the night before when in fact, he was still breaking the speed limit at midnight trying to make the show.

Sure, some judges know and are friends with some exhibitors. Why not? Isn't it better that judges are real people with real involvement in the sport? Those who no longer breed or exhibit need to hear about the heartbreaks and the triumphs of their friends. Even if only by osmosis, they long to experience the highs and lows of the dog game. It keeps them in touch with reality.

AKC-licensed judges are revered worldwide and deservedly so. They are an interesting cross-section of

Ch. The Silver Spoon O'BJ, (Ch. Sea Breeze Grand Wizard x Ch. Goshen's The Silver Lining O'BJ) bred and owned by Barbara Andrews. On loan to Shirley Merritt, she finished with ease as pictured in this B.O.B. and Group II win, from the classes.

them and learn from them instead of wasting time griping about a loss.

Go to any average show and just sit down and study the list of judges. The sum of their knowledge about dogs is astounding and we would do well to look, listen, and learn from these masters. Great judges like Alva Rosenberg are not just "stories" to be told around ringside. There are many Alvas alive today who should be appreciated before they become legends!

You'll soon catch on that longevity as a judge does not take the place of knowledge and judging ability. Before putting a great deal of importance on anyone's opinion, it's a good idea to know what qualifies that person. Being licensed to judge dogs does not in itself make that person qualified to judge every breed. The judge may be brilliant in Sporting breeds but only winging his

Am./Mex. Ch. Inaka Honey Barbara, C.D., P.C. (Ch. O'BJ BigSon's Jake x Ch. Matagi's Nisa On The Lake) is owned by Bill Bobrow. She was Number 1 in Akita News Obedience rankings for Novice class 1988 and Number 2 Novice Class Akita World Rankings, 1988. Breeder, Tamara and Bill Warren.

Ch. O'BJ One-of-A-Kind, ROM (Ch. O'BJ King's Ransom, ROMXP x Ch. The Mad Hatter O'BJ, ROMXP) is a Multi-BB and Group Placing bitch owned by Carol Laubscher, Regalia Akitas. "Uno" is pictured winning BB at the prestigious Ravenna KC under judge Eleanor Evers, handled by Jack Patterson.

way through Working dogs. He or she may be very conversant with the breed standard, may belong to the right clubs and travel in the best social circles, may be the nicest, most sincere person you'll ever meet, but still not know an Akita from an Elkhound. Or maybe he does, but freezes up when confronted with a large class and a lineup of pro handlers. Or maybe he was never a particularly ethical person in his private life and is as inclined to hand out the right considerations to the right people at a dog show as at a board meeting. People are people and by now you've guessed: judges are people too.

The true test of a person's knowledge is in his ability to judge which dogs to put together for matings and to evaluate which puppies to sell as show quality and the ultimate task, judging which one of the litter to keep for themselves. A breeder who has the ability to do this well and do it consistently year after year is indeed a knowledgeable judge. Hopefully, they won't freeze up or be intimidated once they enter the center of the show ring.

Ch. O'BJ Striped Kareem Sky Lake, a Top Ranked Widow-Maker son owned by Susan Charpentier, handled by Dixie Perry to Group I under Jane Anderson.

handler-turned-judge is going to be especially hard to fool.

These people may not have been directly involved in Akitas but you can be pretty sure that they have an innate ability to recognize type, class, and quality in most any breed. It's called an "eye for a dog" and while it can be cultivated by rigorous study, it's rather like musical talent, a gift one is born with.

So don't be discouraged by losers and don't fall back on the old excuse of "politics" when you lose. Put your dog away and go back and sit ringside and study the judge. You just might learn something and if you're honest with yourself, you may be able to see why you lost that day. No dog is perfect. Perhaps your dog has a fault which that judge is particularly fussy about. That doesn't mean he's a bad judge, only that he abhors bad fronts and your dog is east-west and out at the elbows. Of course he lost!

The professional handler who was able to accurately evaluate a new dog, and whose personal integrity didn't allow him to "special" a less than special dog is usually a very good judge. If he consistently presented top-ranked dogs over the years, then this

Better than sitting at ringside after you've shown, sit there for a while before you exhibit. Familiarize yourself with your judge's ring pattern, know what he looks for in a dog, and then be ready to show it to him!

There are three golden keys to winning in the ring. A good dog in top condition shown to a knowledgeable judge. All three keys are within your reach.

If you don't have a good breed specimen and you want to win, then buy one. Don't make the mistake of trying to "breed your bitch up." The odds are against you. Buy a top show puppy before you get so discouraged that you drop out, or before you flood the world with litter after litter of mediocre Akitas.

If you have a basically sound, typy dog, then get him in top con-

Am/Mx/Int'l Ch. O'BJ Sachmo Ko-Son (Ch. O'BJ BigSon of Sachmo, ROMXP x Tetsu-Ko O'BJ) owned by Jorge Hadad made breed history becoming Mexico's Top Dog All Breeds in 1989. Sonny is also a Group winner in the U.S.

Ch. O'BJ BigSon of Sachmo, ROMXP winning his first Group I, as always, breeder-owner-handled. The author considers this his most memorable win, not only because it was the first of so many, but because it reflected the opinion of over a century of judging experience as represented by Group judge Mr. Heywood Hartley and trophy presenter, Mr. E. W. Tipton.

dition. Roadwork, swim, put him on a jogger, bike with him; do whatever is needed to correct any weakness and put him in hard tight condition. Exercise will bloom the coat. Feed him properly, groom him, and see that he's parasite-free.

About that last key. If you're unsure about a judge, give him a try. A good rule of thumb—show three times to any judge before dismissing him and show under three different judges before giving up on a dog.

If you come away without a ribbon in three tries under three different judges, you must reevaluate your handling skills and/or the quality or condition of the dog. If you show under the same judge three times and leave his ring empty-handed while winning with the same dog(s) under other judges, cross him off your list. That may not make him a "bad" judge, just one who doesn't care for your type of dog, so why continue to throw money away and have your good dog demeaned by someone who doesn't appreciate him? Learn to recognize and appreciate those judges who consistently award the best Akitas.

BIS Ch. The Widow-Maker O'BJ, ROMXP (Ch. The Real McCoy O'BJ x Ch. The Same Dame O'BJ, ROMP) winning the Working Group at 15 months of age under one of the most greatly loved All-Breed judges of our time, Mr. E. W. Tipton.

Ch. Chosen's Blaze of Glory (Am/Can. Ch. Allure's Island Shogun x Koma-Inu Alabaster) bred and owned by Jodi and Stephen Higgins, Chosen Akitas. Handled by Kathy Mines Rayner to B.O.S. under judge Mrs. Peter Gunterman.

Katagi's Dai Ichi No Shogun, by Ch. Kuma Ryoshi x Krug's Chiyo Hime No Mai, who was a Tom Cat daughter. Bred by Nick Marinos, "Dai" was a dominant sire for Jade-Shogun Akitas.

Ch. Windom's Imperial Destiny, (Ch. Kin Hozan's Toklat, CD & ROMX x Windom All That Jazz, ROMX) bred by Ed and Adrienne Israel, owned by Janet Kozatek.

Ch. Chiheisen's Fit for A King (BIS Ch. O'BJ King's Ransom, ROMX x Ch. Chiheisen's Holly No Daitan) bred by Sylvia and Frank Thomas and John D'Alessio, she's owned by Roger and Jan Kaplan.

Multi-Group-placing Ch. Tora's MoMo Saku winning her first BIS under Carl Leipmann, handled by Bill Sahloff for breeder-owners Jim and Anne Marie Taylor and son Christoper. "M" (Ch. Bogart's Hill Showdown At BigSky x Am/Can. Ch. Tora's Michiko O Ryan, TT, ROM) finished with four consecutive majors and BOB over specials. At 19 months, "M" was the youngest BIS Akita, setting records like her dam who produced eight champions in her first litter!

Ch. Palace Court's Taisho Napali, (Big D's Palace Court Anjin Son x Ch. Kuma Yama Sykora Star) bred by Pat Van Buskirk, was the first Best In Show Winner in Hawaii. "Tai-Tai," as owners Henry and Nancy Kapali call him, was the #3 Working dog of the Islands in 1990 and was ranked in the top Twenty Akitas Nationally.

Ch. Chiheisen's J. D. V. Hitman, C.D. (Ch. Asahi Yama No Hanashi x Ch. Kebo's Jazie Masumi of Hikari) was ranked in Top Ten Obedience, Akita World, 1987. Owned by Bill Bobrow and Sylvia Thomas, bred by Y. Foreman and P. Schwartz.

Ch. Target Rose O'BJ (Seabreeze Gold Miner O'BJ x Ch. The Dame's On Target O'BJ, ROMPX) finishing her championship under judge Nick Agliano, handled by Norma Gibson. Owner Maurizio Moretto of Santiago Chile, sent "Marra" back to the States to earn her AKC Ch. title and to be mated with Widow-Maker. Marra accomplished both tasks with flair and ease!

Am/Can. Ch. Ashmen's Bronco Bill of Bruin (Ch. Koma-Inu Bronze Bruin, ROM x Ch. Windom's Kaki Kisa No Ashmen) bred and owned by Judy Ashmen. "Bronco" finished from puppy class in only six shows. Shown sparingly as a Special, he was AOM at Westminster and has several Group placements in 1992. The handsome brown dog is also a multi-Group placer in Canada.

Ch. Chiheisen's Take It To The Maxx (Ch. O'BJ Zack The Spotted Bear, ROM x Ch. Kuroi Kao Dallas Alice, ROMX) bred by Chris Weatherman and Priscilla McCune, is a multi-Best In Show winner for the Schippers, the Thomases, and Jose Machline.

O'BJ Ambassador at Chaslads, photo at 9 months. (Ch. The Widow-Maker O'BJ x Ch. The Mad Hatter O'BJ) is owned by Mick Street, Nottingham, England. He is the sire of Specialty Best In Show Winner, Eng. Ch. Chaslad's Captain Cronas.

Ch. E Oka's BigSon's Shadow (Ch. O'BJ BigSon of Sachmo, ROMXP x Ch. O'BJ Kye Kye Go of E Oka) bred and owned by Linda Henson. "Shad" gained his Championship title on the Florida National Specialty circuit, handled by Barbara Andrews and Meg Carpenter of England's Overhill Kennels. He was then owner handled by Linda to Best In Sweeps under Robert Campbell, Okii Yubi.

THE OBEDIENCE RING

One of the most successful owner-trainers I know is John Seaborn of Alberta, Canada. John is well known for his remarkable accomplishments in obedience and for the willing dependability of his Akita's performance both in and out of the obedience ring.

It has been many years since Bill and I instructed obedience and frankly, we have never worked an Akita to an obedience title. As the pressures of conformation competition increased, we ceased formal obedience training our own dogs. The rapport which comes from daily teamwork with one's dog and knowing that the dog is totally tuned in and, more importantly, *understands* what is wanted and expected of him are things every owner should experience. We regret that we were compelled to sacrifice formal obedi-

O'BJ Lochinvar Saisho. Owner-trainer John Seaborn says *"Socialization begins early — a friendly cat helps!"*

ence in favor of the conformation ring. Time limitations aside, there's no reason most owners can't enjoy both!

In any case, I no longer feel qualified to instruct or discuss obedience. While "show training" our youngsters is a form of obedience training, commenting on the more formal aspect is best left up to someone who excels in that competitive arena on a daily basis. For that reason, I asked Mr. Seaborn to contribute to this chapter and we thank him for his generous response.

TRAINING YOUR AKITA
by John Seaborn

Introduction

Every year hundreds of thousands of dogs are destroyed by humane societies and dog pounds across North America. Many of these dogs are purebred. Some of them are Akitas. Reasons that owners give for dumping their dogs were: he grew too big; he destroyed the furniture, lawn, or garden; he jumped up on people and knocked them down; he bit someone; he wouldn't stay home; he was too aggressive; he chased cars or livestock; he couldn't be controlled and he barked too much. Other reasons given are that the owners are moving into a new house, they are expecting a baby or they have allergies. Many of the latter reasons are simply cop outs. The owners don't want to admit they failed their dog. Virtually all of the above problems could have been eliminated through proper socialization and training.

I will not instruct you through step-by-step obedience training. Nor will I deal with problem dogs or problem situations. Entire books have been written on these subjects. Also there are professionally run obedience classes which can guide you. However, few books or obedience classes are written or conducted by people who are knowledgeable about the Akita breed. The breed does present some unique challenges. What I will do is to provide you with some knowledge and training tips specific to the Akita.

Laying the Essential Foundations for Training

There are four essential foundations for training. If present, one can teach a dog almost anything. But if these foundations have not been established, training becomes more difficult if not impossible.

1. The most essential foundation is the *quality of the puppy* itself, its temperament, disposition and physical soundness. Unfortunately puppies are not all equal. A bargain puppy is rarely a bargain. Temperament and disposition are often incorrectly used interchangeably. Temperament refers to a dog's suitability for the purposes for which he was bred.

The Akita temperament should reflect courage and confidence. He should be aggressive, not passive. Aggressiveness is a quality to be sought and should not be equated with viciousness. Aggressiveness is really equated with assertiveness. Akitas are very assertive. An Akita should enter every new situation in a confident manner that commands respect. A timid Akita certainly does not reflect appropriate Akita temperament. A dog that is timid or lacks confidence is harder to train and is rarely totally reliable. In the context of training, temperament is equated to the dog's willingness to do the job for

which he was bred. Akitas are very willing hunters but are much less willing to retrieve a dumbbell. Another Akita temperament trait is independence. Typically Akitas see little need to do something just because their owner wants them to.

Disposition refers to the dog's outlook on the world. A good Akita disposition is characterized by friendliness and curiosity. To such an Akita the world is a challenge to be explored. An Akita with a good disposition is extroverted and outgoing. Soundness means the dog is free of any physical or psychological problems that set limits on what the dog is capable of accomplishing. All good breeders guarantee their stock to be physically and mentally sound.

2. The period from three to 16 weeks is critical in a dog's development. This is the canine *socialization period,* when

Tamarlane's Suki-Yaki and Checan's Ko-Goma on a long "sit stay" for owner John Seaborn of Canada.

Happiness is an armfull of Akita! Shellie Schwark and Ruger celebrate life together. Ruger is a companion Akita in every sense of the word. Unshowable due to an injury, he is nonetheless an outstanding representative.

your Akita learns to bond with you, the owner. It is the period when he learns about the world in which he lives. During this period everything and anything the puppy experiences will make a greater impression on him than at any other time in his life. It is absolutely imperative that your Akita puppy be taken out into the world and exposed to as many things as possible during this formative stage. The puppy must be given house time and be around lots of people. The time spent with your puppy during this critical period of his life will repay itself many times over. Learning during the socialization period is permanent. It is important that your puppy not pick up any bad habits during this time. If your Akita puppy has not been properly socialized, it is almost impossible to overcome this deficiency in later life. Buying your Akita puppy from a conscientious breeder usually guarantees a good foundation has been begun. It is your responsibility to continue to build on it. Be very wary of purchasing an unsocialized kennel-raised Akita. Be especially cautious of purchasing such a dog over the age of four months.

3. Dogs need to learn *how to play.* Toys such as balls and stuffed animals (teddy bears) are essential to your Akita's development. Toys also make motivating a dog during training so much easier. Toys are associated with fun. When used during training, toys make learning fun for the dog. It doesn't take much to transfer a dog's chasing and retrieving a stuffed toy to chasing a dumbbell. An adult dog who has never learned how to play is more difficult to train because it is harder to motivate such a dog.

4. An Akita must *learn who is boss.* Dogs are pack animals. A pack has only one leader. The leader is listened to and obeyed. To more placid breeds, leadership is not so important. They will accept virtually any leader, even an inconsistent and ineffective one. Akitas are dominant, assertive dogs. Knowing who is the pack leader is especially important to an Akita. If the human does not establish a leadership role, the Akita will quickly assert himself and assume this role. An Akita who thinks he is boss is very difficult to train. Leadership is established by lots of loving, gentle, firm, consistent handling. Brute force, beatings, or kicks do not establish leadership, only fear and/or resentment. Your Akita puppy should be handled frequently by all members of the family and as many friendly strangers as possible. His mouth should be gently opened and his teeth examined. He should be lifted onto tables and held there while people go over him. His feet should be handled and his nails trimmed. He should be made to lie on his side to be groomed. Puppies will often resent this. But it is essential you persist. Start with short sessions and build on these. Never give in to the puppy be-

Respecting their Elders, "Kaho", "Kuma", and "Sam" owned by Maria Heldman. Youngsters at this age should always respect an adult dog's authority.

cause he cries or pulls away. Biting, even play biting, is a dog's way of asserting dominance. From earliest puppyhood, biting humans must be discouraged. A biting seven-week-old Akita puppy may seem cute. A biting one-hundred-pound one-year-old is not! By the time a puppy is four months old, he should never bite a human, even in play. Be gentle but firm. If the puppy attempts to bite, put your hand around the puppy's muzzle and say "Nooo" very firmly. Get the puppy used to having food and toys taken out of his mouth. Don't do this in a teasing fashion. On occasion gently and firmly take things away from him. All members of the family should do this. The dog is allowed to resist such attempts in the beginning. He is not allowed to show resentment. Aggression towards other animals must also be strongly discouraged. As pack leader you do not allow fighting. In all of the above cases, discipline your puppy by picking him up by the scruff of the neck (leaving his hind feet on the floor) and saying "Nooo" very firmly. Hold him there for a moment until he whines and then put him down and love him

up. The puppy must learn the meaning of "No." Whenever the puppy is doing something undesirable, use a firm "No" and redirect his behavior. Always follow punishment with love and hugs. This kind of training from earliest puppyhood teaches the puppy his position in his human pack. Obedience training finalizes the question of leadership. The dog is taught to obey. Teaching an Akita who is boss does not mean brutalizing the dog. It means establishing a loving bond between the Akita and you. This bond is built on love, gentleness, consistency and firmness. It is this bond that transforms you from the Akita's owner to his master. It is this bond that motivates your Akita to work for you and, if required, to lay down his life for you. Buying an Akita means you own him. But does not necessarily mean the dog recognizes you as his master. Akitas don't understand the concept of ownership. They do understand leadership. You have to earn an Akita's recognition of you as his master and leader. You can't buy it, but most definitely you can't beat it into him.

Exploding Some Myths

There are many training myths about Akitas and dogs in general. Some of these beliefs can be detrimental to laying essential learning foundations. Others result in inappropriate training methods.

1. *Akitas are untrainable.*

As a consequence of its size, intelligence, temperament and stamina, the Akita is perhaps the most versatile of all breeds. Akitas have been successfully trained to hunt all types of game. They have been used for police work, and as tracking dogs, sled dogs, and cart pullers. Originally bred as hunters, they had to think for themselves. Akitas are very good at thinking for themselves. They are exceptionally intelligent. The downside of this is that they get bored very quickly. Akitas have incredible memories. You can capitalize on this quality in training. Akitas also have a dignity that rebels at being forced. For these reasons Akitas require a slightly different training approach than is commonly used.

2. *You can't teach an old dog new tricks.*

An Akita that has been properly socialized, trained, and is bonded to its owner can be taught virtually anything at any time in his life. An Akita that has not been socialized, trained and has not established a bond with its owner is difficult to train something new because the dog does know how to learn, has hang ups, and is hard to motivate. A second problem arises when it is necessary for an Akita to unlearn something in order to master something new. We all know habits (good or bad) are hard to break. Make certain your Akita does not pick up bad habits. Don't allow your dog to run free in unsupervised, uncontrolled situations. Not only is this dangerous for your dog but he picks up many bad habits. Training should always be done on lead, no matter how good and reliable you think your dog is. A lead gives you total control and allows quick correction and/or prevention of inappropriate behaviors. A good flexi-lead is an invaluable training tool. One mistake—like the dog bolting and running away—can undo months of training. A smart dog like an Akita quickly learns that if he can get away, training is over. From that point on, the Akita is constantly looking for that opportunity. Your Akita should only be given his freedom in completely safe areas and always under your supervision.

3. *A show dog shouldn't be obedience trained.*

The reasoning behind this is that an obedience-trained dog loses the sparkle

Akita Tani's Kageboshi won the first Akita obedience trial. She was a daughter of Akita Tani's Ureshii Kuma who was the first OFA Akita. Handler is Rusty Cunningham Short.

that is required to win in the show ring. This is true to some extent for Akitas who are *improperly* trained. When Akitas are trained using harsh corrections in stressful situations and using repetitive practice techniques, they quickly become bored and disenchanted. However, if proper training techniques are used, this can avoided. A well-trained, bonded, socialized Akita should actually do even better in the show ring.

Ch. Bobrow's Bartok, CDX, PC. Akita World-Top Ten Obedience Winner 1984, photo by A. Bobrow.

4. *You shouldn't begin teaching a puppy until he is six months old.*

Puppies attain their full mental capacity at seven weeks of age. This means a seven-week-old Akita puppy has the same learning capacity as a full-grown dog. He lacks concentration, coordination and physical stamina but not ability to learn. Most importantly, what a puppy learns during the first five months of life is more lasting and permanent than at any other time in his life. Training can actually begin at seven weeks. This does not mean you start formal obedience on a seven-week-old puppy, but rather that you begin the puppy's education. Whether you formally teach your Akita puppy or not, the puppy will start learning at this age. It is essential that the puppy's learning be channelled properly. Because an Akita puppy learns so quickly, has

not yet picked up any bad habits, and is only a fraction of his adult size, puppyhood is an ideal time to start training. If you can, get your Akita into a puppy-socialization or puppy-obedience class as soon as he is old enough. You must be especially careful with a puppy between the ages of eight and 12 weeks old. This period is commonly known as the fear-impact period. Any frightening, painful, or

Ch. Mokusei's Zeus of Daitan-Ni, ROM, a top winner, doing agility work with owner Jeanne Galindo Hayes.

traumatic experience will have a permanent, lasting effect. Training must not be stressful. When your Akita is experiencing fear or reluctance, neither force your dog into a confrontation nor reinforce his fears by praising and petting him. Force will frighten the dog further. Praise will only reinforce that he was right in being afraid. Allow the dog to work out the problem with patience and kindness.

5. *Dogs know when they have done wrong.*

As highly social pack animals, dogs communicate by a wide variety of signs and

has done wrong. All the dog knows is that you are mad. He hasn't the slightest idea why. *Never* punish a dog for anything unless you actually catch him in the act. As with all corrections, timing is critical. Equally important—always show the dog the desired behavior and follow punishment with love. If you catch the dog defecating on your carpet, immediately correct him and get him outside. When he defecates outside in the correct place, praise him.

6. *Bitches are easier to train than dogs.*

Dogs are bigger and stronger than bitches which make them more difficult to handle

"Tina," listening for her next command. Seawood's Tina BearTrap (Ch. Akita Tani's Daimyo x Ch. Golden Sun Seawood Wa Wa L'Wilac) breeder Kelle Clinton, owner Kelle and Alyce Clinton.

signals. When you acquire a dog, the dog becomes a member of your family. You represent his pack. Akitas are experts at picking up subtle human moods and feelings. Picture this scenario. While you are away your Akita has just relieved himself on your carpet. You come in the door and immediately smell the dog's indiscretion. Your mood changes. Your Akita quickly picks up this mood and comes to greet you (or runs away from you depending on his past experience) with a sheepish look. You interpret this to mean that the dog knows he

and correct. Stud dogs are easily distracted. Bitches in heat are very difficult to train. Unless your Akita is of show quality and you have purchased it explicitly for breeding, you should neuter it. Dogs should be castrated at nine months of age. This allows the dog to attain the full benefit of its male hormones for growth and secondary sex characteristics. It capitalizes fully on the benefits of castration: reduced aggression and reduction of the tendency to wander. Bitches should be spayed at six months of age. Bitches spayed before 12 months of age almost never develop mammary tumors. They also develop better and more luxurious coats. Neutering always makes an Akita a better pet and human companion. When neutered, the trainability and manageability of dogs versus bitches is virtually equal.

7. *Dogs can generalize.*

This myth is rarely stated as such. However it often underlies inappropriate training methods and is responsible for creating many problems. Dogs learn specific responses to specific commands for specific situations. They cannot generalize these commands to other situations. In other words they cannot form concepts as can humans. An example will demonstrate this. You have trained your

Ch. and OTCH Langan's Tamashii Drift (Am/Can. Ch. Langan's Cody Bearpaw x Am/Can. Ch. Langan's Aka O'Kashi, ROM) bred by Sheryl Langan, owned by Bob Ottenbrite and Sheryl Langan. She is Canada's first female Dual Champion (second Dual Ch. Akita) and Canada's second OTCH female Akita. She is also a multi-Group placer en route to her Can. Ch.

Akita to "sit" on command. He will sit from a stand or sit automatically when you stop. What the dog really does not understand is that "sit" is a position. He has no idea of the concept of "sit." If you need proof of this, put an Akita who has been well trained for "down-stay" in a down position. Ask him to "sit." Unless the dog has been specifically trained to sit from the down position, he won't understand the command. The dog's lack of ability to generalize means that you have to carefully train your Akita for each and every situation that a specific response is required. Treat each situation as a new training experience for the dog. Where this really becomes important is in the area of "proofing." All dogs trained for obedience competitions need to be proofed on all exercises. Simply stated, proofing means the handler must think of all the ways a dog can do something wrong and specifically train for these situations.

8. *It is better to have a dog trained by a professional.*

It is preferable to have an Akita trained professionally than not trained at all. However, it is far better to train your own dog. The dog is bonded to you, not the professional handler. To compensate for the lack of bonding, the trainer will have to use more force on the Akita. Akitas don't respond well to forced training. Some professional trainers use training methods which are totally unsuitable for an Akita. Some take shortcuts in training. There are no shortcuts. You may force an Akita to do something, but there is always a cost. Training your own dog reinforces your dominance and leadership. If you cannot train your own Akita, there is no guarantee that an Akita who will work for a trainer will necessarily work for you. It is better to take your Akita to obedience classes where you will learn to train your own dog. The best way to pick a class is to go to a dog show in your area. Watch the obedience classes. Ask the owners where they trained their dog. Classes provide a place where you can turn for assistance when you experience problems. And you will experience problems. Every dog trainer does. If you are having a problem teaching your Akita something at home, stop training this exercise. Seek assistance and advice from your trainer.

9. *Attack-trained Akitas make better protectors.*

An Akita should never be attack trained. There are situations where attack training a dog is desirable, as in the case of dogs used for police work and the military. These dogs are working animals. They are not pets. Family pets should never be attack trained. Many cities have special legislation pertaining to dangerous dogs. An attack-trained Akita is considered a dangerous animal. If such a dog bites someone, you face a charge of criminal negligence.

Am/Can. Ch. Kakwa's Orca, ROMPX, turns the crowd on at Madison Square Garden in 1982. Orca is the only white Akita to win BOB at Westminster KC and to have achieved a #1 National Ranking. The multi-Group winner was owned by Bill and Barbara Andrews, handled by Sidney Lamont.

Akitas are intensely loyal to their masters and will naturally protect their master's person and property. If you want to sharpen your Akita's innate protective instincts, raise him in the house. A kennel-raised Akita has nothing to protect. Work especially hard to establish a strong bond with your Akita. Spend as many hours with him as you can. Take him with you to as many places as you can. There is no better natural protection dog in the world than a strongly bonded Akita.

Ch. Ishi Aman, CD, TDX, TT proves that Akitas have brains as well as brawn and beauty. The record breaking Akita is shown tracking with his trainer, Margaret Teague. He is owned by Jeanne Galindo Hayes.

10. *Obedience training is work.*

It takes about half an hour a day to train an Akita. If you don't have the time to spend with your Akita to train him, perhaps you should reconsider buying one. Obedience training should not be considered work. It should be fun both for you and your dog. If you don't enjoy training, chances are your dog won't either. Training offers many rewards both for you and your Akita. A trained Akita is a joy to own and a pride to its owner. It is welcome almost anywhere it goes. The hours spent in training repay themselves thousands of times over. Remember that most dogs were bred for specific purposes such as hunting, herding or sled pulling. Few dogs today have the opportunity to do the jobs for which they were originally bred. A dog needs a job to do or it will become bored. Training provides a job for the dog to do. It gives an Akita a sense of purpose and worth.

11. *Two dogs are better than one.*

One dog is always more easily trained and better bonded than are two dogs. A single dog must rely totally on its owner for companionship. He gives you his undivided attention. Also two dogs require more time and attention. If you decide to get a second Akita, do so after your first Akita has been socialized and trained.

Training Your Akita

Initially your Akita has no idea what is expected of him. You must show the dog what it is you want him to do. When you learn

O'BJ Lochinvar Saisho (Ch. Sea Breeze Bounty Hunter x Ch. O'BJ Giddy-Up Go) is an Obedience Champion, consistently scoring in the high 190's under the tutorship of owner-trainer, John Seaborn.

something, like playing the piano, you learn it in a step-by-step fashion. You don't expect to learn to play a sonata all at once. Dogs are no different. You must break all exercises down into their component parts. Teach each part separately. An example will illustrate how this works. Official obedience requirements say a dog must come in to you quickly when called, sit squarely in front of you and go to the heel position on command. This exercise is really made up of five separate components: (1) come, (2) sit, (3) sit in front, (4) go to heel and (5) sit beside you in the heel position. Each part must be taught separately. First the dog must be taught to "come." His favorite toy is an excellent incentive. The dog must be praised extravagantly for coming. Quite separately teach the dog to "sit." When he understands sit, work on sit in front. Then work on teaching the dog to go around to "heel" and finally after the dog has mastered the going-around part, teach him to sit at heel. When the dog has learned all the component part, start putting them together...one part at a time. If the dog comes in quickly but does not sit, go back and separately work on the sit.

Besides breaking each exercise down into component parts you also must break each component part down into realistic levels of expected performance. You don't expect to play the piano scales perfectly the first time you try. Sticking with the "come" example, the ideal first step is to have the dog come toward you when called. At this point you don't care about the other steps, i.e., front sit or heel (these can be taught in the same training session but as separate and distinct lessons). For this lesson you are only interested in the "come." It is unrealistic to think your Akita will come in quickly and stop right in front of you on the first try. In other words, don't expect perfect performance. Motivation is critical. Every dog will be motivated by something: praise, food, toys, or something. Find out what motivates your dog. Use toys, food, or praise or all

fully if the task can be broken down into two or more components or if the initial expectation level should be lowered. Keep training sessions short. An Akita will learn more in three ten-minute sessions than one 30 minute session. Akitas have an incredible memory. They do remember what they are taught. Usually a dog remembers best the last thing it has learned. That is why it is a good idea to quit a lesson and move on to something else as soon as the dog gets it right. After three successive sessions when

Checan's Ko Guma, performing the broad jump for owner-trainer John Seaborn.

three as appropriate. A realistic first level of performance is for the dog to come when called. You don't particularly care if he ends up in front of you, beside you or behind you. You also don't care how fast he came or if he is bouncing around. It is enough that he came. For this component at this expectation level, this was a perfect performance. Praise effusively each and every effort the dog makes. You may repeat this lesson one more time during a given training session. But don't ask an Akita to repeat his performance ten more times and become bored. If you are having difficulty getting your Akita to do something correctly, consider care-

your Akita performs a lesson perfectly on the first try at the level of expected performance you have set, move on to the next higher level of performance until he has mastered that component of the exercise. When all components of an exercise have been mastered, put them together one part at a time for a polished, finished performance.

Initially, when training, work in distraction-free areas. When you have achieved a finished performance for an entire exercise in a quiet area, introduce distractions slowly. Now that the Akita has the idea of what it is being asked of him, gently introduce negative reinforcement, light leash pops, and/or withholding of the reward (food, toys praise). Repeat the exercise until the dog does it right with distractions. Then praise, praise, praise. At any time during training the dog becomes confused, back up to the step the dog knows how to do and begin again. Remember learning must never be made stressful or boring for an Akita. Under these conditions, an Akita's desire to learn ends and he shuts down. Akitas are particularly prone to shutting down.

Once the dog knows an exercise (a dog does not know an exercise until he can do it in different locations with distractions), intro-

OTCH Langan's Shetu Drift (Am/Can Ch. Toshiro's Karate Drift x Ch. O-Ten Kuro Kogo of Joto Zoku) bred by Sheryl Langan, owned by Kim Ottenbrite, Leitash kennels. Shetu is Canada's first OTCH female Akita and the second Akita to earn the OTCH title.

duce correction. This is the time to use sharp leash pops. The leash is jerked sharply and immediately released. Under no circumstances should you use negative reinforcement or corrections on a puppy under four months of age. The puppy is learning to learn, and learning must be fun. He also could be in his fear-impact period. Akitas do not take kindly to correction. It is far better to praise extravagantly and reward appropriate behavior than to negatively reinforce or correct inappropriate behavior. But corrections are necessary. Be careful when correcting an Akita. For a correction to be effective, the Akita must know how to avoid getting another one. In other words, he must know what is expected. To correct

an Akita repeatedly when the dog hasn't the slightest idea what to do to avoid the correction is stressful and cruel. An Akita will immediately shut down. Follow every negative thing you do to an Akita with praise. Always end every training session on an up note. Have the dog do something he does well and end with praise.

Sometimes corrections have effects quite different from what was intended by the owner. Not infrequently one sees a person give a "come" command to an Akita. The dog rushes in quickly only to be corrected for a poor sit. This discourages the dog from coming in quickly as he never knows what is going to happen to him when he gets there. *Never, never, never punish an Akita*—no matter what he has done—if he comes to you when called. If the dog must be punished, go to him. Never call a dog to you to be punished. The dog must never learn that it is bad to come. Another common mistake many owners make is hitting their dog in the chest with their knees, stepping on their back feet or otherwise punishing them for jumping on them. Why is your dog jumping on you? Because he loves you and is happy to see you. This is the exact behavior you want to encourage. Does thumping, bumping, or stepping on your dog's hind feet encourage him to want to be close to you? Of course not. Does the dog associate these corrections with jumping up? After a few repetitions he might. But you also will have dampened his enthusiasm. The most effective method for training a dog not to jump on you is when he jumps up grab both his front paws, one in each hand. Squeeze just hard enough to cause the dog discomfort. Hang on to him for a full minute. He will pull and whine but hang on. Most importantly while you are hanging on to him and squeezing his feet tell him what

Ch. Jamel-Rojan's Oso Grande (Ch. Bar BJ's Brown Bomber x Jamel's Shortcake) fully mature five and a half years. Breeders, Jackie Towbin and Barbara Hampton. Photos courtesy of owner Roger Kaplan.

a wonderful dog he is, praise him effusively. After a full minute, place his feet back on the ground while still praising him enthusiastically. Repeat this as often as required. It won't take long before the dog gets the idea that while it is nice to be near you and praised, it is also much more comfortable with his feet firmly on the ground. He learns what you wanted him to—not to jump up on you.

As trainer or leader, you must be able to break all exercises up into their component parts and break each component part into reasonable performance levels. You must in short know what it is you want your dog to do. You must also know your dog. You need to know what motivates him, when he is

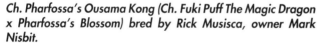

Ch. Pharfossa's Ousama Kong (Ch. Fuki Puff The Magic Dragon x Pharfossa's Blossom) bred by Rick Musisca, owner Mark Nisbit.

getting tired or bored and when he is confused or afraid. Commands must be consistent, meaningful and enforced. Never use mixed commands. For example, "sit" means sit. Never use "sit down" which is really two separate and distinct commands to the dog. Use the same command each and every time. When you give a dog a command, make certain the dog follows through on all occasions. There is no point in enforcing a "down" command during training and not in the house when you are watching TV. If you aren't prepared to enforce a command, don't give it.

The most essential attribute of a good trainer is patience. With patience, even the most inexperienced of trainers will succeed.

Ch. The Joker Is Wild O'BJ (Ch. The Widow-Maker O'BJ, ROMXP x Ch. The Mad Hatter O'BJ, ROMXP) going Best of Breed over top champions at only eleven months of age under Judge Anthony Dinardo. Joker is owner handled by Roger Kaplan.

Never train your dog when you are upset or stressed. There is never justification for kicking, hitting or brutalizing a dog. One 30-second outburst can set your training back weeks, even months. For a puppy, such an outburst can forever alter the dog's attitude towards learning. If you find yourself becoming impatient or angry, cut off the lesson immediately.

On a final note, be certain you have the proper equipment and know how to use it. Essential basic training equipment includes a properly fitting choke collar (never to be left on the dog after training), a 3-foot lead, a 6- to 8-foot lead and an 8-meter flexi-lead (an invaluable piece of training equipment). Obedience instructors and/or pet stores can assist you. Like in anything else, proper equipment makes a difference.

AUTHOR'S CONCLUSION

As the owner of an Akita, you have the responsibility to ensure that your dog is provided with the necessities of life. Few owners would fail to provide their pet with food, water and shelter. Today's society is increasingly becoming less tolerant of undisciplined, unruly dogs. Training is an essential for life. To neglect an Akita's education virtually signs its death warrant. In the event you can no longer keep your Akita, a well-trained, well-disciplined Akita is more easily placed. An unmanageable and undisciplined Akita ends up being abused, neglected and is ultimately destroyed. You owe your Akita better than this.

I hope this discussion has helped you. If you have no interest in breeding and showing, at least you will better understand the seriousness and the difficulty in producing top-quality companion dogs. Exhibitors who persevere and develop a winning dog or line are people that care deeply about the

Ch. Hasu Nikko of Skylake at three and a half years old, repeating her Regional Specialty win under, this time under Judge Dani Canino. Nikko (Ch. The Widow-Maker O'BJ x Ch. O'BJ Kaala Skylake) bred by Susan Charpenter and BJ Andrews, owned by Sue Lopez.

Ch. Crown Royal's The Untouchable (Ch. Crown Royal's Slugo-Go, ROM x Pharfossa's Kenjiko Grisley) bred by Sally Ericksen and Ingrid Linerud. Owner, Barbara J. Morgan handled to this Sweepstake win under judge Marcia Erwin.

sport and, hopefully, about the dogs they own and from whom they breed.

If you do plan to breed your dog, then I hope you have grasped the importance of proving your stock not just for your own edification but from the practical aspect of being able to look a buyer in the eye and tell them your dogs are top quality and you have the "certificates" to prove it!

And there is one other thing we really

other than their own family? If you succeed as a breeder and perhaps later as a judge, your photos will be preserved in books and your memory will live on for generations upon generations. Oh true, we're a small segment of the population, but our sport does encompass the globe, and involvement in dogs presents undreamed-of travel opportunities. Making a lasting contribution in any

Ch. Noji's Hip Chick Maddie (Ch. O'BJ King's Ransom, ROMXP x Ch. Daijobu's Vampirella O'BJ, ROM) bred by Noji Akitas, Bill and Marcia Erwin, owned by Noble Akitas, Susan Puett.

haven't stressed that much. If you succeed in the ring, you will be making a valuable contribution to the sport and to the Akita breed. You will have left an indelible mark in history. This may not sound like much compared to being remembered as President of the U.S. and it sure doesn't compare with the lasting fame of Elvis, but how many people are ever really remembered for anything or by anyone

country ensures that enthusiasts all over the world will acknowledge and emulate your achievements.

So there are many reasons to show, whether you intend to breed or not. One of the most important should never be forgotten. Above all, "The Proving Ground" is the perfect place to acquaint the public with the Akita, one of the most handsome and noble breeds known to man!

The Akita Today

TRULY "RECOGNIZED"

As we move toward the 21st century, much is changing in the sport of purebred dogs. There are many more shows, entries at all events have grown, and many breeds have tripled their numbers.

From being a "rare breed" on AKC litter registration lists, the Akita has moved into the top echelons of enrollment numbers and popularity.

as a sound Working dog with great character and popular appeal.

By the end of the 1980s, the Akita's success in obedience competition had become commonplace rather than remarkable. Overcoming an undeserved reputation for "stubbornness" and lack of trainability, Akitas are competing in increasing numbers and doing so quite successfully. Although still not considered a likely

Ch. Akita Tani's Yoru Bara, the first Akita bitch to obtain a Working Group placement. Pictured being awarded a Five-Point Major by Judge Melbourne Downing in September, 1973. Handled by June Bracisco, she was bred by Liz Harrell, owned by Tom and Sandy Ing.

Seldom given serious consideration in judging rings of the 1970s, the Akita is now a serious Group and Best In Show contender. Judges who previously regarded the breed as generally unsound, unusual in conformation, poorly presented, and sort of a "fad" dog associated with the yuppie generation have now come to respect the breed

choice for devotees of high-level obedience competition, owners are quick to point out that the Akita is one of the most intelligent of all domesticated canines, and many Akitas are consistently achieving high scores and multiple obedience titles.

The impact of the Akita's rapid rise to stardom has been significant. Most changes have been positive, but negative effects will continue to multiply in direct proportion to the increase in breed popularity and the quality of leadership as provided by the parent (ACA) and regional Akita clubs. The AKC, along with a handful of national breed clubs, is beginning to move into areas of genetic and moral responsibility, and we trust that our breed's national club will do likewise.

A major problem the Akita fancy has in common with other national organizations is one of logistics, complicated by a membership with differing goals and motivations. To unite such a diverse group into a like-minded club with altruistic purpose requires some doing. It was easier when the ACA was smaller in numbers and there was a clear-cut goal (AKC recognition) to inspire the idealist. The ACA of the last decade has been plagued with seemingly insolvable discord, but, through it all, Akita owners have never wavered in their "stubborn" hope that we will once again see a national club which is truly dedicated to the Akita dog.

Beyond the bumps and pitfalls of too popular—too fast, many breeders see the next decade as one in which dedicated fanciers will once more unite to protect the breed. From both newcomers and old-timers, there is genuine concern and a growing recognition of our obligation as individuals. Recognition comes in many forms. Acknowledgment of our responsibility to ensure that clubs are in the hands of responsible, ethical leaders is just one of them. Realization that every owner has the potential to help or harm the breed and a concerted demand that clubs become hard-line about ethics and breed welfare are realistic recognition of the current popularity problems.

While there are still enough structural problems to satisfy the devout fault-finder, the past few years have seen a tremendous improvement in once-common faults such as cow hocks, steep shoulders, sagging skin, loose eyes, big ears, and underdeveloped

Ch. Tobe's Tuff Stuff II (Ch. Tobe's Return of The Jedai x Ch. Tobe Krug's Tai Fighter) bred by Beverly Bonadonna, owned by Melinda Spinosa. She's the 1989 National Specialty Grand Futurity Winner, 1990 Region I Specialty BOS Winner, 1990 National Specialty Maturity Winner, and 1991 Canadian National Specialty BW/BOS Winner.

rear quarters. The average Akita one now meets in the city park is an impressive animal easily recognized as a purebred dog. This is in itself the "recognition" only dreamed of in the '60s and '70s.

As we plunged into the '90s, ideals of type and function were even more fervently discussed due to AKC's sudden second "recognition" of the Akita—and of the Japanese Kennel Club as a valid registering body. Sought and expected by the Shiba fancy, AKC's quiet reversal of position came as quite a surprise to Akita breeders. Understandably, great chasms of disagreement opened all across the country. AKC's new policy and the resulting discord will have a profound effect on the breed in the Americas.

The historical first points awarded to a Japanese import were to Winners Bitch at the 1992 National Specialty. Interestingly, this seemed to be a popular decision. Looking around the ring, I witnessed approval from many who were on record as disinclined to import, myself included. But a good Akita is a good Akita and it seemed that is what ringside "recognized" as the lovely Onishi-bred, Sakayeda-owned bitch made her way to WB.

One unfortunate effect of AKC's abrupt reversal is the seeming validation of the defensive "winning doesn't matter" attitude held by a vocal majority of habitual losers. This cop-out attitude is a threatening trend which developed in the late '80s and one which is seemingly vindicated by AKC's acceptance of what many view as a type contradictory to the AKC standard. My comment is simple: it does matter. Challenge has always been vital to the survival of every species, domesticated or wild. Competition is equally crucial in every walk of life, whether it be big business (the development of consumer products, medical advances, etc.) or the ability to produce the finest wool, richest milk, or highest egg production. Not to put the deep emotional involvement of breeding dogs on the same commercial level as a chicken farm, nonetheless, complacency has been the downfall of many once-successful breeding programs. Winning does matter because it keeps breeders involved, attentive, dedicated, and determined to keep producing sound, healthy, beautiful animals.

Perhaps a reflection of the times, canine health problems have increased. Most "new" problems (meaning those which have always been there but are more frequently being defined) are the result of new feeding and rearing practices. In a cruel twist of logic, many deficiencies of the immune

So. Am. Ch. The One To Keep O'BJ (Ch. The Widow-Maker O'BJ, ROMPX x Ch. The Mad Hatter O'BJ, ROMPX) owned by Maurizio Moretto, Santiago, Chile. "Queenie" is the first and thus far, the only female to win the Group in Chile. She is the dam of a multi-Group Winner and BIS winner, The Black Magic Ace.

system are the result of pharmacological advances which promote mass production and marketability of food animals. This technology has been carried over into the production and treatment of companion animals which are obviously not bred to slaughter and which we hope will be long lived and mentally and physically healthy. Pharmacology is a very competitive business. Vets (and owners) are inundated with warnings and inducements to use more and more vaccines, chemicals, additives, and toxic medications...all in the name of improved health. One must weigh the new technology carefully in light of the proven connection between new feeding, vaccination, and environmental practices and the increasing incidence of certain forms of cancer as well as all immune-related diseases.

Don't be shocked at these statements. Instead, consider that today's newscasts are filled with warnings about foodstuffs, products, by-products, and medications which we humans use or consume. From alar to tobacco to dioxin to tranquilizers, we are learning more and more about our home and personal environment and the ways in which our own health is challenged. In terms of genetic health, most breeds, including the Akita, have made notable advances. Veterinary research has opened new doors, placing vital new information at the fingertips of the average practitioner. There is still much confusion regarding what is genetically influenced or induced but universities are making great progress in genetic and molecular research with the result that we are closer than ever to being able to pinpoint particular modes of inheritance.

As one of the most popular breeds in the Americas, the Akita has both benefitted and suffered due to the admiration of the dog-owning public. Akitas have a slight advantage over those breeds which can be housed a dozen-to-a-cage, but this has not protected them from being a profitable commodity for unscrupulous breeders. Commercial breeders have also managed to capitalize on the appeal of the exotic big guard dog.

Conversely, as more and better Akitas are shown, the breed has also attracted experienced, dedicated dog people. New fanciers, who have been successful in other breeds and find themselves hopelessly in love with the Akita, are more than willing to take on the responsibilities and problems associated with Akitas because they know how to solve some of them and are astute enough to know that all breeds have problems. Such people are a credit to the community of Akita owners and a blessing to the breed. Perhaps you are one of them!

Ch. O'BJ Shaka-Khan At C and L (Ch. Tsunami's Flash x Ch. O'BJ Canduit Tuya) earned Award of Merit at the 1991 National Specialty, owner handled by Lynn Doran.

TOP WINNERS

Every breed has its big winners, those legends which inspire us and which establish important goals for each of us. Whether it's a weight-pulling contest, the Iditarod, a herding trial, or the pageantry of the show ring, such competitions represent the last vestiges of "survival of the fittest" in our modern society. This is where the next generation of sires and dams is tested. In theory only the "winners" should be allowed to carry on the species, as in nature. In practice, it isn't always so but that doesn't mean we can disregard the significance and the ultimate benefit to the animals themselves.

The breeder's art is exemplified by publicly comparing our best efforts with those of other breeders. Some people would have you believe that dog-show judges are incompetent or dishonest or politically motivated. Some are. Some are all three! But be assured that American judges are among the most respected and best traveled in the world.

Our group and all-breed judges have opportunity to assess overall trends and to learn from a wide assortment of breeds and the people who safeguard them. The "specialty" judge, who remains closely aligned with only a few breeds rather than branching out to study and judge entire groups, is a valuable asset and serves as a watchful eye on those breeds he or she loves most. It's a good system. Though not without fault, it is quite simply the best in the world!

The American Kennel Club oversees most conformation shows in the United States. There are other U.S. registries and

Ch. North Star's Mad Maxx (Ch. O'BJ Zack The Spotted Bear, ROM x Ch. Kuroi Kao Dallas Alice, ROM) is a Best In Show and National Specialty BB winner. He was #2 Akita 1990 and 1991, is a multi Regional Specialty Winner, received an Award of Merit at the 1990 National and is a multi-Group Winner. Bred by Chris Weatherman and Priscilla McCune, owners Mark and Cathy Schipper and Frank and Sylvia Thomas.

show organizations but the AKC governs most breeds, including the Akita. The American Kennel Club does so by providing certain tools for breeders. It keeps and publishes show and breeding records and funds education and research. In 1990 AKC began to seriously fight anti-dog legislation. But mostly, it maintains a registry based largely on trust. AKC has field investigators and will suspend registration privileges from those it catches defrauding the system, but in actuality the accuracy of the stud book depends entirely on the honesty and integrity of dog owners.

AKC also provides guidance for breed clubs. Although not within the scope of its charter, the AKC recognizes a certain responsibility to assist in maintaining objectivity and stability in breed-club operations. Club policies and administrations change with uncomfortable regularity, and such shifts often take place dramatically and not without political bloodshed. It is therefore important that AKC maintain a steady course and, when need be, assist in the sensible development, preservation, and protection of each breed it registers. The AKC helps formulate by-laws, show plans, and procedures. It protects the "territory" and show dates of clubs.

AKC also licenses those persons considered knowledgeable enough to pass judgement on specific breeds, and it furnishes a list of those people and the breeds for which they are approved. All in all, AKC provides the world's greatest stage upon which breeders compare the quality of their animals.

Then, of course, there are various ratings systems developed by the doggy press. These systems rank dogs against others of their breed and also in what is called inter-breed competition, i.e., group and Best In Show wins. What does this mean to the average dog owner? Why go to all this trouble?

Since the beginning of recorded history, man has taken pride in his animals. Whether it was Stone Age man who felt comforted by the presence of the wild

Ch. O'BJ BigSon of Sachmo, ROMXP (Ch. Okii Yubi's Sachmo of Makoto, ROMXP x Vi-Brook Tonya) winning under National Specialty Judge Mr. Donald Booxbaum. Breeder-owner-handler Barbara Andrews.

dog at his door, or the nobleman who tested his hounds against those of his hunting companions, man has devised ways to exhibit and compare his dogs. Although there are many structured canine competitions, obedience and "bench" (technically, almost a thing of the past but the term persists) shows are the two most popular. Both forms of competition measure the handler's training skills, but, in theory, bench shows less so as they are about judging the structure, soundness, and adherence to breed standard rather than how well the dog performs. Obedience measures the dog's responsiveness to training. Correct breed temperament and type, or even health and soundness, are of little consequence as long as the dog can perform the required exercises.

So the reason for dog shows is a simple one. If a majority of respected judges have decreed that dog "A" is an outstanding specimen, and if that dog has gone head-to-head with other top dogs at big shows and has won his fair share, he's a "good dog." Breeders can refer to that collective opinion when they are about to make breeding or acquisition decisions.

That doesn't mean that the "number one" dog is the perfect mate for every bitch. Being nationally ranked doesn't guarantee a good front or that he's genetically free of mouth faults. It does indicate that, overall, dog "A" is superior to the majority of competition at breed level, or in both breed and group (inter-breed) rings.

While there are variables which have to do with things like where and how often the dog was shown, the keenness of

BIS/BISS Ch. Running Bear's Sunburst (Ch. Big D's Akanboo Akai Palaccort x Am/Mx Ch. Kuma Yama's Palace Court Dani) achieved BIS under the popular judge Mrs. Lee Canalizo, handled by Keith Pautz for owners Mark & Lisa Borlase and Judy L. Gresham.

competition in that area at that time, and how much money was spent in campaigning, advertising and promoting the dog, the verified ring record stands as the *only* objective assessment of a dog's

Ch. Eudora's Dixie Affair, ROM (Ch. Pharfossa's Maximum Overdrive x Naga's Ichiban Nare of Eudora) pictured at seven months as a multiple Group Placer and as of 1991, the Top Winning Puppy Bitch of All Time, pro handled by Fran Keyes. Breeder/owner/handler, Mark Nisbet.

adherence to the breed standard. It incidentally measures stamina; health; and baring drugs, breed temperament. These qualities are of great importance to owners and are vital to breeders who strive to produce a dog which walks like, looks like, and acts like an Akita!

Over the years, there has been an exciting succession of "top winners," many of which had a positive influence on the breed by having had that unique ability to pass on their virtues and few of their faults. There are, of course, dogs which were not successful show dogs, but whose prepotency came forward and is recognized through the Register Of Merit system.

Here, we would like to provide you with a quick summary of top winners. Please bear in mind that this list is not meant to be the last word on accuracy (due to so many various ratings systems and resulting discrepancies) or on the individual quality of these great dogs. I have included this information because we believe that the Akita's ever increasing recognition in the show ring is significant and gratifying to those who believe in its future.

The Canine Chronicle Points System Finals provides the following information: 1980 listed Ch. Tobe's Peking Jumbo as number one, followed closely by the west-coast bitch, Ch. Matsukaze's Holly Go Lightly. Ch. Okii Yubi's Sachmo Of Makoto ranked third that year, followed by another lovely bitch, Ch. Big A Stormy Of Jobe. Ch. Kenjiko Royal Tenji held on another year, finishing ahead of yet another bitch, Ch. Forral's Party Doll, with the last two slots filled by Ch. Tono Hai Of Kirabran, and Ch. O'BJ Zack The Spotted Bear.

The 1981 Finals ranked the brilliantly campaigned pinto, Ch. Matsukaze's Holly Go Lightly as number one Akita and number 15 Working Dog for 1981. She also became the breed's first multiple-Best In Show winner. Ranked in descending order were Ch. Sherisan Keystone Of Kintaro, Ch. HOT's Van Scoten Jones, Jumbo, Sachmo, Ch. Date Tensha All About Chesta, Sakusaku's Ringtail Cat Go, Ch. Okii Yubi's Mr. Judge, and Ch. O'BJ Zack The Spotted Bear. Interestingly, Keystone, Jumbo, and Zack were Sachmo sons and Chesta and Van Scoten Jones were owned by the same kennel.

The year 1982 saw some new names but once again, Holly headed the list. Ch. Kakwa's Orca appeared in the number two spot, followed by Keystone and another new name, Ch. O'BJ BigSon Of Sachmo. Ch. Asahi Yama No Kaminari was just ahead of Ch. Kenjiko Royal Tenji, who left the remaining places to Ch. Cee Jay Rocky Road Of Kibo, Ch. Frakari's Date Tensha Dibotsu, Ch. Great River's Jumbo Jima, and a new silver female, Ch. Jai Laphan's Tiphani.

In 1983, Kennel Review listed BigSon as number one, followed by a new challenger, Ch. Gr Rivers Galloping Gourmet, and then Orca and Abaddon. Ch. Mike Truax' Royal Tikara Pal first appeared on the list, followed by Ch. Hot's Mo's Barnaby Jones, Ch. Blue Max Chikara Buichi, Rocky Road,

Ch. HOT's Lightening Strikes, (Ch. Hot's Ying Yang x Hot's Sandy Paul of Asano) breeder Stephanie & Melvin Olsen. Handled by Pam Lambie to this Major win under Judge Nick Agliano for owner Elaine Hess.

and another new dog in the ninth spot, Ch. Jakura's Pharfossa Michael. Holding one more year despite malicious sabatoge, Keystone finished tenth.

For diehard statisticians, we should explain the slight inconsistencies between the two systems. Kennel Review Magazine reports from October through November Kennel Gazette stats, which closely approximate the calendar year, whereas the Canine Chronicle tallies show results by actual publication dates. Regardless of the system, the top eight or nine dogs are invariably the same.

In 1984 BigSon appeared in Top Ten Working stats while Orca, Gourmet, Abaddon, Tikara Pal, Barnaby Jones, Michael, and other familiar dogs changed breed rankings many times during the year. New names in Akita vocabulary were Ch. Cody R. Coyote, Ch. BigSon's Silverson, and Ch. Frerose's Crime Buster.

1985 was dominated by Tikara Pal, with Abaddon trailing far behind in second place while a newcomer, Ch. Tobes Abrakadabra, edged ahead of Barnaby Jones. The puppy dog, Ch. The Widow-Maker O'BJ, suddenly appeared on the list, joined by a spectacular white bitch, Ch. Cotton Ginny O'BJ. Ch. Storm Trooper O'BJ nudged out Ch. Golden Sun Taki Bi No Taiyo for seventh place and two more young dogs gained rankings, Ch. Hot's Heir To The Throne in ninth with Ch.

Tamarlane's Veni Vidi Vici finishing in tenth place.

1986 saw sweeping change as The Widow-Maker dominated Working Group stats. Ch. Veni Vidi Vici pressed hard, flying from coast to coast. Beginning a strong specials career, Ch. Allures Island Shogun slipped past another eastern competitor, the young Barnaby Jones son, Ch. Brook Staten Deja Vu. Out West, Buichi held on another year, followed by Ch. Asahi Yama No Hanashi, Barnaby Jones, and Ch. To Zu's Gizmo Of Mtn Bear. Storm Trooper also held another year, and Ch. Sho Go's Rambo made his first appearance on the charts along with Ch. Big D's Akanbooakai Palancourt.

The year 1987 wasn't much of a horse race. Widow-Maker ran away with it early in the year, finishing at number 14 Working Dog in only 46 shows. The other favorites, Shogun (who finished first in breed points), Veni Vidi Vici, and Rambo, were worried by two new threats, Ch. O'BJ King's Ransom and Ch. O'BJ Striped Kareem

Ch. Lk. Norman's Pandora, C.D.X. (Ch. O'BJ BigSon of Sachmo, ROMXP x Ch. O'BJ Michiko of Wri, ROM) was Akita World Top Ten Obedience ranked for 1985 and 1987. Breeder Bill and Tamara Warren, owner Bill and Andrea Bobrow.

Ch. Coca Cola Cowgirl O'BJ (Ch. O'BJ BigSon of Sachmo ROMXP x Ch. O'BJ Kotausha-Mo of Westwind, ROMXP) is shown winning B.O.S. under Judge Robert Wills, owner handled by Angie Witherby. Paladin Akitas' first showdog, Coca and Angie proved how easily a good novice dog and handler can succeed.

Sky Lake. Another handsome contender, Ch. Allure-Windrift E Z Ryder, nudged ahead of Hanashi and Buichi, and the year was over.

Ransom cinched 1988 by such a wide margin as to discourage all competitors except his sire, The Widow-Maker, who finished second. A new star emerged, Ch. Tobes Return Of The Jedai. The flashy red pinto moved past Veni Vidi Vici and Shogun, leaving Ch. Soho's Black Star, Ch. Beoths Three Toes Griz, and Rambo to fight it out for all but the last two spots, one of which was claimed by another new name, Ch. Torinoko's Big Jake.

BIS Ch. O'BJ Cherokee Spirit (Ch. Sea Breeze Bounty Hunter x Ch. Goshen's The Silver Lining O'BJ) took several Group placements en route to his Can. Ch. and has numerous placements as a Champion. His first show as a new Ch. he went Best In Show, owner handled! Owner Kim Ottenbrite says Judge Abe Zvonkin "remarked specifically on head and ears and what a wonderful temperament" Rokee has.

With Ransom's death in December, Jedai became number one for 1989, challenged only by Ch. Goshen's Heir Apparent, E Z Ryder, and in fourth place, the semi-retired grandsire of Heir Apparent, Widow-Maker. The remaining contenders were Rambo, Griz, and Kareem who held fast against a new winner, Ch. Obi-San's Dynamite. Driving statisticians crazy, there was actually a tie between Ch. Shogun and a new red pinto, Ch. Windom's Thor Of Walton, thus 1989 records eleven dogs listed in the Top Ten.

1990 saw Jedai firmly in control of eastern rings while west-coast contender Kareem trailed far behind in the second spot. Two new youngsters were beginning to make their presence known, Ch. Goshen's Chariots Of Fire and Ch. North Stars Mad Maxx. Ch. Running Bears Sunburst burst onto the chart with a Best In Show as a striking black dog, Ch. Karma-Ki's Ringside Rumor popped onto the finals list ahead of Ch. Nami's Shokko Of Oka, Big Jake, and Ch. Mtn Bears Teddybear.

1991 was another great year for Jedai, who stayed far in front of Mad Maxx, who was working to stay ahead of a host of challengers. Another new dog, Ch. O'BJ Razz M'Tazz Of Sachmo, grabbed third spot from Ringside Rumor and Chariots Of Fire while a big pinto, Ch. Frakari's D Akambo No Barnaby secured a notch on the list by gaining a Best In Show.

1991 recorded a dramatic "First" in Akita history when two sets of brothers made the Top Ten. Ch. The WW Coal Miner O'BJ made the chart along with his full-brother Chariots Of Fire and then at year's end, Ch. North Stars Siberian Express, a younger brother to Mad Maxx, also made the list! He was followed Ch. Riverview's High Roller and the staunch mid-western dog, Big Jake.

There are as many private ways of compiling statistics as there are contenders for the top honors. Unfortunately, the Akita Club Of America has never kept verified show rankings. Various Akita magazines attempted to provide the fancy with statistics but have never achieved the authenticity of *Kennel Review* and the *Canine Chronicle,* the only two publications (all-breed) that consistently published accurate show ring ratings.

During the first ten years following recognition, the Akita was so rarely awarded at Group level as to make such tabulations interesting but hardly definitive. Dogs considered only average could (and did) garner a Group placement or two and suddenly were "ranked" dogs. Thus the "numbers of dogs defeated" was not always indicative of quality insofar as interbreed ratings. As the Akita moved into the '80s, soundness improved, breed type became a bit more defined, and judges became more selective.

might be underrated as having defeated only average specimens in an area not known for tough competition. The key to understanding the systems is simple.

If any dog regularly places or wins in Group against nationally ranked dogs of other breeds, we can assume he has met and defeated better than "average competition" and he becomes, by any definition, an outstanding representative of his breed.

Breed authorities may find fault with the dog but unless one is considering

Ch. Crown Royal's Count Basie, A.K.A. "Otis" (Ch. Noji's The Count Crown Royal x Am/ Can. Ch. Crown Royal's Akai Okashi, CD) owned by Kerry Much, handled by Ingrid Linerud.

The breed stats are still very meaningful to most breeders. The breed ring is where one can compare things like size and type. When a dog is standing with 30 other breeds of varying size, coat, and structure, only the most knowledgeable can successfully judge him against the finer points of the breed standard. Nonetheless, we can't discount the fact that before a dog can build interbreed rankings, he has to have his ticket to the Group ring—a Best Of Breed win!

There are many who will argue that the breed-level quality of competition at many local shows is negligible. We agree. But it's equally possible that a truly great dog

breeding to him, what difference does it make? No dog is perfect. The important thing is that we can all rest assured that the breed is being well represented to the public and to the ever-discerning eye of ringside.

In closing this section of top winners, it seems appropriate to provide you with a summation of those dogs which have been designated as all-time top winners. Fortunately, all-breed statisticians provide us with accurate information.

In 1986 *Kennel Review Magazine* ranked Ch. Mike Traux's Royal Tikara Pal (two BIS). and Ch. Matsukaze's Holly Go Lightly (three BIS) as the top winning male and female all time. By 1989 it was a whole new ball game as The Widow-Maker continued to build a Best In Show record that had already tripled Holly's, and his young son, King's Ransom, became the all-time number-two top winner. Retired in 1989, Widow-Maker held as *Kennel Review's* top Akita all time through 1990 but Jedai was rolling and by 1991, he was firmly established as the top Akita all time, by all systems. No bitch has as yet challenged Holly's record as the top Akita bitch all time. Owners of such outstanding bitches face a hard decision. Between blowing coat and heat cycles, campaigning a bitch is decidedly more difficult than running a dog. But the real problem is that it's almost impossible to attend the number of shows required to achieve those top rankings— and still pass greatness on to the next generation. As in Holly's case, many great show girls never produce that dreamed-for litter.

Presently, the list of Best In Show winners has grown to impressive length. Only a decade ago, there were fewer than five BIS Akitas. Today there are more than 25. The number of Akitas which will attain the most thrilling and meaningful "letters" customarily attached to the dog's registered name can be expected to more than double over the next ten years.

Although AKC does not officially designate a dog as BIS Ch. Great Dog, the dog

Ch. O'BJ A-Head of The Game is shown winning Best of Breed over Top Ranked Champions - from the Puppy Class. Judge Joe Gregory, breeder/owner/handled by Barbara Andrews. "Header" is by Ch. O'BJ King's Ransom, ROMPX x Ch. The Dame's On Target O'BJ, ROMXP.

fancy and its publications customarily use the "BIS" title. When a dog has achieved more than one Best In Show, many owners precede the title with "Multi-" and so I have used the appropriate title for those dogs which I know have won two or more Bests In Show. Those dogs entitled to use the ultimate show ring title are:

BIS Ch. Allure-Windrift's EZ Ryder (Ch. Fu-Ki's Hideki Tojo x Ch. Windrift's Oriental Express). Breeder-owners, Laura and Alan Armstrong.

BIS Ch. Asahi Yama No Kaminari, CD (Ch. Kin Hozan's Toklat, CD, ROMX x Ch. Swanee Cho Cho San). Breeders, Werner and Veldta Oetmann. Owner, Elizabeth Greco.

BIS Ch. Big A's Stormy Of Jobe (Ch. Shuso Saki Tumi Of Okii Yubi x Juho Mariko No Kin Hozan, ROMP). Breeder, Keith Marshall. Owners, Gary and Janet Voss.

BIS Ch. Brook-Staten Deja Vu (BIS Ch. Hot's Mo's Barnaby Jones, ROMX x Ch. HOT's Messiah-d Krisje). Breeder, John D'Alessio. Owners, John D'Alessio and Charmayne Wiltshire.

BIS Ch. Frakari D's Akambo No Barnaby (BIS Ch. Hot's Mo's Barnaby Jones, ROMX x Ch. Date Tensha Pot Luck). Breeder, Ira Winkelman. Owner, Lois Harris.

BIS Ch. Gaylee's O'Kaminaga, ROM (Rowdy-San x Miko-Go). Breeder, C. Clifford. Owner, Leon Nogue.

Multi-BIS Ch. Goshen's Chariot's O'Fire,

ROM (Multi-BIS Ch. O'BJ King's Ransom, ROMXP x Ch. The Dame's On Target O'BJ, ROMXP). Breeder, BJ Andrews. Owners, Lewis and Julie Hoehn.

BIS Ch. Goshen's Heir Apparent (Multi-BIS Ch. O'BJ King's Ransom, ROMXP x Hikari's High Hope). Breeders, Julie Hoehn and Pat Schwarz. Owners, Lewis and Julie Hoehn.

BIS Ch. HOT's Mo's Barnaby Jones, ROMX (Ch. HOT's Melvin O, ROMP x Ch. Frerose's Annie Till, ROMP). Breeders, Stephanie and Melvin Olsen. Owner, John D'Alessio.

BIS Ch. Karma-Ki's Ringside Rumor (BIS Ch. Tobes Abrakadabra, ROM x Ch. Tobe's Sno-Storm Baracuda). Breeder-owner, Nancy Bowen.

Multi-BIS Ch. Matsu Kaze's Holly Go Lightly (Kin Hozan's Kazan Go x Kofuku No's Shoga Hime, ROMX). Breeder, Gus Bell. Owners, Bea Hunt and the Estate of Gus Bell.

Multi-BIS Ch. Mike Truax's Royal Tikara Pal, ROM (Ch. Kim-Sai's Royal Jikara Kuma, ROMP x Smith's Princess Neisha). Breeder, Frederick Evans. Owners, Bill and Marcia Erwin.

BIS Ch. North Star's Mad Maxx (Ch. O'BJ Zack The Spotted Bear, ROM x Ch. Kuroi Kao Dallas Alice, ROM). Breeder, Chris Weatherman and Priscilla McCune. Owners, Mark and Cathy Schipper and Frank and Sylvia Thomas.

Multi-BIS Ch. O'BJ King's Ransom, ROMXP (Multi-BIS Ch. The Widow-Maker O'BJ, ROMXP x Ch. The Mad Hatter O'BJ, ROMXP). Breeder, BJ Andrews. Owners, Lewis and Julie Hoehn.

BIS Ch. Palace Court's Taisho Of Napali (Big D's Palace Court Anjin Son x Ch. Kuma Yama Sykora Star). Breeder, Pat Van Buskirk. Owners, Henry and Nancy Kapali.

BIS Ch. Running Bear's Sunburst (Ch. Big D's Akanbooakai Palaccort x Ch.

Ch. Daijobu's Nichiko (Ch. O'BJ BigSon of Sachmo, ROMXP x Ch. Maxwell's Kuro Ban Kuma, ROM) at about seven months, handled by Bill Andrews for breeder-owner Charles D. Bell. Nichiko became a multi-Best of Breed and Specialty winner, earning top National rankings.

Ch. Hino Maru Yasashii Hyoiin CAS, T.T. "Congo" is owned by Cindy Smith, bred by Teruko Arima, and handled by James Taylor.

Kuma Yama's Palace Court Dani). Breeder, Judy Gresham. Owners, Lisa Ravina, Mark Borlase, and Judy Gresham.

BIS Ch. Sho-Go's Rambo (Ch. Sho-Go's Joboy Tuff-N-Stuff, ROM x Ch. Frerose's Dark Moon Of Sho-Go, ROM). Breeder-owners, Warren and Deborah Shields.

BIS Ch. Tamarlane's Veni Vidi Vici, ROM (Ch. Pharfossa Outlaw Josey Wales, ROMP x Ch. Tamarlane's Mi Magic, ROMP). Breeders, Diane Foster and Sophia Kaluzniaki, DVM. Owners, Sophia Kaluzniaki, DVM and Carolyn Rennie.

BIS Ch. Tentei's Sak'e Tuem (Kirabran's Asa Kaje Boshi x Breens Notorious Ninja). Breeder-owners, Beverly and James Johnson.

Multi-BIS Ch. The Widow-Maker O'BJ, ROMXP (Ch. The Real McCoy O'BJ x Ch. The Same Dame O'BJ, ROMP). Breeder-owner, BJ Andrews.

BIS Ch. Tobe's Abrakadabra, ROM (Ch. Yamakuma's Itazura Sama x Ch. Tobe's Princess Leia Organa). Breeder-owner, Beverly Bonadonna.

Multi-BIS Ch. Tobe's Return Of The Jedai, ROM (Ch. Tobe's Adam Of Genesis, ROMP x Jag's Lois-T). Breeder, Evelyn Geiger. Owners, Ruth Winston and Beverly Bonadonna.

BIS Ch. Wanchan's Akagumo (Akita Tani's Kuro Yama x Tusko's Star). (Breeder, Pete Lagus. Owners, Pete Lagus, Sonja Lagus and Carol Foti.

The only other prefix of perhaps equal importance is BISS which indicates the dog was best in specialty show, i.e., Best Of Breed winner at the National Specialty Show. We have included not only those distinguished dogs but the other major National Specialty winners as well.

Depending on the size and quality of the entry, and the whims or long-standing preferences of the judge, National Specialties may or may not bring forth the best Akitas of the year. All agree that Nationals provide a mind-boggling array of Akitas to fit every style and preference, and a wonderful social setting. Most important of all, the National provides an opportunity to cast speculative looks at other dogs which we have only seen in photos. Nationals are where many breeding decisions are made, based not so much on the winners of the event as on which dogs, viewed up close and personal, are truly right for a particular bitch.

THE NATIONAL SPECIALTY

The historical first Akita Club Of America National Specialty show was held in October 1976 in San Fernando, California. The judge was J. Council Parker, who awarded BOB to Ch. Gaylee's O'Kaminaga and BOS to Ch. Akita Tani's Kori Of Koshi-Ki. Sweepstakes were judged by AKC-licensed judge

A lovely trophy from the 1982 National Specialty awarded to RWB, Ch. Voodoo Doll O'BJ, bred/owned by Barbara Andrews.

Ch. O'BJ Char-Ko (Ch. Minkee's Arcturus Mekan x Ch. Okii Yubi's Dragon House Ko-Go, ROMXP) on her way to a Working Group II, under All-rounder Tom Gately breeder-owner-handled. She became the Top Winning Puppy Bitch of All Time at seven months of age.

Am/Mex. Ch. Inaka's Sophisticated Lady (Ch. Raiden of Jo-Uba x Ch. Inaka's Shiroi Oboko) bred by Bill and Tamara Warren, owned by Bill Bobrows and Tamara Warren.

C. L. Savage, whose top winner was another Gaylee dog, Gaylee's Fonzie No Kosetsu.

The year 1977 saw the Nationals in Massachusetts, judged by Mrs. Carolyn Thomas, with her husband Robert Thomas doing Sweeps. BOB was the multi-Group placer who became one of the breed's most consistent winners, Ch. Gin-Gin Haiyaku-Go Of Sakusaku. BOS went to Ch. Yamakumo's Okami and Best In Sweeps to Indian Hy's Grizzly Bear.

The Specialty moved to Indiana in 1978, where breed judge Mr. Dale McMackin awarded BOB to the popular mid-west winner, Ch. Nan Chao's Samurai No Chenko and BOS to one of the breed's two Best In Show bitches, Ch. Big A's Stormy Of Jobe. Breeder Joan Linderman made the Winners Dog (and future Group winner) Frakari's Date Tensha Dibotsu her Best In Sweeps.

It was back to California for 1979 with Ch. Gaylee's O'Kaminaga repeating his BOB win, this time under Thelma Brown. BOS went to Ch. Jo-San's Seibo No Kosetsu. Mr. James Hohe put Edo's Satoichi No Jo San Best In Sweeps.

At the 1980 National in Houston, Derek Rayne awarded BOB to the top bitch, Ch. Big A's Stormy Of Jobe. BOS went to Ch. Okii Yubi's Mr. Man and breeder Joan Harper gave the Sweeps win to Echol's Honesty Best Policy.

An interesting puzzle began to take shape at Houston. The 1976 entry at the first National was 121. The second National was only 43 dogs, but if memory serves me, it was held in the middle of the week, in the middle of a blazing July summer, and (apologies to all the good folks from Massachusetts) sort of in the middle of nowhere. The mid-west entry climbed back to 102, and populous California drew a record 133. One would think Houston would also draw a crowd but instead, the 1980 entry dropped to only 91 dogs. Back to California the next year, it shot up to 170, continued to climb to 190 in Ohio and 195 in Illinois. By 1990, entries were up to 400, with 422 in 1991 and then, back to Houston in 1992 for a disappointing entry of only 289.

The 1981 National in California was judged by a popular Canadian, Mr. Robert Waters. He made the west-coast star Ch. Matsu-kaze's Holly Go Lightly his BOB with BOS going to the dog, Ch. Satori's Asahi Go. Breeder Terry Arndt judged Sweeps and her winner was Kuma Yama's Kazan Of Koshi-Ki.

It was Ohio for 1982 with BOB going to east coast dog Ch. Kenjiko Royal Tenji and BOS to Holly. Mill Creek Bozo Jo was WD and BOW under Mr. John Patterson. For the first time, two judges were used for the regular classes. Mr. John Stanek judged bitches, with Kelly's Tara Chino going WB. Breeder Jerry Hoskins made Eastwind Glacier Fox Of Northland his Best in Sweeps.

It was chilly in Illy for the 1983 National, but not for the popular BOB winner Ch. Kenjiko Royal Tenji, winning under Dr. M. Denio. Sachmo's power was evident as his son Cheloy's Naughty Ninja went WD and his daughter Ch. O'BJ Kye Kye-Go Of E Oka took BOS. WB, judged by Mr. John Cramer, was Daijobu's Vampirella O'BJ, a BigSon daughter/Sachmo granddaughter. Breeder Carol Foti judged Sweeps with future big winner Blue Max's Chikara Buichi getting her approval.

1984 was judged by Japanese all-breed judge, Mr. Hideo Ito, who made Ch. Asahi Yama No Hanashi his Best Of Breed, Ch. Jo-San's Seibo No Kosetsu his BOS, and Langans Task Force his WD and BOW. Bitches were judged by Mrs. Marie Moore and Crown Royal's No No Narrett was the victor. Breeder James Sailer excused a couple of dogs for lack of merit (a first!) and made Wanchan's Buntaro his Best In Sweeps. The Oregon show drew 288 dogs.

Florida seemed like a good place to go in January of 1985, especially as the National was part of the country's most hotly contested circuit of the year. Despite the great circuit and vacation-like locale, entries were down by a hundred dogs, perhaps because of the geographical difficulties in driving to the Tampa Bay area. Long-time breed supporter Mrs. Virginia Hampton made big eastern winner Ch. Hot's Mo's Barnaby Jones

her BOB dog and her Winners Dog/Best Of Winners was Jens Smokie-Jo Of Rainbow, a double Sachmo grandson, as was breeder Robert Campbell's Best In Sweeps, E Oka's Big Son's Shadow. Best Of Opposite went to the lovely Veteran Bitch Ch. Toshiros, who incidentally had been WB at the 1979 National in San Jose. Mr. Edward Stevenson found his WB in Hot's Gemini Ginja Brown.

The Nationals moved back to California again for the first Independent National Specialty and Obedience Trial. A record 289 dogs, not counting obedience, validated the concept of an independently held event. Mr. Patrick Doniere, Jr. chose the son of last year's BOB winner by naming Ch. Brook-Staten Deja Vu as BOB. His WD was Kinoshita's Atama Kabu and BOS went to Ch. Crown Royal Akai O Kashi, a Group-winning bitch. Mrs. Joan Frailey awarded WB to Lucky's Red J.E.M. No Jo-San and breeder Janet Voss made Bar-BJ's Super Slo Mo her Sweeps winner. High In Trial Obedience winner was a bitch, Uchida's Sashika, CDX.

The Independent National introduced a new format, one which is used in several other breeds and which received rave reviews from everyone. The Best Of Breed judge selects several other dogs from those competing in Best Of Breed class that he or she feels are worthy of an Award Of Merit. The number of awards given out are determined by the size of the entry. These Awards Of Merit are not given in any order; in other words, all of those dogs so awarded are considered equal. The first AOM recipients were: Ch. Kakwa's Orca, Ch. Toshiros, Ch. Tamarlane's Veni Vidi Vici, Ch. Cee Jay's Rocky Road Of Kibo, Ch. Gaylee's Artic Fury Of Northland, Ch. Asahi Yamo No Hanashi, and Ch. Big D's Akanbooakai Palacourt.

Connecticut was bitterly cold with inadequate tenting for exhibitors and dogs. Spectators braved the sleet and rain for short periods, then hastened back to the shelter of the motel. The 350 dogs loved it! The 1987 BOB winner, chosen by Mrs. Jacqueline Quiros-Kubat, was Ch.

Tamarlane's Veni Vidi Vici, and BOS was Ch. Frakari's Date Tensha Pot Luck (sired by 1978's WD and Sweeps winner, Ch. Dibotsu). The future top winner of all time, Tobe's Return Of The Jedai began his illustrious career as WD and Best Of Winners. Mr. John Connolly awarded WB to Kazesan's Pica No Kando and breeder Donald Lusk chose Tadashii's Okii Konan as his Best In Sweeps. This was the last year to date that a non-breeder has judged Sweeps classes. High Score Obedience Akita was Foulk Run's Cowboy.

Awards Of Merit went to Ch. Cotton Ginny O'BJ, Ch. Big D's Akanbooakai Palaccort, Ch. Shuso Black Star, Ch. Bishamon's Day Of The Sun, Ch. Windom's Imperial Destiny, and Ch. Tobe's Tar Baby.

Not everyone made it to Denver for a Rocky Mountain high in 1988. The entry was down to 176 for the first National judged by a breeder-judge.

As difficult as it is to acknowledge the shallowness of some show people, it would be terribly unfair to allow the low entry to stand against Mr. Reed Keffer's reputation. A small but powerful faction within the breed resented his selection (by vote of the majority of the ACA membership) and consequently, a concerted effort was made to besmirch Mr. Keffer's reputation and to sabotage the entry. In an incredible display of petty stubbornness, the ACA board attempted to break the legal contract for Mr. Keffer's services, and failing that, it brought ethics charges against him. Rumors spread like an oil slick and damage to the reputation of the club and other involved parties was considerable. Many who might have gone to Denver did not. It is not my place to qualify Mr. Keffer's judgement on that day; the record of the dogs he awarded are of

sufficient comment. Although he was "tried" immediately following completion of his judging assignment, no ethics charges were sustained.

From a total entry of 176, Mr. Keffer selected Ch. Brook-Staten's Maxwell Smart (sired by National Specialty BOB winner, Barnaby Jones) as BOB and BOS to Ch. Kuroi Kao Dallas Alice, with WD and Best Of Winners going to Noji's Demons Be Gone (Ransom son out of National Specialty WB, Vampirella). Two previous National Specialty BOB winners, Ch. Asahi Yama No Hanashi and Ch. Hot's Mo's Barnaby Jones, received Awards Of Merit, along with Ch. Allure's Island Shogun, Ch. E Oka's Cloak N'Dagger, and Ch. Allure-Windrift's EZ Rider.

Am/Can Ch. Seawood's Cayuse, (Ch. Akita Tani's Daimyo, ROM x Ch. Golden Sun Seawood Wa Wa L'Wilac, ROM.) known as "Little Bear" pictured at three years, taking a Group Placement under judge John McNichol. Breeder/Owner is Kelle Clinton, Seawood Akitas.

Bitch classes were judged by Mrs. Irene Biven. WB was Magic Mountain's Big Splash. Best In Sweeps judge was Mrs. Beatrice Hunt, who awarded the bitch, Langan's Masumi No Miryoko. High Score Obedience was Spotted Bear's Kuma San, holding a Utility Dog title. Obedience judge was Mrs. Patricia Maynard.

In 1989, the Nationals added Futurity classes and grew to a three-day event with 278 Akitas. For the fifth time, it was held in California. Mr. Robert Ward awarded BOB to Ch. Sho-Go's Rambo and BOW to Wesaka's Japanese Warrior. He gave Awards Of Merit to Ch. Sho-Go's Joboy Tuff-N-Stuff, ROM, Ch. Crown Royal's Count Basie, Ch. E-Oka's Nihon No Akai, Ch. Tobe's Return Of The Jedai, and he included the WB, and the WD, Wesaka's Japanese Warrior in the awards.

Lt. Col. Wallace H. Pede officiated over bitch classes, with WB going to Nishi Taiyo Hannah Bachiyr.

Ch. E Oka's Broadway Bear (Ch. E Oka's Puttin On The Ritz x Ch. E Oka's Cloak N Dagger) going B.O.B. at three years, handled by Fran Wasserman. He's owned by Cheryl and Mark Balitzer, bred by Linda Henson.

Sweeps were judged by Ms. Barbara Hampton who made B-Line's Royal Valinu Samson her Best In Sweeps. Futurity judge Mr. Frank Nishimura's Grand Prize winner was Tobe's Tuff Stuff II. Langan's Makkuro Bushi Go, TDX was the High Scoring Obedience dog under Mr. Peter C. Schuessler.

The 1990 event went South to Tennessee, drawing 400 dogs. Mr. Mike Window from the United Kingdom would have been that exciting "unknown factor" except that he is well known in England and, prior to his assignment here, had imported a top winner from this country, Ch. Tamarlane's Veni Vidi Vici.

Mr. Window's WD and BOW was Kosetsu No Kimosabe. Breed judging began before lunch and after examining about half of the one hundred Specials, including Ch. Tobes Return Of The Jedai, lunch break was announced. After the Specials class had left the ring, in a presumed attempt to quell the controversy over the dog's size, Mr. Window measured Ch. Jedai in the ring. Unfortunately, it was not done during the judging but at a time when most people were busy gathering coats, chairs, and dogs, or had already departed ringside. Those who failed to see the measuring process were assured by Beverly Bonadonna's "victory lap" around the ring. "Ben" (as Jedai was well known) had officially measured in.

Mr. Window's final selection for BOB was the famous Top Winner, Ch. Tobe's Return Of The Jedai. BOS winner was Ch. Panmark's Musicmaker Of Seisan. Awards Of Merit were given to Ch. Fu-Ki's Hideki Tojo, Ch. Tamarlane's Spytfyr O'Kindamar, Ch. Karma- Ki's Ringside Rumor, Ch. Bar-BJ's Desperado, Ch. North Star's Max Maxx, Ch. Tamarlane's Rocket's Red Glare, Ch.

Allure's Island Shogun, and to Winners Dog and Winners Bitch.

Mr. Patrick Doniere, Jr. awarded WB to Big Benz Glory Be, and handler Mr. Edward J. Finnegan Jr. made Jedai's son, Frakari's Rockets Red Glare, his Best In Sweeps.

Futurity and Maturity competition was judged by Mrs. Madeleine B. Fish, who named Frakari's George M as Futurity Winner and the 1989 Grand Futurity Winner, Ch. Tobe's Tuff Stuff II, was Grand Maturity Winner. High Score Akita was Shoho's Don't Mess With My Tutu, a UD-titled bitch.

The 1991 National moved back to California. Four hundred twenty two dogs were entered, many competing in multiple events over a three-day

Am/Can. Ch. Seawood's Hi Flyer with breeder/owner/handler Kelli Clinton. Three year old "Flyer" is by Ch. Akita Tani's Daimyo, ROM x Ch. Golden Sun Seawood Wa Wa L'Wilac, ROM.

spectacular. Mr. Samuel Pizzino judged dogs. His BOB winner, Ch. Northstar's Mad Maxx, a 1990 Award Of Merit winner, was a popular decision. BOS went to Frakari's Martha Washington, who was also Grand Maturity Winner under breeder Bettye Krug.

A person may not judge a dog that he has recently owned or, in the case of Ms. Wasserman, she may not judge a dog owned by someone with whom she lives. Rather a complicated issue but such rules are meant to prevent a conflict of interest. In the case of Martha Washington, AKC rescinded her wins and ordered all ribbons and trophies returned. There was, therefore, no Best Of Opposite Sex or Maturity Winner at the 1991 National Specialty, a rueful situation for all other bitch owners who might have claimed those prestigious wins.

Bitch classes were judged by Mr. Donald Booxbaum. Winners Bitch was Joy's Cho Cho and his Veteran Bitch winner was Ch.

Crown Royal's Akai O Kashi, CD, the 1986 BOS winner.

The Veteran Dogs class winner, Ch. Tamarlane's Veni Vidi Vici, received an Award Of Merit, as did Ch. Hinomaru Daitani Diamond Back, Ch. The WW Coal Miner O'BJ, Ch. Karma-Ki's Ringside Rumor, Ch. Inaka's Sophisticated Lady, Ch. Noble Tandy Son Of Bartok, Ch. Running Bear's Sunburst, and Ch. O'BJ Shaka-Khan At C and L.

Stud Dog winner was Ch. Noji's The Count Crown Royal and Brood Bitch Winner was Ch. Kuroi Kao Dallas Alice, the 1988 BOS winner and the dam of Mad Maxx. I didn't see Brace competition but there were several entries with Ch. Kobu's Kyrion and Kobu's Allah A-K-Bar taking first place.

Ms. Fran Wasserman judged Sweeps, awarding Best Junior and Best In Sweeps to Apogee's Mac Paint, who was also Futurity Grand Prize Winner under Mrs. Bettye Krug.

As we remember the 1992 entry dropped to 289 at Houston. Dr. Richard Greathouse judged dogs and intersex, awarding WD and BOW to ten-month-old Big-O Winter Storm Of Rowsaw. His Veteran Class winner was Ch. Allure's Island Shogun, thus setting the stage for a hot contest in Specials class.

Mrs. Betty Leininger judged bitches, and she and a white-masked red Japanese import made breed history. Her WB was Hachihime Of Onishi Kensha. The five-year-old bitch received strong support as the judging progressed and ringside became less stunned and more charmed by her personality and type. She did not lack bone, substance, nor size. Mrs. Leininger awarded Veteran Bitch class to Ch. Kobu's Ka-Aba, CD.

To the beat of tumultuous applause, Dr. Greathouse selected the Veteran Dog, Ch. Allure's Island Shogun as BOB. In what many considered to be "restitution" for her previous loss, he then awarded BOS to Ch. Frakari's Martha Washington. From a Best Of Breed ring filled with great dogs, Dr. Greathouse designated Ch. Tobe's Return Of The Jedai, Ch. Orions Walk The Dinosaur, Ch. Tamarlane's Veni Vidi Vici, Ch. Erin's Heart Of A Rebel, Ch. Hinomaru Daitani Diamond Back, Ch. Karma-Ki's Ringside Rumor, Ch. Esko Shadazar Tango, and Ch. Kobu's Ka-Aba, CD as Award Of Merit winners.

Judging both Stud and Brood classes, Dr. Greathouse selected Ch. Hinomaru Daitani Diamond Back from a large entry of Stud Dogs and Ch. Tora's Michiko O Ryan, TT as Brood Bitch winner.

Obedience was judged by Mrs. Judith Brown and High Score Obedience winner was Maxine II, a former rescue Akita. Sweeps were judged by Mrs. Catherine Bell, who made Bighorn's Lord Of The Changsi her Best In Sweeps. Mrs. Joan M. Linderman awarded the Futurity Grand Prize to the eight-month-old dog, Daitan's Just Be Cos. From an entry of seven, Mrs. Linderman's

Can. Ch. O'BJ King's Pistol (Ch. The Widow-Maker O'BJ x Ch. The Mad Hatter O'BJ) is a multi-Best Puppy In Show and adult Group Winner. He is a Regional Specialty Best In Sweeps Winner and the following year, was BB at the Canadian Nationals, owner handler by Serje Desforges.

The Akita breed in England owes its present-day status to the USA, from where most of the foundation dogs were imported. It took until the 1980s for the breed to get on its feet. Photograph by Robert Smith.

selection for Grand Maturity Winner was the dog, Apogee Dances With Wolves.

There are other Akitas who have excelled in the ring and as producers. More importantly, there are thousands of Akitas who have earned an even more important award—"Best" of friends for each of their owners. Each one will live on in the hearts and memories of owners everywhere.

THE AKITA IN ENGLAND
by Mrs. Wendy Bell, Kysami Akitas

The first Akitas known of in Great Britain were imported by a Japanese gentleman called Mr. Smith, some time in the 1940s. Although the dogs were registered and were also shown at Crufts Dog Show, the breed didn't catch on. Nothing more was heard about the Akita until another was imported in the 1950s, but as this dog was never registered, it was obviously someone's family pet.

At the end of the 1970s—early 1980s, interest was finally taken in the Akita breed. A number of people imported animals. The first was brought in from Canada by Miss Marian Sargent; her name was Davos Watakyshi Tomo-Dach. That was in April 1981, followed by Kosho Ki's Ki Ki in August, imported by Gerald and Kath Mitchell. Two were also imported from Japan; a bitch Yukihimi-Go by Mrs. Beryl Mason, and a dog, Fujimatsu-Go by Mr. and Mrs. Frank Green.

By 1984, 12 Akitas had been registered with the Kennel Club, seven bitches and five dogs; nine from the USA, one from Canada and two from Japan.

The first litter to be born in Great Britain was whelped on October 23, 1983. Dam Am. Ch. O'BJ Sachette No Okii Yubi, Sire O'BJ Aces High, bred by Meg Purnell-Carpenter of the Overhills Kennels. The second litter was bred by Mr. and Mrs. Mitchell of Kiskas Kennels, born on November 2, 1983; dam Kosho Ki KiKi, sire Kosho Ki Song For Adam Otk. Also in December 1983, Beryl Mason's bitch Yukihimi-Go produced a litter to Fujimatsu-Go.

A Japanese Akita photographed in England in 1994—only in the 1990s has England registered a fair number of Akitas. Photograph by Robert Smith.

classified at Crufts in 1985. Best Of Breed was The Steel Glove O'BJ. More classes began to be offered to Akitas, and the breed started to have an impact.

The Akita "took off," not surprisingly as they are so magnificent and come in such beautiful colors. So we went from none registered in 1980, to an excess of 600 registered for 1990, and now have around 3000 in the country.

As with all breeds of dog, and the Akita is no different, there are now a number of different types in the show ring, which sometimes gives the judges a headache.

February 1990 brought great changes with the fact that for the first time Challenge Certificates were on offer to Akitas. The first were awarded at Crufts by judge Mr. Ken Bullock, with Am. Ch. Tamarlane's Veni Vidi Vici getting the dog CC and Keskas Jezabel, the bitch CC. Am. Ch. Tarmalanes Veni Vidi Vici went on to become the first

Overhills and Kiskas were the two top kennels in the early 1980s, joined by Mike Window and Marian Sargent of Tegwani Kennels—most dogs in this country are founded on one or two of these kennels' breeding.

In the early days, registrations were low and the only classes available were the Any Variety Not Separately Classified. The first to achieve Best Puppy at a Championship Show was Kosho Ki's Kimono Of Kiskas. In February 1985 at Crufts, Overhill's Lizzys Girl was Best Of Breed AVNSC, being the first Akita to win this top honor. Lizzys Girl was from the first litter born here. She and her litter sisters, Overhills Marlows Miracle and Overhill's Kita Mori, were very successful, as was Kiska's Triad, an impressive black and white male from the second litter. He unfortunately died at the young age of 18 months with bone cancer.

Classes for Akitas were first

The many attractive colors and patterns of the Akita attract British newcomers to the breed. Breeders should pay some attention to breeding dogs with vibrant colors lest the English Akita will wash out into fawns and grays. Photograph by Robert Smith.

As an estate guardian, the Akita has as many virtues as he does as a show dog and companion animal. A soundly built and temperamentally stable Akita is the only Akita to own and breed. Photograph by Robert Smith.

Akitas. On the same day, Ch. Brandeezi Quite A Gent, a beautiful black and white male bred by Pauline Hayes, gained his crown as did Ch. Lizda Zee Zee Flash, a bitch bred by Dave and Liz Killilea.

As with any new breed, breeders need to be more selective with their matings. We need to pay attention to ears and ear set. Colors in the ring at the moment are fading. The rainbow of Akitas you once saw in the ring has become mainly fawns or faded black and whites. Too many are breeding to top winners and not evaluating what is good for their particular bitch's problems. Possibly because they are such a striking breed and can command good prices for puppies, this is one reason.

Coat textures are many and varied, as is size. I suppose all breeds go through this period until the money goes from the breed and dedicated breeders get down to the betterment of the breed.

THE GOLDEN CARPET

The Akita has found friends all over the world. The Latin countries have taken the breed into heart and home.

Akita champion in Great Britain, being awarded his third CC by Meg Purnell-Carpenter at the Welsh Kennel Club Championship Show. By this time, Am. Ch. Goshen's Heir Apparent had been imported to the UK and it was neck and neck with these two dogs as to who was to be the first champion. On the day of Veni Vidi Vici's earning his championship, he went on to Best In Show, the first Akita to gain such an award at a Championship Show.

1991 saw the first British-bred champion Northern Mexico has always been a hotbed of competition as state-side owners went south for Mexican Championships prior to AKC recognition of the Akita. Mexico became the first country to see an Akita become Number One Dog, All Breeds. This spectacular accomplishment was achieved in 1989 by Am/Mex/Intl. Ch. O'BJ Sachmo Ko-Son (Ch. O'BJ BigSon Of Sachmo, ROMXP x Tetsu-Ko O'BJ) owned by Jorge Haddad, Jr.

South America has also shown an increased interest in the breed with many countries already claiming a Best In Show Akita. Mr. Moretto in Chile has had several Best In Show wins which failed to dim the excitement of owning of the first female Group winner, Ch. The One-To-Keep O'BJ. The Jucep Kennels of Dr. Parra in Columbia has also had tremendous interbreed success with his big pinto, Ch. "Ziggy."

The breed has gained great popularity in Australia, sparked by the early success of an American import, Australian Ch. and BIS winner, O'BJ Piece Of The Rock, owned by Ken Taylor. Many other great Akitas followed and strong bloodlines have developed in the vast land "down under."

In all countries, temperament is at a crossroads. There is a real danger that the basic character of this proud and dominant breed will be eroded away by those who desire a more "saleable" product. As stated by so many authorities, the Akita is not suitable for every family. Neither is the delightfully busy Shiba, the distinguished Wolfhound, or the sturdy little Corgi. Every breed has a distinctive personality and character which appeals to one family but not another. If we try to change the Akita into *something else,* he will no longer be desirable to those families who appreciate a dignified, discriminating, brave, stable, and innately unique *guard dog* companion.

Over the last half century, many breeds have been tampered with in the interest of marketability. As a result, many hunting breeds no longer interest sportsmen; not a few herding breeds have lost the keen instincts which man so carefully developed. Sadly, in a society that recognizes the inherent danger in firearms yet longs for assurance of personal security, many working breeds have become only cotton-candy caricatures of once-noble protectors. The tradition of an extra family member, capable of guarding his home and family, is in danger of being lost in the mad rush for uniformity of physical attributes and non-bothersome personalities. Prospective owners desiring a canine ornament to complete the family portrait would be happier with a

cat or non-mammalian species. They are far less trouble than most canine breeds, which brings up another point.

It would be easy to soft-pedal the issue of dominance and guarding instinct. Many "breed books" do so quite smoothly, but this author feels that the Akita is so near-perfect that we need not change nor disguise him.

We must only be honest. In today's litigious society, ownership liability and the moral and legal obligations of the breeder are of great importance. Owners should be told that this is a dominant breed with strong guarding instincts and breeders must not attempt to mislead the public. It isn't fair to buyers but most of all, it's grossly unfair to the dogs.

An unfortunate example is the AKC video wherein the Akita is portrayed as a sled dog. We see an exceptional and exceptionally *well-trained* team of Akitas working together in total harmony even though the Akita Standard clearly states, "Temperament— Aggressive toward other dogs." At no time is the viewer told that it's an unusual function or that the footage isn't meant to indicate a history of sled use. Such misinformation can lead to heartbreaking disappointment for a multi-dog family who would purchase an Akita believing it would fit right in with their other dogs.

Breeders, who assure prospective purchasers that the Akita is going to "get along just fine with other dogs" and who would have the buyer believe it's just an oversized teddy bear, are flirting with a lawsuit should the dog ever harm another dog or person. The wishy-washy (or white-washy) position held by some breeders is, and will continue to be, a detriment to the future of the Akita. No one need apologize for striving to produce a steadfast family protector; we need only to be honest with the public.

For those breeders who advocate "correcting" the Akita temperament, may I point out that almost without exception, attempts to change instinctive thought and reaction patterns of well established breeds have proven disastrous. There is a welcome place in society for stable, discriminating family protectors. To those who might disagree, I offer AKC registration statistics which indisputably demonstrate the public's continued attraction to those breeds commonly known to have strong guarding instincts.

It would be unwise to attempt to dilute the Akita's courage and determination to protect those he loves. Even worse than losing those precious attributes is the sad results of market-place breeding. The public is not equipped to deal with the genetic psychosis which result from the amateur muddlings of fad breeders. We have only to look around at the increasing numbers of dogs which are anxiety-ridden fear-biters, or overly aggressive bullies, or outright canine sociopaths, to know that we should have left well enough alone in many breeds!

If prospective owners were objectively educated about both positive and negative aspects of each breed, they could then make informed decisions as to which breeds would best reflect their tastes and lifestyle. If that were the case, the right families would choose the right breeds and be happy to keep them forever. There would be no strays; there would be no needless destruction of former pets; and there would be no......

"Sasha" a 4 year old rescued female. Now living the good life with her new family.

AKITA RESCUE

Every Akita owner should be aware of the existence and, more to the point, the need for animal rescue organizations. Probably the best known of these breed-affiliated rescue groups is the Akita Rescue Society of America, known as ARSA. Secretary and editor of the Parent Chapter newsletter is Barbara Bouyet, 237 Venus

"Denali", a four year old male stray found on a PA highway. A beautifully trained dog who is always searching the horizon for his lost owner!

Street, Thousand Oaks, CA 91360. There are ARSA chapters throughout the United States serving along with many other unaffiliated Akita or all-breed rescue organizations. All are of vital importance as buyer demand is met by hundreds of money-grubbers and ego-seekers who have no genuine concern for the quality, health, or welfare of the dogs they produce.

Akita rescue groups perform a valuable service. Without them, many of our noble breed would languish in pounds and so-called "humane" societies around the country. For those who understand the Akita's depth of character, the very thought of such a proud animal forced to survive as a beggar, robbed of all dignity and even worse, deprived of the one-on-one contact that the breed thrives upon is a nightmare of the worst sort.

Despite the good they do after the fact, rescue organizations have been unable to control the root of the problem. It is shameful that breed clubs count among their members many persons whose activities are known to swell the population of rescue facilities! That such people are allowed to remain as members, their despicable activities shielded from the wrath of fellow members, may be partially attributable to the position taken by most rescue groups. It is a complicated issue. For instance, if individuals are publicly exposed, it might cause more Akitas to be secretly put to sleep rather than risk certain censure by turning the dog in to a rescue group. On the other hand, if callous owners and irresponsible breeders were held accountable, perhaps fewer people would find it so easy to shirk their responsibilities. Perhaps, in the long run, fewer Akitas would be neglected, abused, misrepresented, and over-bred.

It's a sensitive matter and one which each group handles carefully. Before purchase, you may wish to verify that none of the breeder's dogs have been abandoned to rescue. This could happen without their knowledge but when the breeder is known, rescue workers will always contact them. Most have gratefully claimed the dog which they created or have at least paid boarding and medical expense until a good home could be found.

The problems generated by irresponsible breeding and ownership grow daily. Anti-pet legislation is spreading, but a strong rescue network can reduce the numbers of Akitas that terminate in "shelters," thus preventing unfavorable notoriety for the breed. Simply put, it is unforgivable for any Akita to ever spend more than 24 hours in custody. Everyone must do his part; if you cannot provide temporary housing for one or more rescue dogs, you can surely help finance the efforts of the various Akita rescue organizations.

I asked ARSA and Delaware Valley Akita Rescue (DVAR) to provide us with a firsthand look at rescue work and tell us how we can help. DVAR

"Tomo Dachi" 3 year old male, a former abuse case. He came in weighing only 38 pounds and with multiple health problems. Thousands of dollars later, he is a healthy and handsome 95 pound success story!

responded, for which we are most grateful:

"As with all breeds of dogs, Akitas need rescue groups. Owners give up their Akitas for various reasons which are in no way the 'fault' of the dog. Delaware Valley Akita Rescue receives dogs from well-known breeders, backyard breeders, and pet-store acquisitions and we find homes for all whose breeder cannot or will not resume responsibility. Rescue dogs come in all degrees of conformation, from ugly to gorgeous.

"Delaware Valley Akita Rescue rarely gets puppies under the age of six months. Most Akitas come into rescue between the ages of one to four years. Some are owner turn-ins to shelters, some are strays, but the majority are given directly to us by caring owners who fear for the fate of their beloved pet if they were to leave it in a shelter. Consequently, we have a lot of background on most Akitas in our rescue, and we make every effort to learn/verify as much as possible about each Akita before adopting it out. We take *no* people-aggressive Akitas but will deal with animal-aggression if the Akita is controllable. Abused Akitas are rarely seen and seldom taken on; a few of our dogs have been neglected, and they make the most appreciative, 'second childhood gleeful' pets. Most are already exceptionally good pets, are exuberantly eager to please after losing their first homes, and will bond strongly to their new families when given a small period of adjustment.

"All of DVAR's Akitas are spayed/neutered prior to adoption, current on shots, on heartworm preventative and thyroid medication if needed, and in good health. Potential adopters are educated about both the advantages and disadvantages of owning the breed, screened through vet and reference checks, and their homes, yards and neighborhoods are inspected. Great care is

"Shogun" is a 6 year old "stud dog" confiscated from a puppy mill. He was in deplorable shape, having lived on a chain for six years. The SPCA gave him medical attention and DVAR housebroke and socialized him. Shogun now goes to nursing homes to visit the elderly - a truly rescued dog serving a noble purpose.

taken to match the right Akita with the right home —and the Akita has to show enthusiasm for his new owners! A lengthy, legally binding contract is signed which stipulates such matters as acceptable housing, training, exercising, no soy food, daily rather than monthly heartworm medication, etc. The new owners have a month with the dog in which to decide if this is indeed the right dog for them; if not, they return the Akita and their adoption fee is remitted in full. Adoption fees are meant to cover expenses; we make no profit.

"The two women who constitute DVAR (and who both have full-time jobs otherwise) succeeded in placing over 40 dogs in 1991 alone. DVAR broke the news of the Kansas puppymill shutdown to the Akita fancy at the National Specialty, and, through articles we prepared for national magazines such as *Dog World* and *Dog Fancy,* we helped the Kansas Humane Society of Wichita place more than 20 of these unfortunate but difficult dogs directly into homes throughout the country during 1991.

"Delaware Valley Akita Rescue mans informational booths at dog shows and dog-oriented functions, answers innumerable phone inquiries about all facets of Akita ownership (whether or not their Akita came from us), writes a semi-annual newsletter for adopters and other friends of rescue, evaluates dog problems and refers them to appropriate experts, and helps other breed rescues through references, transportation and sometimes temporary housing and emergency vetting.

"Akita rescue work is emotionally, physically, and financially draining, but seeing a needy, deserving Akita united with a delighted adoptive family is a great reward! Akita rescues are necessary for the dogs' sakes, and they educate about responsible dog ownership. Well-run Akita rescues deserve broad-based support and respect from the Akita fancy; through them, every friend of our breed can contribute his or her share in helping Akitas in need."

By Kathy Dewees
and Margie Rutbell

Akitas need your help. If you would like more information, can offer assistance to the breed, would like to adopt, or would like to make a tax-deductible donation; please contact your local rescue group, or write to:

Delaware Valley Akita Rescue, P.O. Box 578 Rancocas, NJ 08073; The Akita Club of America, or any of the many local rescue organizations.

Ownership means an obligation to prevent pain and suffering for all animals and most Akita owners find it impossible to look into the eyes of their beloved dog and not see the hopelessness and pain of a hundred other Akitas. Won't you help?

Sam and his friend Tahoe at one year. They are owned by Maria Heldman, Mariah Akitas.

Akitas on Parade, photo courtesy of Director Patricia A. Happel. This group of Baltimore area owners take special pride in displaying their Akitas in such a dazzling and positive way.

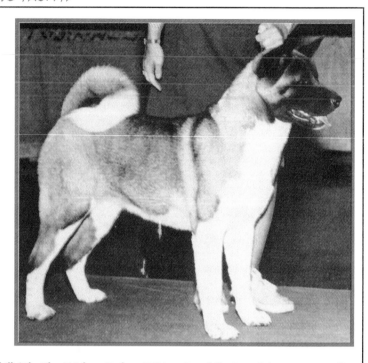

Ch. To-Zu's Misty Morning, ROMP, October 19, 1980 - October 20, 1989. By Ch. Akita Tani's Daimyo, ROMPX x Ch. Me-Tu of To-Zu, ROMP, Misty was 1989 Region #1 Akita Specialty Show Brood Bitch Winner and Veteran Bitch Winner. Owners, Ruth and Robert Broskin.

The Humming Bird Is Overhill (Ch. The Widow-Maker O'BJ x Overhills Pacer) is an outstanding youngster from a litter co-bred by the author and Meg Carpenter, Pensford, England. This unusual arrangement led to Mrs. Carpenter being perhaps the first breeder of American AND English Champion Akitas!

The West Camp Kennel of Steve and Abbie Schiff produces Working Akitas as well as show winners. Thier son Mike enjoys his rides as much as the dogs enjoy the sport.

Can. Ch. O'BJ King's Pistol (Ch. The Widow-Maker O'BJ x Ch. The Mad Hatter O'BJ) pictured taking his first Group placement, at 10 months. Owner handled by Serje Desforges, Ontario Canada. He is a multi-Group winner and National Specialty B.O.B. winner.

International Champion Top of The Line O'BJ (Ch. O'BJ Mighty Maverick x Ch. The Cat In The Hat O'BJ) shown winning second place in the International show in 1993. This outstanding youngster is owned by Cinsilu Akitas, Guatemala, Central America.

Am/Mex. Ch. Kuma Yama's Palace Court Dani (Big D's Palace Court Anji Son x Ch. Kuma Yama's Sykora Star) is the dam of BIS winner, Ch. Running Bear's Sunburst. Dani was bred by Patricia Van Buskirk and is owned by Judy Gresham and Mark and Lisa Borlase.

Ch. Eudora's The Highlander (Ch. The Widow-Maker O'BJ, ROMPX x Ch. Eudora's Dixie Affair, ROM) finishing his Championship at only eight months with two owner handled BOB wins and two Group placements. He has several more Ch. or pointed littermates, all bred by Mark Nisbet, Eudora Akitas.

Can. Ch. Serdess Shadow Warrior "Bobby", by Can. Ch. O'BJ King's Pistol x Can. Ch. Cindy Caprice De Lauclair) was WD and Best Puppy at the Canadian National Specialty and is pictured at 9 months, taking B.O.B. from the classes. He finished at 10 months. Handler Shelly McHugh, owner David Hancock, of Ontario.

Ch. O'BJ Kuroyama Jade (Ch. Raiden of Jo-Uba, ROMX x Ch. The Dame's On Target, ROMXP) taking his first Group placement at eighteen months, handled by Bryan Martin for owners Michael and Eileen Shedd.

Can. Ch. Matsutake's Cody Bearpaw, ROM, (Can. Ch. Kakwa's Nehwa, ROM x Can Ch. Davos Bianca) owned by Bev Wilkinson, bred by Deborah Wald.

Overhill's Cherokee Lite Fut (Am. Ch. The Widow-Maker O'BJ x Overhills Kita Mouri) is well developed at ten and a half months. Being female, she is at a prime "puppy show" stage of development, including front and rear angulation whereas many male pups will be steeply angulated or high in the rear at this age. Bred and owned by Meg Carpenter, Overhill Kennels, Pensford England.

Tenkohime of Shikoku Hanoka Kensha, known as LuLu, is a Japanese import by Tenichimaru of Kawashha Kensha out of Midori of Atsugi Fumoto. She's bred by Kaichiro Hanaoka, owned by Kiyoshi Yamazaki.

Breeding the Best

THE COMMITMENT

There's only one path to success as a breeder and I have to tell you, it's mostly uphill, winding across the rocky terrain of commitment in such a way as to get a lot of people lost. We can set goals by the dozens, be blessed with good looks, good dogs and a huge bank account. We may hire the best handlers, read all the right books, and travel in the best circles. We can soak up knowledge like a sponge and spew out platitudes by the hour. While these advantages may bring short term satisfaction, there's only one thing which earns respect from one's peers and lasting success as a breeder. It's not elusive; it's not a mystery.

Failure to commit to ethics and excellence explains why so many would-be breeders wander aimlessly from one dead end to another. AKC records reveal that it takes about five years before most people give up. Only a handful spurn the short cuts, and, making a personal resolution to arrive at their destination, they begin the climb to higher ground.

Make no mistake: walking the lofty path of commitment is the exact opposite of having one's head in the clouds! It means having a realistic obligation to the breed, to the sport, and most of all, to personal standards of integrity. It means sacrifice. Believe me, it's not always convenient. That thing called commitment can get in the way just when you think you've arrived.....

Many years ago, I wrote a piece for *Kennel Review,* one of America's premier dog magazines. It was picked up and reprinted by several other publications so I suppose it pretty well explains what commitment means to dog people.

WHAT IS A BREEDER?

Webster's gives us some interesting definitions of breed: "Nourish, cherish... generate, engender... cause, occasion... bring up, nurse and foster," and more to the point, "produce by special selection of parents or progenitors."

Anyone who puts two animals together for the purpose of producing young does "generate, engender, cause, or occasion" the propagation of that species or breed. Most breeders, thankfully, "nourish, cherish, bring up, nurse, and foster."

Ahh, but here's the rub: Only a handful of persons involved in the production of companion animals can be said to "produce by special selection of parents or progenitors."

A Breeder (with a capital "B") is one who thirsts for knowledge and never really knows it all, one who wrestles with decisions of conscience, convenience, and commitment.

A Breeder is one who sacrifices personal interests, finances, time, friendships, fancy furniture, and deep pile carpeting! She gives up the dream of a long, luxurious cruise in favor of turning that all-important specialty show into this year's "vacation." The Breeder goes without sleep (but never without coffee) while watching anxiously over the birth process, and afterwards, every little sneeze, wiggle, or cry.

The Breeder skips dinner parties because a litter is due or the puppies have to be fed at eight. He disregards birth fluids and puts mouth to mouth to save a gasping newborn, literally blowing life into a tiny, helpless creature that may be the culmination of a lifetime of dreams.

A Breeder's lap is a marvelous place where generations of proud and noble champions once snoozed. A Breeder's hands are strong and firm and often soiled, but ever so gentle and sensitive to the thrusts of a puppy's wet nose. A Breeder's knees are usually arthritic from stooping, bending, and lifting puppies, but are strong enough to enable the Breeder to show the keeper pup in Sweeps!

A Breeder's shoulders are stooped and often heaped with abuse from competitors, but they're wide enough to support the weight of a thousand defeats and frustrations. A breeder's arms are always able to wield a mop, support an armful of puppies, or lend a helping hand to a newcomer.

A Breeder's ears are wondrous things, strangely shaped (from being pressed against a phone receiver), deaf to criticism, yet always fine-tuned to the whimper of a sick pup. A Breeder's eyes are blurred from pedigree research and sometimes blind to his own dog's shortcomings, but they are ever so keen to the competition's faults and are always, always searching for the perfect specimen.

A Breeder's brain is foggy on faces, but recalls pedigrees faster than an IBM. It's so full of knowledge that sometimes it blows a fuse; it catalogs thousands of good fronts, hocky rears, and perfect heads... and buries in the soul the failures and the ones that didn't turn out. The Breeder's heart is often broken, but it beats strongly with hope everlasting—and it's always in the right place!

"My Three Sons" Puppies bred by Susan Duncan, (by Ch. Daitan's Watakushi No Kokoro, TT x Kyojin Mitsu Kuma Go, TT, TDI) left to right, Tanoshii Yogi Bear (owner Maria Wight) Am/Can/Mx/CACIB Ch. Tanoshii Akuto TD, TDI & Am/Mx TT (owner Buford and Susan Duncan) and Tanoshii Kalohe Honey Bandit (owner Arnold Ywen. Photo by Jeanne Galindo Hayes.

Oh yes, there are breeders, and then, there are Breeders.

LEARNING THE ROPES

The true dog person loves all dogs, but especially his own breed. All of them. Even the ugly ones. It's not enough just to be responsible for our own dogs or those we bred. For every breeder who muddies up the gene pool, there must be a Breeder willing to pick up the pieces and repair the damage.

If you are already "in" dogs or if you feel yourself drawn to the sport, stop and consider which path you will take. If you are willing to sacrifice your time and resources with little hope of financial recovery, and with the understanding that should you rise to the top, you become an easy target for jealous detractors; if you are willing to exchange personal vanity for integrity; if you are willing to use your finances and intelligence to benefit all animals and not just your chosen breed; then read on. You have spoken the vows. You are ready to become a Breeder.

The next time you go to a dog show, look around. While just about everybody is having fun (and there's a lot to be said for that!), the majority of those exhibitors lugging crates, rapturously clutching the purple ribbon, or dozing off at ringside after a long night's drive; most will be gone from the sport within a few years. They will have had fun, and piled up a ton of memories but finally decided the

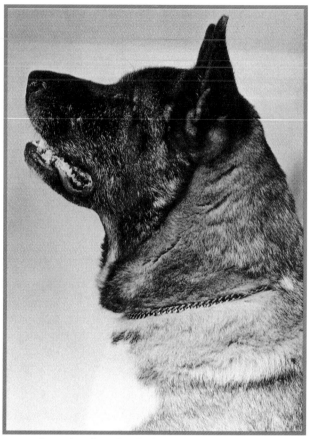

Magnificent head study of Akita Tani's Shoyo-Go (Jap. Ch. Kinsho Go x Akarui Kokoro) bred/owned by Liz Harrell.

Ch. Akita Tani's Kyoko, photographed at six years, is the fourth of four Champion litter sisters from the fortuitous mating of Akita Tani's Tatsumaki to Akita Tani's Kuro Shusu, a breeding which produced the Akita Tani's Champions Arashii, Yoru Bara, Kashi Kuma, and the famous sire, Daimyo!

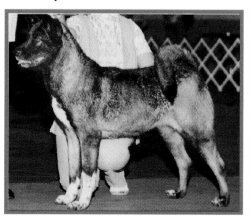

disappointments outweighed the rewards and so they "cut back" or "got out." They are seldom missed for there is a constant supply of new faces and new dogs.

And then, there's the small group which I like to think of as the brainstem of the sport. They are the faces you see inside *and* outside the Group rings show after show, year after year. They may be owners, they may be handlers. You'll probably see them in the magazines now or eventually, you'll see them in center ring; they are the judges of the future.

You can participate at any level of involvement which suits the amount of time you have, the intensity of your desire to excel in the sport, and your long-range plans. Many people don't plan at all, they just find that their love for dogs and all that has to do with dogs is one of the most

Ch. O'BJ Shoshoni Sunrise, (Ch. O'BJ King's Ransom, ROMPX x Ch. The Dames On Target O'BJ, ROMP) owned by Carolee McKnight. Even as a youngster, Shoni demonstrates the solid four-square stance so desirable in the Akita.

your goal of producing Akitas which will be a satisfying reflection of your personal taste and talent, you must have more than just a female dog. She must be sound, healthy, well bred, and of show quality. Don't be tempted by the very first sidetrack you encounter—the sign that says "Breeder Quality, Cheap Route to Success."

The term "breeder quality" is usually synonymous with "pet quality"—but with a slightly higher price tag. No matter how terrific her phenotype, she is not "breeder quality" unless she has a dependable pedigree (genotype) and you know who to breed her to!

If you already own a female, don't succumb to temptation. Consider whether she really has anything to offer the breed. If your desire to mate her is prompted by love and a belief that everyone should have an Akita "just like her," or curiosity about what she might produce, or the idea of providing a good learning experience for the children, or to recover your investment, then please

gratifying things in their lives. If the rest of the family feels the same way, they become the progenitors of second- and third-generation "dog people."

If you've given it some thought and want to know more, this discussion is for you. With but a couple of exceptions, the information isn't new. It's tried and true. Just about every book ever written about breeding will tell you the same thing. Read one. This book is about Akitas and intended only to give you basic guidelines, not try to prove them to you. You must satisfy yourself as to the validity of my comments.

The starting point for your trip up the breeder's path is pretty obvious. It's marked "Female Dog." We want you to do more than play the game, we want you to succeed, so here comes basic tip number one. In order to realize

Krug's Cindy (Ch. Krug's Akai Osama x Krug's Sheba) breeder Bettye Krug. Cindy was purchased by the Andrews, to be mated to Sachmo. He died before that could be accomplished so she was bred to Am/Can Ch. Kakwa's Orca. The litter contained only one noteworthy pup, O'BJ Aces High, a big strong dog who is behind several English and Australian pedigrees.

understand that such reasons lead to hundreds of unwanted Akitas in shelters all across the country. It's fun to study pedigrees, plan breedings, talk to stud dog owners, and dream of a wonderful litter of furry little darlings, but when it comes down to making that final decision, think carefully. It will be your first conscious act of commitment.

If your bitch has proven herself in the show ring and you are reasonably certain about her genetic probabilities, then and only then are you ready to decide upon a mating which would be favorable for her and a credit to you. Your responsibility as a breeder does not end with rearing the puppies. The logical consequence of seeing her through gestation and rearing the puppies is that you have to sell them.

If the bitch's pedigree is in demand and you have bred her wisely, you should have developed a list of prospective show homes. If you practice sound rearing techniques and are conversant with callers, then you should have no problem selling your pets to wonderful families who will love them as much as you do. If those shoes don't fit, the really uncomfortable fact is that you could have a problem selling the litter.

If you do a mating believing that you have plenty of friends just dying for one of the puppies, you may discover that people have a way of moving, going on vacation, acquiring some other pet, and, in general, changing their minds. Realistically, you are more apt to find yourself with eight hungry puppies which are outgrowing their quarters, beginning to have puppy squabbles, and creating an unbelievable waste disposal problem! What to do? If you love your puppies, you'll live up to your commitment. You will keep them until the right homes are found, regardless of zoning violations, neighbor disputes, and vet bills!

The stud dog owner is also confronted with decisions of commitment. He must not be tempted by rationale such as "if I don't breed her, they'll just breed to a lesser

Ch. Sierra West Jun Kin Makura by Ch. O'BJ High-N-Mighty No Goshen, ROM x Ch. Skylake's Tokyo Rose. He's owned by Judy Pillow.

quality stud." Thinking to provide service for a pet-quality bitch is usually only an excuse to compromise ethics. If it doesn't feel right, if you would have trouble justifying the mating to other conscientious fanciers, don't do it.

Ethics aside, let's be purely practical. If a mediocre bitch with a mediocre pedigree is bred to your stud dog, it's almost certain that she will produce mediocre puppies or worse yet, serious genetic defects. No matter how much you love your stud dog

tionship with at least the basic rules of inheritance. Those books you find especially interesting should be purchased and committed to your library shelf for future reference. Trust me, it's worth going back to school for a little while because if you own a sound, healthy, show-quality adult with proper breed character, it's only because the people who created him did their homework. You owe owners of subsequent generations no less.

To apply your newfound knowledge of

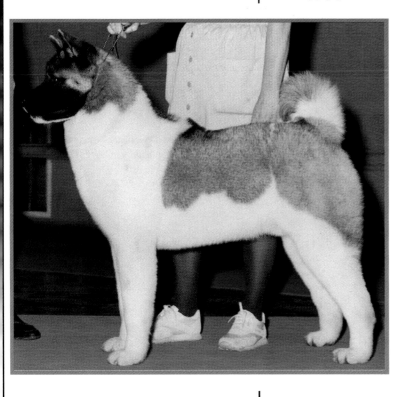

Ch. O'BJ Tribute to Ransom (Ch. O'BJ King's Ransom, ROMPX x Ch. The Dame's On Target O'BJ, ROMPX) pictured taking BOB over top specials at only nine months old under judge Charlotte McGowan who also awarded him a strong Group placement, owner handled by Peggy Casselberry.

and believe in his genetic prowess, the odds are against him. If you own a top-winning stud, you can expect some pets to be sold as show quality, based on the stud's reputation. It won't take many such breedings before his stud career is ruined. Better to miss an "iffy" service than suffer the loss of future stud services, the inevitable result of one too many compromises.

Like any other hobby, help is available. Start out with a library card. Right. Check out several books on genetics. If you plan to breed, you must develop a working rela-

genetics, you must understand pedigrees. Most people think they do, but there is one never discussed factor which can throw your calculations totally out of whack. Will we discuss it? Of course we will.

Many people throw the genetics primer in the trash when, having studied all the theory, the impossible happens anyway. There is often a reason, and rather than see you discouraged or muddling on doing random thoughtless breedings because the basics didn't work, I'll tell you the unpleasant truth.

Am./Can. Ch. Frerose's Rev. Jesse at 4-1/2 months and at 2 years of age. Owned by Frederick O. Duane and Diane Murphy, handled by Diane Murphy, judge Melbourne Downing. An outstanding young dog, proving dominant for his many virtues.

Proven Pedigrees

Before creating a litter, you must truly understand the importance of "pedigree." Every dog recorded by one of the world's registry associations has one. Some demand purity of lineage; some aren't so fussy. The American Kennel Club, the Canadian Kennel Club, The Kennel Club (En-gland), and other registries in the western world demand that all ancestors are of the same breed. None of the associations offer assurance of quality by any definition such as type, health, temperament, or structural soundness. Dog shows were invented for that purpose!

To an experienced breeder, the genealogy record may or may not be a pedigree. The hard truth is that a pedigree is not always an accurate record of ancestors and, therefore, may be useless in terms of genetic values. A person has usually struggled well past the five-year fallout period before arriving at this discomforting truth but sooner or later, everyone does. "Out" or "crossbreedings" are often alluded to in closed circles; a little dash of Papillon into a Longcoat Chihuahua breeding for example. Other mixes are known to have occurred, are dealt with by that generation of breeders, and forgotten by the next. As recently as the 1990s, AKC approved the introduction of Pointer blood into the Dalmatian breed in an effort to correct a genetic kidney problem. It caused quite an uproar among dedicated Dalmatian breeders who insisted that the problem could be avoided by selective breeding within established Dalmatian lines. They were outraged at the mere thought of another breed's "impure" characteristics filtering through their lines. Despite the controversy, by the close of this century, Dalmatian fanciers who are unknowingly working with lines descended from that "outcross" would argue that it never could have happened!

Inaccurate or dishonest listing of parents is much more common within breed lines. The sire or dam is recorded as the famous sibling instead of the non-champion, and the breeder rationalizes it as "being the same pedigree." Worse yet, the commercial operation has little concern for which male mated which bitch as long as "it's all the same breed." When confronted with the options of aborting the bitch, culling the entire litter, or selling them all as pets with no papers, even the usually honest breeder may give in to the temptation to make a "best guess" as to the sire of an accidental mating.

Make no mistake, fraudulent records exist and to those who really know the breed, they are the only logical explanation for the "unaccountable" faults which crop up in carefully bred litters. Pity the bitch owner who, having done months of careful research, makes a breeding which is guaranteed not to produce the fault he is determined to avoid, and then sure enough, the dreaded problem makes its appearance in that dream litter.

If it couldn't have happened but it did, then all you have is a piece of paper, not a pedigree.

To further complicate the intricacies of pedigree research, a widespread black market in blue slips was detailed in the *Canine Chronicle* during 1991. The operation was reported as an organized ring whose activities were well known to the AKC Board of Directors. AKC makes every attempt to protect the integrity of its stud book, but freely admits a pedigree is only as valid as the honesty of the breeder.

Although the Hershey case was curtailed by law enforcement and the AKC, the effect such huge operations have had on what is commonly referred to as "junk pedigrees" is beyond comprehension. Whether by deliberate design or genuine mixups, the likelihood of falsification increases in direct proportion to the haphazard breedings evident in a "junk pedigree."

This is not to say every champion on a pedigree actually made any great contribution to the genetic pool, but it does indicate owner commitment and the probability that such owners would no more falsify a pedigree than they would the birth records of their own children! A pedigree heavy in well-known champions and top producers is one's best assurance of accuracy in recorded lineage.

While we hope that a pedigree is a certificate of authenticity, it should also be a document which attests to careful selection of breeding partners by people who understand genetic principles. Just as important, they should have the wherewithal to develop and apply their ideals in a constructive manner. The pedigree should demonstrate a clear pattern of mating related dogs (linebreeding) which excel in overall breed type, genetic health, and proper temperament. Anything less will not reliably reproduce these qualities even though it may be a champion dog.

If you're serious about establishing a winning, healthy, dominant line which will be in demand, then the way is simple. Buy from an established, winning, healthy, dominant line! Starting with anything less puts you in a downhill mode before you've bred your first litter.

Multi-BIS Ch. O'BJ King's Ransom, ROMPX (Multi-BIS Ch. The Widow-Maker O'BJ, ROMXP x Ch. The Mad Hatter O'BJ, ROMXP) currently the #3 Top Winner of All Time. Breeder, BJ Andrews; Owner, Lewis and Julie Hoehn. Ransom represents seven generations of ROM-P sires and is the second of three generations of Best In Show winners.

Drawing the Line

Avoid pedigrees which are only a journal of haphazard matings to the day's top winners. While such matings may produce the occasional good representative, they always include unacceptable percentages of non-showable dogs.

Linebreeding (and possibly inbreeding) will be apparent on the best pedigrees. Inbreeding may be defined as combining two intensely related animals such as littermates, father–daughter, mother–son. Linebreeding is the mating of more distantly related individuals such as aunt–nephew, grandsire–granddaughter, etc. What sometimes appears to be linebreeding may actually be inbreeding due to previous in-breedings or repeated tight linebreeding. Thus, a half-brother–sister mating might actually be as inbred as a full-brother–sister breeding.

Outcrossing is mating two animals of the same breed which are in no way related. True outcrossing is almost impossible in breeds with a small gene pool. It isn't as bad as it might have been because the Akita was not a pure breed in Japan, consequently early imports represented a diverse genetic spectrum. The occasional crossbreeding (to a mongrel or a different breed) continued in this country. It wasn't until the AKC stud book closed, precluding the occasional "registered" but crossbred litter that the gene pool of the Akita became as restricted as most other breeds.

The breeding of closely related dogs will reduce the variances in the gene pool. This brings forth both good and bad characteristics, in roughly the same ratio as they existed in the parents. Wise breeders not only build a strong gene pool by linebreeding, they know how to clean the genes by deliberately bringing forth hidden characteristics so they can be identified and eliminated.

The phenotype is that which is visible to the eye: the dog as he stands before you. What you see may not be a true indication of his genotype, the invisible characteristics that he is likely to pass on as phenotype in his offspring. Tight linebreeding or inbreeding is used to strengthen genotype. One interesting form of inbreeding is mating an individual once to its parent and once to one of its outstanding offspring. The results are then compared, enabling the breeder to do a sort of genetic blueprint for that individual. If the results are extraordinary, the progeny may be back-crossed to each other, thus setting (hopefully) the desired characteristics and moving the faults even further into the remote background.

Another system of establishing a consistent line is one which I call a one-two-punch: the mating of an outstanding sire to two half-sisters which share a common parent of outstanding quality. A glance at O'BJ foundation pedigrees reveals this system at its ideal best. Sachmo (Mikado son) working with Ko-Go and Nikki, both outstanding girls sired by Yukan (half-brother to Mikado through Ashibaya Kuma), both girls out of litter sisters sired by Mikado.

Ch. O'BJ Cody of Spotted Bear, an inbred 8 week old female by Ch. Sachmo x Ch. O'BJ Nikki No Nikki. The classic father-daughter breeding earned Nikki her ROMP title.

No matter the system, inbreeding and successive linebreeding is successful only when based on outstanding individuals who are themselves free of serious genetic flaws. If you scan a pedigree and note a close breeding on an unfinished dog, you have to be very skeptical of the reasons. They are usually based only on convenience or economy.

Having said that, I can also assure you are living, breathing, cuddly puppies who have a right to live and be loved. If that's not possible due to the nature of the mistake, a breeder must mercifully destroy them. A heart-rending decision, experimental breedings are best left to those who have the fortitude to ethically handle any unpleasant results. Moreover, I can find no justification for the use of any animal with a potentially life-threatening genetic problem in order to

Am/Can. Ch. Allure's Island Shogun, ROMP (Am/Can Ch. Fu-Ki's Hideki Tojo, ROM x Am/Can Ch. Windrift's Orient Express, ROM) owned by Ruth and Robert Broskin and handled by Skip and Kathy Rayner, was #1 Akita in Breed point systems in 1986 and 1987. He ranked #3 for 1986 and #2 in 1987 Group points systems. Shogun was BB from Veteran's Class at the 1992 National Specialty.

that there is no "gene troll" living under the bridge of inbreeding. No indeed, the real bridge tender's name is "kennel blind" and it stands at both ends, taking its toll when we refuse to acknowledge the fact that only one dog in ten thousand is worthy of inbreeding on!

We must also face the probable result of trial breedings. Test matings are inherently (pun intended) likely to bring forth undesirable characteristics. In order to establish a tight line, one must make such breedings, but what on earth does one do with the unsatisfactory results? Those "mistakes"

test-mate a supposedly healthy dog. I know it has been done, but carefully kept breeding records and the moral courage to neuter both parents if the defect shows up in the progeny are the much more humane solution. There's no need to deliberately create sickly or deformed animals just to satisfy some warped need to prove one's dog to be clear of a specific problem.

Successful breeders never become obsessed with setting one virtue while letting other desirable traits become weakened. Tight linebreeding or inbreeding has many pitfalls but they are as crevices to the mountain climber. When skillfully negotiated, the satisfaction and the thrill of arriving at the summit make it more than worthwhile.

The bottom line is this: Don't try to reinvent the wheel before you know how to drive the car. Makes no sense to start out with unnecessary unknowns and uncertainties. There will be enough of those no matter how skilled you become at matching dominants and recessives. Save the experiments for a time when you're better prepared to deal with them. Take full advantage of the hard work that other breeders have put into establishing reliable bloodlines. It's the cheapest time you will ever buy!

Alphabet Superiority

OK, now let's get into the nuts and bolts of reading a pedigree and understanding all those confusing abbreviations or "letters." And by the way, don't make the mistake of buying into the letters game. Letters are important and indicate breeder commitment, but

Ch. Kicho's Dai Ichi Hotei by Ch. Cee Jay's Climax No Noroshi x Yot Club's Kicho Shuko. "Ko" is owned by Pat and Homer Ramsey.

they must be measured against the overall quality of the dog and not construed as some sort of breeding stamp of approval.

You can avoid costly mistakes. If we take off the rose-colored glasses and go to the record books, we will get a good dose of reality. The AKC stud book reveals that over 70 percent of the time even champion to champion matings produce no titled dogs. Assessing overall health and freedom from genetic defects are much more difficult, but, on average the results still fall far short of possible achievement levels. You can narrow those odds by learning how to weigh all the factors which add up to genetic strength,

prepotency, and compatibility with your bitch.

Let's examine beauty or "bench" titles which precede the name. You should be pleased if the pedigree lists the champions (Ch.) in red and, as we say, you've "gotta a lotta red." You should be even more pleased if you have other abbreviations such as Can., Mex., or Eng. preceding the Ch. title. These letters indicate the dog is a Ch. in Canada, Mexico, England, or some other country. Currently, the Fédération Cynologique Internationale (FCI), which conducts international shows, does not officially recognize American type, black-masked Akitas. Although the quality of competition and the difficulty of attaining the title varies, it is a distinct honor to achieve a Ch. title in more than one country, and it's a good indication of the owner's dedication.

"BISS" before the dog's name denotes a Best in Specialty Show win. In other words, the dog was considered by the judge of the day to be the Best Of Breed at a show held only for Akitas. That does not necessarily mean the big once-a-year National Specialty. Many regional Specialties have only a handful of semi-local champions in competition.

When trying to ascertain the value of the title or a particular win, it's helpful to know whether the dog has achieved other important wins under other judges. It's not uncommon for a dog to be flown across the country to compete under a favorable judge when a big win is up for grabs.

"BIS" signifies that a dog has gone Best In Show over all breeds. This is much more difficult for it means the dog not only had to win Best Of Breed, he also had to win the Working Group, probably under a different judge than the one who awarded him BOB. He then had to go on to defeat all the other winners of their respective Groups, usually under yet another judge. In so doing, he may have defeated as few as three or four hundred dogs at a remote show in the middle of nowhere to several thousand dogs of the highest caliber at one of the very prestigious shows.

Following the dog's name, one may run into a confusing jumble of letters, some of which are intended to indicate soundness, intelligence, or genetic dominance. Various letters are awarded by AKC for Field and Obedience titles such as CD, CDX, UD, etc. Field Ch. or OTCh. (Obedience Trial Ch.) preceding the name are usually coupled with individual Obedience titles listed after the registered name.

Other letters which may append the proper name are Register Of Merit titles. The basic "ROM" indicates a male has sired ten or more AKC champions and a female has produced five or more. An "X" means the Akita has produced at least twice that number, while the letter "P" denotes the dog has also produced ROM-titled progeny. To the serious breeder, these are the most important letters in a pedigree for they proclaim genetic strength in *all* areas by which a dog's quality can be measured. American pedigrees and

advertisements frequently contain initials such as OFA, CERF, or terms like "thyroid clear" or "vWD clear," all good indications that a dog has been certified clear of a particular health problem. There is disagreement as to which are simple hereditary problems and which are not, and to the need for routine re-certification for all developmental health problems.

The concern is that unlike the easily authenticated AKC letters, health clearances are seldom definitive and not easily verified. Eye (CERF) certification must be done yearly to remain valid. "Thyroid clear" claims are especially meaningless due to unreliable lab results, unknown breed normals, and fluctuations related to medications, stress, and other external

Ch. Mokusei's Zeus of Daitan-Ni, ROM by Ch. Golden Sun Taki Bi No Taiyo x Ch. Golden Sun Tai of Mokusei. Breeders are Curt and Sally Van Allen, and Merry and Frank Atkinson. "Zeus by the Sea" is pictured at 15 months with his owner Jeanne Galindo Hayes.

Ch. O'BJ No Jacket Required, (Ch. The Widow-Maker O'BJ x The Shadow Knows O'BJ) breeders, BJ Andrews and Ronnie Boyter. "Hanten" is owned by Sam Dasalla, Jessam Akitas, handled by Dixie Ray Perry.

so negligible as to be incalculable. Yet the OFA has raised age limits from one year to two years and cautions that dysplasia may develop after two years of age. Even more disturbing is that once a dog has received the OFA letters, it is highly unlikely to ever be re-x-rayed, even (especially) if problems develop.

In other words, a dog may be so cow-hocked, east-west, sway-backed, malformed, sickly, or lacking in type and temperament as to render it totally unfit to reproduce the species, but it can still receive "health" clearances, which to the uninformed, may be interpreted as a license to breed the dog.

I've never been nimble-footed enough to skirt slippery territory, so I'll go ahead and warn you that fraud connected with health certification is disturbingly common. One cannot charge the veterinarian with knowing each and every dog that a breeder may present. Vets see many dogs, and presenting a fawn dog over and over and over for certification in which the dog's color is not even noted can gain many false certificates for dogs which could not possibly pass examination. Tattooing is so simple nowadays, particularly when a dog is already under anesthesia, we should hope for the day when tattoo or microchip implant identification will be required before any form of health certification is given.

Even more disconcerting is the knowledge that if a suspected hip, hormone, bleeding disorder or eye problem develops, the dog isn't likely to be presented for re-certification. It may, however, continue to produce offspring while resting on the laurels of meaningless "letters."

So it is that one must take health certification with the proverbial grain of salt. The intent is admirable, but until such time as all

influences. They must be repeated at least yearly due to changing metabolism. VWD tests must also be repeated for the same reasons and are even more easily corrupted by medicines, hormonal status, injury, or poor handling of the test medium.

The initials "OFA" indicate the dog has been certified free of hip dysplasia by the Orthopedic Foundation for Animals. "X-ray clear" means essentially the same thing but may or may not indicate veterinary expertise in that field. To be "OFA certified" or "x-ray clear" means that the hip sockets were considered normal for age and breed at the time of x-ray. The certification does not mean any other joints are normal nor does it offer assurance that the animal is "sound" in the clinical sense. Because of the inconvenience and the risk of anesthesia, the percentage of re-x-rays of certified dogs is

Ch. The Sharper Image O'BJ (Ch. The Widow-Maker O'BJ, ROMXP x Ch. The Mad Hatter O'BJ, ROMXP) going B.O.B. from the classes under Lt. Col. Wallace H. Pede. Mirage is owner handled by Maria Heldman, Mariah Akitas.

dogs can be positively identified, and the official designation contains the date of the most recent certification, "letters" other than those earned in the AKC show ring and authenticated by AKC records must remain secondary to first-hand observation and careful pedigree research.

Although there have been instances of "ringers" in the show ring, it is not common. Champion and advanced obedience titles are a pretty safe bet as indicative of both mental and physical soundness. A dog which is mentally unstable, overly aggressive or timid, or which suffers from a debilitating physical impairment is unlikely to attain AKC letters either before or after the name.

Linear and Non-linear Logic

Studying pedigrees and all the wondrous information contained therein can become truly fascinating, so a word to the wise may be in order here. A person may spend years shuffling through stacks of pedigrees until he becomes so bogged down in a mass of data that he loses sight of his original goal and becomes what is commonly referred to in the sport as a "pedigree freak." This person can quote the lineage of almost any prominent dog, but has yet to breed a multi-champion litter or own a top dog.

Receiving help from other novices is to be expected when one becomes involved in a new hobby or sport. It's all part of the excitement of exploring a new interest, but when it comes to making mistakes that live on to remind us of how gullible we once were, it isn't so funny. Most advice is given in a spirit of generosity and fellowship, but it can also be prompted by resentment, jealousy, or a desire to be noticed. It's not always easy to separate well-meant advice from meaningless chitchat or even from that which is designed to mislead.

One of the most confusing bits of advice is the inevitable warning about certain "lines" or dogs said to produce bad temperaments, thyroid, long coats, missing testicles, hip dysplasia, auto-

303

Ch. Mike Truax's Pal Sunny Boy (Ch. Mike Truax's Royal Tikara Pal ROM x Ch. Tozu's Misty Morning ROM) on his way to a Group I, owner handled by Paula Ebner. Sunny's breeders are Larry Simons and Chris Weatherman.

immune, etc., etc. The list may be quite long depending on the person's repertoire and need for recognition.

Most such advice falls apart under scrutiny and raises more questions than answers when approached as a genetic practicality. For example, many of the standard bugaboos have not been established as hereditary. In addition, anyone who breeds more than three litters of differing sire–dam combinations will produce one or more of the problems that novices whisper about. But most frustrating of all, there are very few "lines" of Akitas. The breed is, after all, relatively new in this country and many breeders tend to flit from one "sure combination" to another. By definition, if it doesn't

breed notably true, it isn't a line, it's only a list of dogs which carry the same kennel name.

A *line* has been deliberately developed according to a specific pattern and has resulted in a gene pool with recognizable consistency in phenotype and genotype. A person might breed dogs for 20 years, but if they dabble in first one type and then another, crossing dogs from various kennels, which themselves are not of a line, they would have created nothing more than a hodgepodge of pedigrees. Longevity of that sort is common in all breeds but shouldn't be confused with the genetic definition of a bloodline.

Let's assume you have found the ideal

"look" and identified a line or family group which breeds true for that which you so admire. Do not then be dissuaded by the inevitable and non-specific rumors regarding "problems in the line." *All* lines have problems of one sort or another. After all, if anyone had a line proven to be clear of all undesirable common genetic problems, I'm sure they would have hastened to advertise this incredible fact! Actually, one rather well-known Akita breeder did run just such an ad in the mid-'80s. It was a joke to everyone except the innocent buyers who were taken in and publically ridiculed, and so she

must be based on a minimum of a hundred pups, let's look at just one rather common example. I know of no dog which is proven free of the longcoat gene. This does not mean only that he has sired one hundred correctly coated pups from closely related genetic combinations, but that he has done so with various partners, and that several of those bitches either are themselves longcoated or have previously produced longcoats. I know of two dogs which produced no longcoated puppies when bred to a longcoat bitch. The owners were ecstatic. But then both dogs produced coated pups

Ch. Paper Doll O'BJ at ten years young, owned by Charles T. and Nancy Calloway. She's from an all-champion litter of five (Ch. O'BJ BigSon of Sachmo, ROMXP x Ch. O'BJ Michiko of Wri, ROM) bred by Bill Warren and BJ Andrews.

dropped the idea. Other than that silly exception, I've never seen an ad which proclaimed a dog, a family of dogs, or a bloodline incapable of producing those problems which have challenged ten decades of dedicated breeders.

Perhaps as genetic engineering becomes a reality, someone will be able to honestly lay claim to having established a line free of hereditary faults. Whether such genetically engineered dogs would still resemble their respective breeds is a matter of serious debate among long-time fanciers.

Remembering that genetic conclusions

when bred to a normal-coated bitch of a different genetic combination. The owners were crushed.

Another example is that of an intensely inbred Sachmo son which was mated to a number of closely related bitches. There were no longcoats and, after several litters, we dared to claim that this marvelous dog with such a restricted genetic makeup was obviously dominant for short coats. He was subsequently bred to an outcrossed bitch and sired longcoats! We should have known better. I repeat, I know of no Akita proven clear of the longcoat gene.

It could as easily be any other recessive characteristic. Turn the logic around. Obviously, there has never been a dog who always and without fail produced spectacular heads; or tails, or rears, or whatever. Don't we wish?

Health problems must be our primary concern, but the causes won't be found in our competitor's backyard. If we are to find a solution to the increasing incidence of health-related problems, we must view the problem through something more than the wrong end of a telescope. An objective discussion of health problems can not be about bloodlines or a competitor's dog. Physical and temperament deficiencies are a reality of our time, and rather than listen to unfounded claims or advice, the wise owner will listen to his vet...and to a good friend called Common Sense.

Genetics: Health and Memory

Many breeds which have been drastically altered by man are plagued with gross physical deformities and a heavy burden of genetic abnormalities. The Akita has not yet been exaggerated in the quest for uniqueness or extremity of features which is a prerequisite for ring success in some breeds. The design of the Akita is in harmony with nature: free of exaggerated body proportions or size deviations, abnormally short legs, excessive angulation, or head characteristics which interfere with breathing, normal eye health, or other such vital functions.

One of the most whispered about and by far the most serious health concerns is auto-immune disease and, unfortunately, all breeds are vulnerable. There are many theories as to the cause for deteriorating immune systems in both humans and animals. At present, it has not proven to be hereditary but we do note a higher incidence of certain diseases within family groups. Again, that could have to do with rearing practices, geographical, or environmental influences. No one knows.

Predecessors of today's Akita suffered various degrees of radioactive exposure and lingering aftereffects. In terms of a timeframe easy to relate to, the bombing occurred only seven dog-lives ago. Radiation is known to cause genetic mutations and I'm afraid we can not overlook the possibility that the somewhat higher incidence of immune-mediated problems in the Akita and a few other breeds could be, at least in part, attributable to ancestral radiation exposure.

The increasing incidence of immune-related problems in all Western World countries (I'm not sure about other developed nations) could point towards some other broad influence. Perhaps our pets are the canaries of the 20th century. I will leave that to scientists. My purpose is simply to make you aware of a growing problem which so far has only been hinted at and is little understood.

We do know that the immune system can be challenged and weakened by certain drugs, chemicals, and antibiotics, and we should accept the possibility that the Akita may be slightly more susceptible than some other breeds.

Reproductive problems are also on the increase. Opinions as to the cause vary from one expert to another. Some experts attribute low sex drive or infertility to problems of the immune system, others to environmental influences, including the prodigious amount of vaccines in use today. Others believe it results from increasing human interference and the inevitable distancing of the canine from its natural environment.

As an aside, in 1993 the result of a study on human sperm counts was released. My figures could be off by a million or so, but the interesting fact is that 50 years ago human sperm count worldwide averaged over 300 million. The new report shows human sperm count has dropped to under 60 million in every developed country save one. Finnish men average 112 million. While discussion tactfully centers around whether or not the much lower pollution rate of Finland

Am/Can Ch. Seawood's U.S.S. Buckwheat, (Ch. Akita Tani's Daimyo, ROM x Ch. Golden Sun Seawood Wa Wa L'Wilac, ROM) is Canada's #2 Akita for 1985, owned by Alyce and Kelle Clinton. Photographed by breeder, Kelle Clinton.

Ch. Sea Breeze MS. Pinafore (Ch. O'BJ BigSon of Sachmo, ROMXP x Ch. Ali's Storm Warning, ROM) is a beautiful "hooded" bitch who finished easily and is pictured winning B.O.S. under National Specialty judge Samuel Pizzino, handled by Joel Rosenblatt for breeder Linn Greene.

contributes to higher fertility, my first thoughts were on the implications as it relates to companion animals, but I confess, my mind quickly moved on to trying to calculate the extinction of the human race based on the incredibly rapid decline of fertility rates. Incidentally, one scientist speculates that the ever-increasing levels of estrogen in the food supply are a major problem in human fertility...

Let's face it—it's far easier to base breeding decisions on more tangible, easily defined characteristics. A good front is a good front. An ugly head is something hard to hide and all the opinions or certificates in the world will not change your mind about that dog's head. While we must always consider the genotype and while the careful breeder will do everything possible to determine which recessives may crop up in a proposed mating, the successful breeder will deal with that which he can see and prove and will seek counsel only from those who have themselves achieved notable success.

Before we move on, there is one other subject which I have never found discussed in dog books. To date, genetic memory is unproven and perhaps that's why most writers avoid discussing this fascinating facet of genetic manipulation. But you guessed it, we will explore this intriguing theory first proposed by Marais in 1911. Scientists are only beginning to unlock the secrets of DNA, so who is to say that in another ten years genetic memory will not become an accepted consideration when the well-educated breeder plans a mating?

Above and Below: Am./Can. Ch. Frerose's Mr. Moto at 3 months and at 18 months, owned by Frederick O. Duane and Diane Murphy, handled by Diane Murphy.

If we first accept the premise of genetic memory, we can see that the effects are often so profound that one has to wonder why it hasn't been more widely utilized by breeders of companion animals? Simply put, here's how it works.

The mechanics of inheritance which dictate physical and emotional traits are believed to go far beyond known factors of transmission. How much of what animals do is "instinct" and how much is actually deeply imbedded memory function? Just as the DNA carries a unique code which determines eye color, bone structure, predisposition to specific diseases, biological clock, and such infinitesimally minute details as the shape and thickness of your fingernails, scientists and geneticists believe

it also carries *knowledge and abilities* pre-determined by the experiences of the individual's ancestors.

Even more bizarre, laboratory experiments proved that worms "educated" by electric stimulus and then ground up and fed to "uneducated" worms passed on the acquired knowledge. The uneducated worms avoided the electrical shocks. Although this experiment had nothing to do with *genetic* memory study, it coincidentally proved that some memories are stored at the cellular level.

Let's look at something really simple and basic. How many generations have passed since dogs had to turn 'round and 'round to flatten the grass for a bed. Why does your dog push the floor around, trying to bury the treat you just handed him? Instinct? OK, that's a good catch-all word but let's not stop there. Suppose instinct can be modified by learned behavior passed on through genetic or cellular memory? Some dogs just flop down on the bathroom floor and some simply ignore an unwanted treat.

Let me give you a couple of otherwise inexplicable examples. One of our stud dogs produced an extremely high percentage of fence-walkers. They didn't just trot the fence, they were always *upright*, walking up and down along the fence like circus

Am/Can. Ch. Sea Breeze Grand Wizard (Ch. Koma-Inu's Nukum x Ch. Alii's Storm Warning, ROM) is a multi-Group placer bred by Linn Greene, Sea Breeze Akitas.

bears. Distinctly different from the common "dancing bear act" which most Akitas will perform for their humans. Fence-walkers do it for their own amusement; they just prefer the upright position.

And then there's the left-wrist-over-right-leg pose. Many Akitas cross their front feet in some manner but a high percentage of Orca kids laid *exactly* the same way as dad, with the front feet crossed *exactly* the same way. Another stud owner has told me that her dog's progeny folds the right foot back under the leg, bending the pastern joint double. Only that foot. They never cross it over the left leg, they always bend it double and tuck it under, *exactly* like their sire.

Many Widow-Maker kids toss their heads in that expressive way which owners know means "C'mon." Ko-Go girls wagged their tails just like mom. Sachmo sons thought they were tractors and although BigSon lived with his dad, he did not learn how to pull like that from watching his sire. All Akitas pull but not that way.

In addition to owning Akitas, we have cats also, so let me give you another example. The Asian Leopard Cat defecates in water. Don't ask me why. Probably because an ancestor lived by water and was too lazy to dig in the dirt, who knows? But the incredible thing is that when the Asian

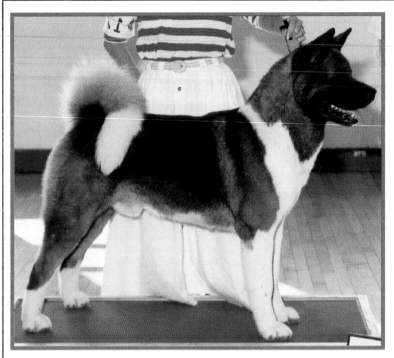

Am/Can. Ch. Torinoko's Big Jake (Ch. Ketket's Hug-a-Tuck of Khalea x Ch. Desert Sun's Kenya of Kuro) bred by Penny Trevithick and owned by Dolores Hart. Jake was ranked in the Top Ten all four years he was shown, (1988 - 1991) and racked up over thirty Group placements from a remarkably consistent string of Breed wins, handled by Don and Rhanda Glenn.

Leopard Cat is bred to domestic cats (hence the Bengal breed), it spawns a whole new behavior patten in the hybrid domestic descendants. A high percentage of F_1 and F_2 Bengal cats defecate in their water bowls. Most breeders suspend water containers to thwart the practice. Is this "instinct"? Or is it genetic memory passed on from their great-grandparents which still live in the jungle?

I'm not a scientist but it seems to me that instinct can be separated from acquired/learned behavior and genetic memory. My definition is that instinct governs that which is life-preserving or necessary to perpetuate the species. We instinctively seek shelter, build houses, grow food, and flee from danger. We do not instinctively know how to play musical instruments or fly planes. Some children do......

Not to be confused with savants, there are many documented accounts of "gifted" children who suddenly "knew" how to play an instrument...or compose a concerto. In the '50s, a 12-year-old boy darted across an airfield during an air show, managed to elude his parents and a host of would-be captors, and was next spotted as he taxied down the runway. He took off without inci-dent, flew a few loops, and then to the amazement of onlookers, landed the bi-plane safely. The incident was reported by the press, but most people buried what they had witnessed that day in the place the brain reserves for stuff it just can't catalog or accept. There have been many other examples, including the odd sensation of *deja-vu*. Perhaps you *have* "been there" before.... Genetic memory fits the acceptable level of Western philosophy much more comfortably than does reincarnation. Think about that.

Then consider why do quarter horses have "cow sense," some more than others? Cow sense is no more instinctive than is "the eye" of a Border Collie. As a student of animal behavior, I believe that these special abilities are the result of genetic memory. Somewhere along the line, a highly capable horse, blessed with extraordinary agility and responsive to an especially competent trainer, learned how to anticipate and thwart the (instinctive) attempt of a cow to return to its herd. Trust me, a horse has no instinctive desire to frustrate a cow and it's definitely not something the average ranch horse could get excited about! The above-average ability of that special horse was recognized, and built upon by wise breeders and trainers until a specific type within a breed was developed: horses with cow sense; horses with ability; horses with genetic memory upon which to build even greater skills.

Athletic skills are more difficult to attribute to genetic memory because everything has to match up just right. In addition to receiving the knowledge needed to perform a particular function, the descendent must also inherit the physical and muscular coordination. An indefinable number of genetic factors must combine in a very precise way in order for Michael Jordan's son to become a tall, hand-to-eye coordinated superstar of the basketball court. But Hank Williams's great vocal chords and musical talent could just as easily have passed on to a daughter instead of his famous son Hank, Jr.

What does this have to do with breeding superior Akitas? Everything. I ask you, what is more important to the average family? A handsome dog or one which is keenly intelligent, incorruptibly loyal, attuned to the family, dependably level-headed, non-destructive, staunchly protective, calm and courageous, and adaptable to changes in lifestyle or environment? Is it possible to develop, define, and genetically influence these behavioral characteristics? I

believe it is although I concede that it's a whole lot more intricate than figuring out genetic combinations for good fronts or little ears. As an educated public now selects specific breeds for specific lifestyles, we breeders have an obligation to provide Akitas which fit the above description. After all, haven't we already created a new generation of domestic canines who "instinctively" respond to the sound of a refrigerator door opening! Now I ask you.

COAT AND COLOR

It's usually the owners of the longcoats who speak the most eloquently in their behalf, but perhaps the strongest statement I can make about longcoats is this: To date, we have never had a dissatisfied longcoat owner. Never. To my knowledge, each and every one of our longcoats lived out their lives with their first and only family.

Donald See of Carbondale, Illinois owns

Ch. Eudoras Hugo Express (Ch. Pharfossa Maximum Overdrive x Nagas Ichiban Nare of Eudora) Breeder/Owner Mark Nisbet.

a beautiful longcoat and he says, "I truly hope all breeders who may have longcoats in their litters realize that there are a lot of people out there who do in fact *prefer* the impressive beauty of these coated Akitas. I guess if it were left up to people like (name deleted) there would never have been any Wire Fox Terriers, Rough Collies and Saints, or Longhaired Dachshunds. What a world we live in. And it gives me the shivers to think what lives in our world!!"

Donald touches on a very sad fact. Unbelievably, there are breeders who publicly state that they have or would kill longcoated puppies. Attempts to rationalize such incredibly cruel practices have even led to charges that the length of a dog's coat has some deleterious effect on health! One letter-to-the- editor queried, "Why would Akita breeders want to hide or subdue such occurrences if the longcoat has no health stigma attached to it?"

To many, that seems a reasonable enough question. The answer is so logically simple that it disgusts all ethical breeders. The public has been fed such ridiculous excuses as, it's "bad type" or that they

"Cleo" is a beautiful longcoat female owned by Donald and Janet See. Her color pattern is commonly referred to as "hooded."

require a bit more grooming, and some come closer to the truth in stating that they are "harder to sell." But what really causes all the disproportionate discussion about long coats? Only one thing. Long coats are distinctively different than short coats. While some unscrupulous breeders have actually represented that difference as being "rare" and therefore desirable, most prospective buyers nowadays are aware that excessively long coats are considered a fault. Therefore, longcoated puppies are pets because they are not so likely to win in the ring, although it is important to remember that the standard *does not disqualify* a longcoat. As a matter of fact, light bone or rangy bodies are faults specified as *serious* in the breed standard. Long coats are not.

The bottom line is and has always been: longcoats cannot be passed off as "possible show" or "breeding stock" and are therefore *economically* undesirable. The potential buyer cannot be told the fault will get better as the pup gets older, as is so often promised about light-boned, sickle-tailed, or grossly unsound puppies purported to be show quality. That, my friends, is the sole reason for all the to-do about long coats. They make wonderful pets and are just as much "Akita" as their top show-quality littermates with shorter coats. And by the way, the length of the coat is actually of less significance than is the texture and the presence of a thick wooly undercoat.

Color is another issue which just about everyone has an opinion on, including the Japanese Kennel Club. In summer of 1991 there erupted a great controversy spurred by the JKC's proposal to bar American Akitas from competition. The JKC would limit acceptable colors to white, brindle, self mask (same as basic body color) and reds with white mask and white points but *not* white markings. This proposal would, of course, disallow 99 percent of American- or British-bred dogs.

The Japanese are very astute "exporters" and no doubt are a bit more far-sighted than some of us suspect. The JKC action may have been, at least in part, a reaction to AKC's acceptance of all JKC-registered dogs. While that seems great for Japan on the surface, it was of not much benefit to the Natural Monument, the Akita. It would hardly have promoted any degree of mass importation. After all, few Japanese dogs of the past decade would be competitive under the AKC standard. Among other things, we prefer a larger, heavier boned, and overall better quartered dog than is currently favored in Japan. The banning of all "American" type, whether by design or coincidence, has resulted in a strong movement to separate the two dissimilar types, thus creating a potential export market for Japanese Akitas as a separate breed.

A few breeders began to import the type currently favored in Japan. The most popular color is the white-masked red, no doubt because it was considered "rare" in this country and therefore thought to be very saleable as distinctively Japanese. Never mind that this color pattern has existed in the U.S. since the first imports but was shunned by almost all show breeders because it unfailingly covered a dog lacking in many features required by the AKC standard!

The white-masked red color pattern (mask, throat, underbelly, etc.) is most com-

"Shibumi", a magnificent longcoat by Ch. Raiden of Jo-Uba, ROMX x Ch. Ninjo Kara Suteki, ROM, bred by Judythe Dunn, owned by Chosen Akitas, Jodi Higgins. Photo by Pawtraits.

monly found in primitive canines such as the Ethiopian Jackal, Australian Dingo, and closer to home, the Japanese Shiba. The reflective pattern is also found in wild felines such as the Tiger, Asian Leopards, Cheetah, and Jaguar. White points and undersides on an orange or rust base color are innately intriguing to most animal lovers because the pattern is usually found only in the wild. Some breeders, myself included, speculate on whether or not we truly want to introduce a primitive color pattern which could be linked to equally primitive behavorial characteristics. The American-type Akita comes in a far bigger package than the Jackal or Shiba.

It is a well-documented fact that certain colors are linked to specific genetic and physical characteristics. Solid white, not necessarily albino, has been linked to deafness and other genetic defects in many species, including canines. The early White Bull Terrier was crossed to the brindle terrier in order to eliminate deafness. It is still considered important that a White Bullie carry a color gene and many top breeders prefer a visible brindle head marking.

Going beyond the often lethal genes, to those which are linked to desirable physical features, one might note that harlequin Great Danes usually have excellent bone or that blue Dobermans have full dentition but are prone to sparse coat and skin problems as compared to the black Doberman, which is more likely to have an excellent coat. Such generalizations are found in horses, birds, cats and probably many other exhibition species.

Although no definitive study has been done in Akitas, coat color often seems linked to other physical features and possibly to genetic characteristics as well. For example, the clear fawns, golden fawns, and shaded silvers almost always have excellent coat texture with proper density and full thick undercoat. Black coats are often of a softer, shinier texture and frequently lack the dense wooly undercoat. Color-bred brindle often represents the old Oriental type and seldom covers a large dog. Japanese writings indicate that a desirable full bristling coat found on a brindle was worthy of comment. Muzzles will often be finer and bone structure somewhat more oval on reds. Whites usually have excellent coat thickness and texture and yet the percentage of white longcoats is thought to be lower.

Researchers now study pigment because of its effect on other fundamental body functions. For instance, many genes which dictate color or pattern also affect development of the fetus. They guide the cells of an embryo to its proper destination (when all goes well) so that ear cells go to the ear and

Kysami Kyodai Seiko, a Widow-Maker grandson owned by Wendy Bell in England.

an animal can hear. New discoveries have shown that defects in the agouti gene can not only wash out color but too much agouti peptide will likely result in an animal which is obese, suffers from diabetes, and is highly prone to tumors of the liver and other organs.

On the other hand, we must not confuse genetically linked color-physical-health-temperament characteristics with traits which are instead representative of a particular breeding program. It may be that marked traits are reflective of the breeder's preference and that the line is only incidentally clothed in a particular coat color.

Most breeders treasure the wide range of colors and patterns which make each Akita distinctively unique. Very few AKC breeds allow "all colors" and, to most, the exciting variations afforded under our breed standard are a constant delight. With the acceptance of Japanese-bred dogs, there is a growing interest in color specifics, so a little background on color genetics may be helpful to those who find themselves drawn to a particular color. First we should stipulate that the "white mask" (associated with white-masked reds) isn't truly white: it's a very pale cream. It isn't the same as the white muzzle markings, blaze, or stripe usually found on a dog with an otherwise black mask. Nor is it associated with the spotting "S" gene which accounts for white body and leg markings. The pale cream points are almost a perfect reverse of the Siamese gene, which darkens the extremities and face where body temperature is lower. The pattern is the result of a temperature-sensitive version of the enzyme tyrosinase, which manufactures either of the two basic pigmentations: black-brown or yellow-red. Where the animal's body is warm, tyrosinase breaks down and the melanocyte barely make any pigment at all. Perhaps the "reverse-pointed" Akita has an excessive amount of melanocyte or a reverse temperature-sensitive tyrosinase enzyme.

Reverse-point is a very primitive color package, which may explain why canines of this coloration are generally lighter in bone structure and overall substance when compared to many long-domesticated "managed" canines. Many owners report them to be of a more light-hearted, less protective temperament and also remark that they are not as dominant as Akitas of other color patterns. If this is so, it may be directly linked to the instinctive pack-orientation of similarly colored wild canines such as the Dingo and Jackal, two species which exhibit the same color pattern.

True albinism (a genetic alteration which destroys the ability of melanocytes to produce tyrosinase) is extremely rare in Akitas. A white Akita is probably a colored dog whose masking gene limits the amount of visible color. This is important because of potential problems from paired doses of the protein-altering genes associatedand

albinism, which may be lethal or result in deafness, sterility, or anemia.

Interestingly, whites come in different degrees of whiteness as is evident on the rare occasions when two whites are seen together in the ring. Breeding white to white will *not* make a whiter white any more than breeding white to red will produce lighter reds. Actually, the reverse is true; one may get more brilliant reds when one parent is white!

The spotting gene provides the white leg, tail, and chest markings (not to be confused with reverse-points). Head markings indicate the genetic color of an otherwise white dog with a strong masking gene whereas minimal body markings (mismarked pinto) represents incomplete expression of the spotting (S) gene. Most breeders wouldn't care much one way or the other except for the controversy surrounding "hooded" and "under-marked pintos." Knowing for sure whether hooded, head-marked, and under-marked pintos are all the same genetic expression would be helpful to those who wish to avoid pintos and to anyone intending to employ a white dog to brighten color but doesn't want to risk the pigment problems so often encountered in true "W" whites.

Eng/Am. Ch. Tamarlane's Veni Vidi Vici ROM (Ch. Pharfossa Outlaw Josey Wales ROM x Tamarlane's Mi-Magic, ROM). "Victor" was a top winner in both the U.S. and England where he went on lease to Mike Window for two years. He won the first ticket to Akitas in the U.K. by winning the Breed at Crufts. He became the first English champion being awarded his third ticket by Meg Purnell at the Welsh Kennel Club show, where he also won BIS that same day. He won several all-breed and specialty BISs and BOB at the national specialty. Breeder-owner, Dr. Sophia Kaluzniacki. His handler in the U.S. was always Rusty Short.

It could be that all markings are simply the result of a single spotting gene but I think not. We have personally noted a high incidence of beautifully marked pintos produced by hooded and pure white dogs as compared to those with incomplete head markings such as goggles or ear color. This would lead one to speculate that there is another gene involved.

Another interesting speculation is that a white with an honest black nose may not be a "W" white at all. He may be a hooded dog whose color ran right off the end of his muzzle, leaving behind the black nose pigment found on colored dogs! Now that may seem a simplistic way to put it but we're exploring color in layman's terms. One thing we can be sure of is whether head markings on a "W" dog, or pinto on an "S" dog, the colored portion of the coat is the dog's genetic color code.

Am/Can. Ch. Kakwa's Orca, ROMPX (Am/Can. Ch. Shuso Saki Tumi of Okii Yubi x Am/Can Ch. Langan's Amaretsu O-Mi-Kami) winning under National Specialty judge (now deceased) Mr. Edward Stevenson. Orca was bred by Andy Russell, imported by Bill and Barbara Andrews, and handled to #1 Akita Dog by Sidney Lamont.

Even though the complexities of pigmentation and cell distribution are being unraveled by universities such as Oregon Health Sciences and Vanderbilt in Tennessee, broad based color genetics research in our breed is severely hampered by the poorly designed AKC "blue slips" which effectively prevent breeders from accurately coding color. For example, silvering is a distinct limiting or bleaching gene which can no more be defined as "silver gray" than can a shaded black or black smoke simply be called "black." In cats, the smoke and the shaded genes are linked to definite physical and personality traits and, no doubt, if dog breeders had a uniform color code, we would uncover many important color-linked characteristics. Most Akitas have a lighter undercoat with the middle coat adding even more interest to a three-layered coat. The silvering gene is distinctly different than the sable gene, and that's vital if one is trying to establish a link between color and other physical characteristics, or to set a particular color within a line.

Even scholarly discussions about the stated preference for rich, brilliant color rarely make reference to yellowish or gray tarnished white markings. No amount of washing will make them white because it is a persistent manifestation of the agouti gene bleeding over the spotting gene. Most fanciers agree that tarnished markings can not be considered "clear" or "brilliant," but have no idea how to correct the problem from a genetic standpoint. Many newcomers don't even notice it and so the tarnishing gene spreads unchecked.

Mottled markings are not "clear" and "brilliant," and some breeders argue that such markings (almost always associated with tarnished whites) fail to meet the standard. Body freckles and spotting as is common in Pointers may be limited only to the white markings or they may be distributed over the body. A white body coat which is roaned, ticked, or flecked with color represents an entirely different gene than one which is "S" spotted. It is also argued that even when the white portion of the coat is a clear white, the overall effect is not one of brilliance and clarity.

Hideo Ito, a highly respected judge in both Japan and America, told me that he considers such spotting "not good." In an interview conducted in 1984, Mr. Ito referred to it as "Dalmatian" but we were interrupted before his interpreter could explain whether he meant only that it was like Dalmatian spotting or that Dalmatians were interbred with the Akita.

Predicting adult color isn't easy. Many the puppy matures. White blazes, collars, and other body markings become proportionately smaller as the body grows but the colored patches on pintos will spread and become further apart as the torso develops.

Breeders were as curious about color genetics in the 1950s as they are now. Mr. Hiraizumi, Akiho judge and officer, was questioned about how to eliminate the Kongo color. Someone wondered if breeding red to red in order to produce red would work. Mr. Hiraizumi's response is no less true today: "The concept of color breeding is good in theory, but is not so in practice.

Ch. Asahi Yama's Yuki-Ko No Shogun (Am./Can. Ch. Kin Hozan's Toklat x Aitochi's Yuki Tori) is a litter sister to Ch. Hanashi. Bred by Vel Oetmann, owned by Terry Arndt.

puppies are born very dark but lighten as they grow older. Born-black puppies may change to dark chocolate or become "shaded" by the time they are a week old. The deep chocolate puppies may continue to lighten until they are fawn or they may become rich reds at maturity. "Grizzled" puppies with distinctly black guard hair will become shaded silver or silver fawn.

The portion that is white at birth will remain white *except* that the white may become tarnished, blotched, or ticked as For some unknown reason, it was found that breeding two dogs of the same color did not produce the desired color. For example, breeding white with white did not produce a pure white."

Despite Mr. Hiraizumi's observation, Japanese breeders have often let an obsession with color get in the way of quality, a particularly frustrating situation for breed purists who try to keep up with faddish changes in Japan. Despite the current narrow scope of color and markings required by the JKC and subsequently, the FCI, mid-century Japanese breeders knew that color is linked to other physical traits. Mr. Hiraizumi demonstrates this understanding by stating, "The aka-goma Akitas produced Akitas with a tight skin and a better overall structure than the kuro-goma. Because of this, they were used heavily as stud dogs. In other words, they won prizes not because they were aka-goma but because they had a better overall structure, stronger joints, and tighter skin."

Asked why the kuro-goma coloring is undesirable, Mr. Hiraizumi explained, "dogs of the kuro-goma coloring, which began with Kongo, are generally found to display the undesirable traits of loose skin, wrinkles, and poor coat condition as depicted in Kongo. In contrast, dogs with the brindle coloring generally have a tighter skin, a good coat condition, and a better overall structure." He also stated that brindles possessed better traits both here and in Japan but warned of the difficulty in producing brindles with good facial traits.

Fujimatsu-Go, one of two original Japanese imports.

Following the Nisei Week Show, Mr. Watanabe repeated the comments of Mr. Hiraizumi. He cautioned, "as a practice, we do not try to perpetuate a single color or qualities and breed for that purpose." Egos, economy, and eclectic events have certainly changed the breeding programs in Japan some 40 years later!

Despite the Japanese preference for whites, they have not had great success in this country due to pigment problems and the confusion about butterfly noses. In the Spring 1976 *Akita Handbook*, Carol Foti summed up the dismal future of the white in a guest editorial entitled, "The White Akita ... Its American Future": "White Akitas will continue to be disqualified from the show ring... many of these animals will be of excellent conformation, temperament, and type. There is only so much stoicism in a person to persist in showing a white Akita that at any time may be disqualified, whether he is a champion or an upcoming hopeful. There will be only so many 'martyrs' for the cause as time passes."

Biscuit-colored dogs are often mistaken for "off-whites" or whites with biscuit ears. There is a distinct genetic difference in the creams, which we now believe is caused by too much agouti peptide, which blocks the melanocyte receptors that determines the depth of color. Biscuit or creams are diluted reds whereas fawns (definite beige-brown tones) are a dilute of brown, which is a dilute of black. Two entirely different genetic codes, neither of which should be confused with white. The genetic symbol for "red" is "O," meaning the natural orange color found on many mammals, including canines. "Red" Akitas are usually shades ranging from apricot to bright orange. Some are in fact sable, black over orange.

Upon close examination, seemingly white (W) dogs may also be identified as biscuit pintos. A breeder hoping for the extra depth of color often obtained by using a solid white (or possibly a hooded dog) will be sorely disappointed if he unknowingly uses a cream or a biscuit pinto instead.

Because biscuits and creams are not white, they must have black pigment. The lovely pastel shades are perfectly acceptable provided they are of clear rich tones, free of the dingy, muddy effect of an agouti coat or a dark undercoat. While the standard states the "undercoat may be a different color from outercoat," if it is darker than the outer coat and shows through, it dulls the overall coloration and can not be considered brilliant or clear.

One can twist the standard and its intent any which way, but if the coat is clear, sparkling, brilliant, and pleasing to the eye, it's okay. The wise breeder will not get caught up in fads or debates of ignorance. Perspective is vital to a successful breeding program. In other words, a dog with a weak "S" spotting factor resulting in brilliant patches of color which fail to "cover more than one-third of the body" is certainly as proper as one with tarnished or freckled white markings, a light outer coat dulled by dark undercoat, a mottled brindle, or a white dog with freckles or "Dalmatian" spots. Personally, I have found the "S" gene to be easily moved to the back burner by using good solid or self color whereas tarnished or blotched markings or body color can prove difficult to eradicate.

Based on the 1993 JKC standard, it would seem that Japan has forgotten Mr. Watanabe and Mr. Hiraizumi's insightful comments. Wise breeders in the Western countries will neither disregard established links between physical qualities and coat

Eng. Ch. Brandeezi Quite A Gent, a British-bred champion.

color nor will they breed for color at the expense of other virtues.

MATING MISTAKES

Relying on vaginal cytology (smears) to determine when a bitch should be bred is risky. There are several new advances in veterinary technology, one being the use of blood samples to measure progesterone levels. As with smears, it's important to do several tests beginning early in the bitch's estrous cycle, thereby establishing a baseline from which a more accurate prediction of ovulation can be made. Not to discount any of the marvelous scientific advances, but by far the most reliable test is the experienced stud dog!

Before we go one step further, please, read this paragraph twice! Never attempt a mating during the heat of the day. Never use a stud dog when he's just been fed. Never allow him to "tank up" during or immediately after a mating attempt. A stud with a belly full of food or water is not at his best. More important, the likelihood of gastric torsion brought on by strenuous exercise is a very real danger. Remember when your mom wouldn't let you eat and then go swimming? Remember those stomach cramps she warned you about? Well, your stomach is better situated than a dog's, which is "suspended" and very prone to twisting when it's overly full and jostled about during exercise. "Bloat" in dogs can be fatal within 30 minutes.

Did you read it twice? Please. Whether you own a stud dog or not. Be aware. It doesn't just happen during ill-timed matings. Any form of hard exercise immediately before or after food or in conjunction with the consumption of large amounts of water is likely to produce bloat.

It's up to the stud dog owner to study Mr. Macho's signals. With experience and a good rapport, the stud owner will usually be able to predict precisely how many days until the bitch will be ready for mating.

All dogs have their own style of romancing the bitch but working (active) studs soon learn the practicality of a courtesy mount. The experienced stud dog, having first said hello, then checked her scent (particularly in her urine), will double check what his nose told him by placing a foot across her back. If she stands, he will apply a little more pressure, actually rising up on his back legs. If she continues to stand, he will quickly straddle her, swing his rear quarters around in alignment with hers, and grabbing her about the waist, he will attempt penetration.

It may be a successful first attempt but many bitches flirt, flag, and even tolerate a courtesy mount for a day or so before they stand for actual penetration. If the working stud dog indicates "all systems go" and smears or progesterone tests support his conclusion, and yet all efforts to effect a tie have failed, owners should consider artificial insemination rather than

let her peak ovulation period go by.

Akita bitches do not ovulate on the eleventh day. Or the ninth day. Or any other specific day that the books say hormone levels will peak, and especially not on the days bitch owners have scheduled for the trip! Some ovulate as early as the third day of noticeable discharge. This may follow a "silent" season of a few days' duration. Some very fertile bitches wait well over two weeks in order to ensure a full entourage of suitors! Many breeders note that good matings which occur at 16 to 20 days often produce exceptionally large litters.

Some bitches really throw schedules out of kilter by having a "split" or "wolf" season. They seem to be in estrus, discharge begins, they flirt and flag, but good studs are not keen about breeding them and within a few days, the season subsides! Just about the time the owners and vets have quit wondering what happened and gone on to worry about something else...usually two or three weeks later, she comes into a full season. Were she in the wild, the primitive cycling pattern would ensure that all males in her area have been alerted and are standing by for the onset of the important event. It's just part of nature's wondrous plan for ensuring continuation of the species.

A "visiting" bitch which is severely stressed may go out of season. If a vet disputes this statement, change vets. Even more amazing, if she's allowed to stay near the stud dog and she comes to trust the new surroundings, she may resume cycling within a few days! Her instincts told her to "shut down," that the new territory might not support her litter. This is not really remarkable to those who understand canine reproduction. Just as the number of daylight hours control the onset of estrus, stress and uncertainty may entirely halt the process. Unless the bitch can be delivered to the stud well in advance of her breeding time, it's better to present her when she's in full-standing heat—just as the follicles are about to rupture or the eggs have just been shed.

Never, never muzzle the stud dog. That's like asking a pro golfer to play with one hand tied behind his back! If truly necessary, a soft velcro muzzle may be used on a really difficult bitch, but it is far better to let time, Mother Nature, and a little courting accomplish the feat. We have a saying that a glass of wine works wonders....not for the dogs, but for the nervous owners who keep getting in the way!

Speaking of courtship, allow the dogs to engage in a bit of play. It's safer to do this on lead (being careful not to tangle them up) in case the play gets too rough or the male attempts to mount too hastily. A good working stud dog will readily breed while on leash and in fact, many males prefer their owner's help. Older dogs especially appreciate a steadying hand on a giddy bitch. They are not as interested in the preliminaries; they just want to get down to business.

One of the most frequently heard complaints involving the mating itself is not

Ch. Daijobu's Joto (Ch. O'BJ BigSon of Sachmo, ROMXP x Ch. Maxwell's Kuro Ban Kuma, ROM) bred and owned by Charles T. Bell. Pictured at 5 months, Joto finished at 9 months, and later became the sire of Ch. The Mad Hatter O'BJ, ROMXP.

achieving a tie. While it's not necessary for conception, a tie is certainly regarded as an integral part of a successful mating. Failure to tie may be due to many factors, most of which are easily solved by time, patience, and a little expert advice. In order to facilitate the full penetration necessary to effect

Regalia's Mountain Man (Ch. The W. W. Coal Miner O'BJ x Ch. O'BJ One-of-A-Kind) bred and owned by Carol Laubscher, shows exceptional development for a seven months old puppy. "Timber" is the result of double-up linebreeding on Ch. The Widow-Maker O'BJ, ROMXP and Ch. The Mad Hatter O'BJ, ROMXP.

Am./Can. Ch. Frerose's Tugger The Slugger at 3 months, and at a very impressive 7 years 10 months old. Owned by Frederick O. Duane and Diane Murphy.

heat, she will either not tilt her pelvis or worse yet, she'll hump her back, drop her tail, and actually cause the pelvis to slant at a downward angle. More emphatically, she may simply "sit on it."

It's up to the stud dog owner to accurately diagnose the problem. If she's physically ready but is frightened; or she's dog aggressive and resents the dominant posture the male takes in the courtesy mount; or she's inhibited by the owner's presence; or perhaps she has a good temperament but simply hates the sight of the stud dog; then chose the right solution—wait a day, comfort the bitch, tell the owner to go hide, or resort to artificial insemination (AI).

If, however, the bitch is in standing estrus, the stud dog is valiantly attempting to achieve his goals, and still no tie is happening, you may consider an obstructive membrane (hymen) as the probable problem. The bitch owner should request the veterinarian who issues a brucellosis certificate to perform a complete health, reproductive workup, and pre-breeding digital exam on a maiden bitch. It's not uncommon for Akitas to have an extremely thick vaginal membrane which can cause confusion for the inexperienced owners and, unbelievably, even for their vets. A simple and solvable problem becomes compounded if the stud-dog owner hates to admit that his dog can't tie the bitch. Often the bitch just doesn't get bred, the owner isn't told the truth, and therefore has no idea of the problem the next time she is sent to be mated.

Any good vet can do a simple digital examination to determine if a persistent membrane is present. If an obstruction is detected in a maiden bitch, minor surgery will be necessary. The membrane need not be removed, only incised, and this can be done by a veterinarian with no, repeat, no anesthesia. It's a simple procedure which most bitches tolerate very well. Akitas have a very high pain threshold and the estrous bitch is unusually

a tie, the bitch must lift her pelvis. This is called "flagging." Flipping her tail to one side, she will tilt her posterior, thus "presenting" the stud dog with the proper angle needed to achieve a tie. If the bitch is frightened, shy, sensitive, inhibited, or, as is more often the case, not in full-standing

tolerant of vaginal pain. Let her stand right up on the table. Do not force her to lie down; it isn't necessary and will only upset her. It will only take a minute. Do not leave her at the clinic. If the vet can't do it then, take her elsewhere or bring her back later in the day. Hold her head and scratch her under the tummy. The incision will bleed a bit but she can be mated immediately afterward and in fact, this is probably less painful than it would be to wait until the next day when some degree of soreness has set in.

If the veterinarian feels it's a big deal, or says he must anesthetize her, seek a second opinion. If he suggests artificially inseminating her, with the thought that delivery of the whelps will rupture the membrane, by all means, get a second opinion. There is rarely any reason to risk the bitch to anesthesia; a mild tranquilizer and gentle handling will be sufficient for even a very nervous, wiggly bitch. And there is never a valid reason to risk the whelps or subject the bitch to a cesarean section. It would be next to impossible for the first puppy to push through a membrane which defeated the efforts of a working stud! Dilation of the cervix will not rupture or stretch it enough to allow normal delivery of the whelp. I believe this undiagnosed or uncorrected condition accounts for many emergency C-sections, particularly when the second litter brings about a second cesarean.

Another problem is a small vulva, or a dry or tight vagina. If the two partners are willing and anxious but unable to accomplish the tie, try applying a water-based personal lubricant or some other non-spermicidal lubricant. It will make things much easier for both animals and alleviate anxiety for their respective owners!

Am./Can. Ch. Kim-Sai's Buster of Frerose as a fully mature animal. He was the #1 Akita in Canada in 1981, bred and owned by Frerose Akitas and Shibas. Our thanks to Fred Duane and Diane Murphy for helping depict growth and development stages in some of the breed's most famous dogs.

When the mating is completed, encourage the male to urinate. Always make sure he is fully retracted before putting him away and be sure the penile sheath is turned right side out again, particularly if the tie is broken or interrupted. On rare occasions, a dry sheath may turn inward as the penis retracts, causing unnatural swelling. Permanent and serious damage can quickly result.

Two breedings are standard although some young males which are seldom used will benefit from three or more. If the bitch is willing, allow them to mate three or four times over a four- to six-day span. Some bitches will stand only a day or so, some will remain in standing estrus for a full week. When either dog says "enough," consider her well covered.

One more tip. Put the bitch on raspberry tea leaves within a week or two after mating—dried leaves on her food (no need to brew them!). They do work, particularly in older bitches who may be prone to uterine inertia. We put moms-to-be on them as soon as they are bred and continue through the first week post-whelp.

WHELPING TO WEANING

Count 58 days from the first mating. I know the books say 63 but this book is about Akitas and they rarely go past 60 days before presenting an astounded owner with the first puppy. Gestations of 58 days have been documented. Short gestation may also explain why Akita pups open their eyes later than most breeds. They arrived early and therefore their 13th day may be only the tenth. Who knows? Just don't expect to see eyes on the tenth day and as long as there is no sign of infection, don't worry about them.

A couple of other points. Please don't drive your bitch crazy by constantly removing her bedding during whelping. Wherever you have put her for the whelping (which should have been done at least a week before her first due date) is her *nest*. In the wild, it would be undisturbed through the whelping process. She would have tunneled under a log, into the side of a bank, or some similar protected spot. The pups would be delivered in a hollowed-out depression onto clean, absorbent earth and she would eat the afterbirth, thus keeping the nest clean.

Even the most experienced brood bitch, who has long ago learned to tolerate our helpful interference, will be stressed by the constant upheaval of her nest. Invariably she's interrupted and made to get up just as she's about to have a productive contraction. And then we wonder why even young bitches suffer from uterine inertia or prolonged labor!

The solution? Have a waste pail, several rolls of good-quality paper towels, some old bath towels, a handy stool (I use an antique milking stool, it's perfect) and a roll of *un*printed newspaper on hand. Line the center of

A six-week-old puppy out of two of the breed greats, Sachmo and Ko-Go. Breeders, BJ and Bill Andrews.

A children's wading pool is the best possible whelping area because it's circular. In the wild, dogs dig round (not rectangular) holes to whelp their litters. Healthy moms keep their puppies clean all the time.

the plastic child's wading pool with the clean newspaper. (I did tell you to throw away those cumbersome, *square,* unsanitary, expensive "whelping boxes," didn't I?)

Oh, and about newsprint. Newspapers were designed to be read, not consumed, and the amount of ink ingested and absorbed during whelping is nothing less than frightening. If you doubt this, rub your hand over a page of newsprint. Then imagine your dirty hand had been a wet sponge. Many of the colored inks are toxic. While the bitch may lie in wait on newspapers and shred them to her heart's content, be sure to change to unprinted paper and paper towels before the actual birth process.

When the first pup is about to arrive, raise the bitch's tail and tuck several thicknesses of paper towel right below her vulva. When the whelp pops out, the paper towels will catch the gush of birth fluids. While she's busy cleaning him, lift her tail (wiping it if need be) and change the paper towel padding. She may catch you at it and be suspicious that you are stealing what looks like a puppy, so let her check it out. She will wonder why you want that paper but, be assured, it will stress her much less than tearing newspaper out from under

her, lifting, and rolling her back and forth while you struggle to put clean paper back under her body.

Between pups, use the soft paper to tidy up her rear quarters and tail. Do not lift or otherwise disturb her. The paper towels will absorb the drainage which occurs as she strains between pups, and you can remove it to your heart's content without upsetting the new mom. If you're whelping her in a plastic pool (you should be), a shallow channel will develop at the outer circumference. Keep this handy depression lined with paper towels. As she moves and scoots around the *natural* circular whelping pool, you can keep a fresh thickness of paper toweling tucked under her tail.

If need be, you will also find paper towels do a much better job drying the pup, instantly drawing moisture from the baby so that you can quickly give it back to mom rather than continue to handle it. Caution, if necessary to sling a gasping or stillborn pup, wrap it in a terry-cloth towel to prevent the possibility of losing your grip.

What to do with those bath towels I told you to have ready? We are frequently asked why our incidence of hip dysplasia is so low as compared to the norm for the breed. We believe that the development of hip dysplasia can be prevented by a number of commonsense precautions taken by the breeder, the first having to do with the whelping environment. Man has never been able to improve on Nature's grand design, but smart breeders will take a lesson here. No self-respecting mother dog would injure and frustrate her newborns by causing them to struggle and over-extend their little legs, trying to muscle up to the milk bar. If we didn't interfere, they would be born on Mother Earth where they could use those well-developed toe nails to gain traction. On newspaper? They spend every waking moment trying to go somewhere on a slippery surface, rather like you trying to walk up a frozen slope day in and day out. Since we won't let her dig a hole in our king-size bed, or (to her preference) under the house, we can at least provide good traction for her babies! So, fold a towel double and place it along the bitch's belly, taking care to lift and tuck it under the lower row of faucets as whelping progresses and her milk really begins to flow. As she scoots or gets up and lays back down, re-anchor the towel under her brisket, breasts, and back thigh. It will become soiled during delivery but if you wait until she's already up, or being walked, or busy with a new arrival, you can quickly remove the wet towel and replace it with a clean one, put down right over the "soiled" pad of newspapers so that it still smells like her nest. The next day you can replace it with a pretty throw rug if you insist.

If the bitch wants to remove the afterbirth in her own practical way, do not interfere with her. Consuming the placenta will do her no harm, in fact, Nature conveniently planned it to nutritionally sustain her through several days of "laying in."

If you didn't buy a child's plastic wading pool, the kind with no built-in seats or slides, please, try to find one now. Your regular department stores always display them during the summer months. The 40-inch diameter (across the bottom) is perfect for the Akita. A piece of carpet under the pool will prevent it from scooting or clattering on hard floors, especially if used with one of those anti-skid carpet mats designed to hold throw rugs in place on hardwood floors.

When she has completely finished whelping and had that deep sleep, which you will come to know means she *is* done, you may replace the old newspapers with a piece of jute-backed carpet, cut to fit inside the pool. A soft cotton (receiving) blanket should be used to cover the carpet and can be easily changed and washed. Polyester or nylon blankets are hot and uncomfortable. Furthermore, whelps will often develop irritated tummies from the friction of materials high in static electricity and low in absorbency.

You may need to turn the carpet over so that she can lie on the bare backing. If she's too warm, she'll scratch up the bed, instinctively trying to "dig" down to cooler earth. A comfortable bitch is less likely to dig, thus covering her puppies and increasing the likelihood that she will inadvertently lie down or step on one.

I realize that most books advise that puppies must be kept in 80-degree temperatures for the first few days but trust me, this does not apply to Akita puppies! I couldn't begin to count the number of calls I've had from frantic owners with problems such as "the bitch won't stay with the puppies," "the puppies keep crying and crawling around," "she keeps laying on them," "she keeps scratching up her bedding." All of these problems are the result of overheating. Only a really cold nest box will require a heat lamp or pad, and then only for the first 48 hours or so *and* only in one-third of the nest.

Pups should be just a little cool when not lined up against mom's warm tummy. It keeps them gathered up, "piled" as puppies should be. Mama dog must be able to get in and out of her bed without treading on puppies which are scattered in all directions. Puppies which are too hot will not pile. They crawl away from uncomfortable heat, even mom's breasts! Don't let anyone tell you that their little thermostats are not yet operating. Just be observant and act accordingly.

External deformities will be obvious at birth and should be dealt with by your veterinarian. Internal abnormalities may be

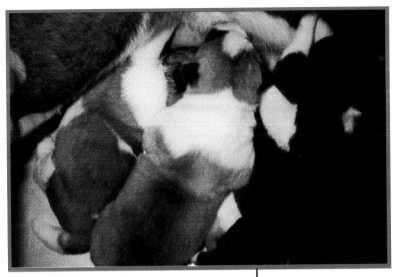

While the puppies are nursing from their dam, their waste is licked away by the dam. Once the puppies begin to eat solid food, the dam no longer cleans their feces.

suspected in the tiny, weak, or fading whelp who fails to dramatically respond to extra help. Frail or underdeveloped whelps are a discretionary decision on the part of the breeder. Everyone has heard about the runt that wound up being the largest in the litter or went on to become a Best In Show winner. While such things do happen, the odds are astronomically against it.

Akitas are remarkably resilient dogs, even as newborns. A puppy which was crowded in the uterus or which is born weak or exhausted from a prolonged arrival will usually do quite well if given assistance for the first 24 hours. You may need to mark the puppy for identification so you can be sure that it finds and retains a nipple until his tummy is full. Remember that pups quickly develop nipple preference and ranking so make sure you put the weak pup to a nipple he likes and then use the same one each feeding. Once an otherwise normal but weak puppy has missed a few feedings or been repeatedly rooted away from his place at the lunch bar, he will quickly fall even further behind.

Happy, healthy, unstressed moms keep their pups spanking clean, licking them to stimulate bladder and bowel. This continues until they begin to eat meat, which in the natural environment, she would regurgitate for them. (Although I firmly believe in natural methods, I draw the line at fixing the pup's first "natural" meat meal!) When the pups begin to eat solid food, the feces is no longer a by-product of the dam's own body fluids and she will cease to lick the pups to stimulate them. No problem. Instinctively, the pups begin to move further from the sleeping part of the nest to relieve bladder and bowels and if not already climbing over the sides, they must be taken out of the whelping pool by 21 days. By four weeks, they insist on going outside the "den" area to eliminate and the wise owner will provide a larger area for them.

Older bitches or those which are in soft, flabby condition may experience prolonged labor, during which calcium levels drop, and this in turn leads to uterine inertia. We hate to disturb a bitch for a trip to the veterinarian. Firstly, the cervix is open, making her very vulnerable to infection. Secondly, it would be extremely stressful at a time when her resistance is lowered and the vet's office is the most likely place to encounter germs—that's where sick dogs go. The birthing should not be interrupted unless you and your vet have agreed by telephone that it is an emergency and not just nervousness on your part.

The bitch may need a hormone shot

but it often isn't as effective in the bitches who need it most due to decreased calcium levels. We always offer powdered nonfat milk diluted in cool water, which seems to help keep the calcium level up and the uterus contracting properly. And, of course, hard-working moms get very thirsty and love the milk.

If a bitch becomes nervous and you are sure it's not the onset of eclampsia (which must be immediately treated by your vet), she should respond to a calcium tablet combined with 500 mg vitamin C. Both have a calming effect and vitamin C is one of those water soluble vitamins which are depleted by stress. Repeat in two hours if needed and continue daily vitamin C.

If she has only one surviving pup, you should stimulate him mentally and physically several times a day. Push him off the nipple, move him away from the bitch's udder. Roll him gently from side to side to help prevent "swimmer" syndrome. He has no sibling competition and will suffer for it in many ways unless you help him to develop normally.

I know you have been told to wean the pups onto baby cereal or soaked puppy food. Don't. Again, no food manufacturer can improve on Mother Nature's plan. Carnivores are intended to eat meat. With weanlings, the first meat meal will probably be the regurgitated remains of the hunt.

Relax, I'm not suggesting that. There are limits! But lean fresh ground hamburger? You betcha! Start small at day 21 and

Three-month-old "Nacho" with his Gumabone® Wishbone® enjoying a rest from puppy games.

graduate to golf-ball sized meatballs twice daily by 28 days, then you can begin to mix the meat with ever-increasing portions of soaked puppy food.

Large-breed dogs do quite well on two feedings a day; puppies are no exception. We encourage nursing and allow mom to sleep with the pups well into the seventh week (sometimes longer!) so they are getting milk from her during the long night and early in the morning before you prepare breakfast. Good-quality kibble, veggies, and meat, served morning and evening, will raise healthy pups with good muscle tone and sturdy bodies.

If you insist on weaning them early to sell them early, this discussion isn't for you. If you want to raise the babies properly, that also means allowing a good mother dog to do her job properly! If we didn't interfere, she would continue to nurse them well past eight weeks. That's why those sharp little fangs are called "milk teeth." They aren't much good for anything other than hanging onto the faucet.

Treat for internal parasites. We worm three times before the pups go to new homes. Today's wormers are relatively safe. Certainly, they are less harmful than a belly full of worms.

Don't over stress the immune system with too many shots. We give the first combination shots at seven weeks and booster every three to four weeks until 16 weeks of age. There is growing concern over modified live vaccines and it would be prudent to do your homework regarding this subject. You should consider possible long term

Tamara Warren is presenting a pup to Ch. Ko-Go, who always loved puppies (a necessary trait for a bitch who would become the #2 Dam of All Time).

effects now when planning your vaccination program for the babies.

So what does this all mean? What does it take to breed the best? First, the ability to truly read a pedigree. The certain knowledge that it *is* a pedigree. Then the assurance that like does beget like. Handsome, sound, properly constructed dogs who move well, show well, and hold up under the stress of a successful show career are those who are most likely to produce offspring with the same characteristics.

One must have the ability to recognize quality, even in it's roughest form. How else is one to know a truly sound, typy dog? The ability to assess quality is known as having "an eye for a dog." Even some beginners have that talent. Lastly and most important of all, one must make the complete commitment: A steadfast commitment to excellence and an uncompromising but ethical pursuit of the total dog. The truth is, volumes have been written about breeding top show dogs, but, my friends, it's just that simple!

At ten weeks of age, Tex weighs in at 25 pounds. Tex is owned by Jim Clark and bred by the author.

Hall Of Fame

WHY REGISTER OF MERIT?

It has been said that a poor-quality bitch bred every season can achieve her ROM title; likewise a stud dog who services dozens of bitches is sure to earn his Register of Merit. Both hypotheses are possible but, in actual fact, it rarely happens.

Only the most outstanding male would be likely to have more than a dozen bitch owners interested in his services and willing to pay the proportionately hefty stud fee. And if that super dog was unable to transmit his superior quality or produced too many genetic problems, he would soon be dismissed by smart breeders. Then too, if a popular stud, or one used heavily by his owner, failed to produce more virtues than faults, simple math tells us that the number of inferior puppies would be noticed. Bitch owners would wise up and "Super Stud" would eventually fall from favor.

True, there are breeders who are so determined to have an ROM-titled dog that they personally show every pup that has even a slight chance to finish. Some breeders foot the bills in order to ensure that owners gain a championship on as many pups as can be added to a list. While anything is possible, these examples are notable exceptions to the way most dogs earn their ROM.

And nothing changes the bottom line. No matter how it's gained, an ROM title is five to ten times more elusive than a Ch. title because that's how many champions it takes in order to earn the ROM.

For the mathematician in you, here's a sobering statistic: for every ROM title earned by truly outstanding sires and dams, there are several hundred so-so litters produced. Only an infinitesimal number of Akitas that produce multiple litters ever achieve their ROM title.

Therefore, the inescapable conclusion is that "ROM" places a dog or bitch in the top two or three percent of all breeding animals. And that's a very clear statement of genetic superiority.

Ch. Sakusaku's Tom Cat Go, ROMP (Jap. Gr. Ch. Teddy Bear of Toyo Haishi Seiko x Jap. Gr. Ch. Haru Hime) was bred by Don and Barbara Confer. He was owned by Joan Linderman, later sold to Terry Wright. A dominant sire, Tom Cat's most famous son was "Chester" formally known as Ch. Gin Gin's Haiyaku Go of Sakusaku. Photo courtesy of Terry Arndt.

EARLY ROM

We're often asked , "How did the Register Of Merit get started?" Most fanciers assume that ACA has always kept those records. Well, ain't so, so let's set the record straight, pun intended.

One must remember that this is a relatively new breed and in the '50s and '60s, Akita owners were a dedicated but mostly inexperienced group of dog lovers. Even as local clubs began to evolve, most were formed by people new to the sport and none were very farsighted about record keeping. Even the new Akita Club Of America was unconcerned with record keeping or archives and the same can be said now, a ,few decades later.

Genetic research was virtually impossible, show records were inaccessible to average owners, and outrageous claims went unchallenged. Some sort of order and reliable information was desperately needed. Sue Oswald, in an article about the Register Of Merit, sums up the early '70s very well, "When I first came into the breed, there was a pitiful lack of information. The Akita Club Of America was virtually nonexistent due to internal problems, there were no publications, few local clubs. My goal was set early—to become a respected breeder. But to accomplish that, I needed facts."

She found them in a labor of love by this author called the *Akita Handbook.* Having published the well-received *Rottweiler Handbook,* I felt that something similar was needed for students of the Akita breed. With the help of my teenage daughter, I published the *Akita Handbook* in 1973. Along with complete show reports, pedigrees, and photos, it included the first AKC report of Top Producers—a statistical list dubbed Register Of Merit. The *Akita Handbooks* were the only comprehensive record of the breed's development in U.S. show rings. Just recently, the *Handbooks* were liberally quoted in a *Dog News* Breed Histories series by renowned statistician and AKC judge Harold Schlintz.

Ch. Akita Tani's Daimyo, ROMXP. Son of Akita Tani's Tatsumaki, bred by Liz Harrell. He was owned by E. Martinelli and G. Kerr and is one of the top producing sires of all time.

The requirements for ROM titles were upgraded in the 1974 *Akita Handbook* and by 1975, second-generation ROM dogs were appearing and prepotency patterns were emerging. In 1976, the last year the *Akita Handbook* was published, I once again stiffened ROM requirements, still giving credit for ROM progeny.

The '70s were boom-time for the breed. The point system was low (four of the same sex made a major) and most dogs were owner-handled. It has been said that ROM titles came easily back then and, to some extent, that is true. But when one looks at the Early Register Of Merit (EROM) dogs and their descendants, one is impressed by the positive influence many of them had on the breed.

EARLY REGISTER OF MERIT (EROM)

CH HOZAN OF MATSU KAZE *sired:*

CH MATSU KAZE'S KAYALA OF KINOUK	(f)	9/01/74
CH MATSU-KAZE'S KUROSHIMI	(m)	2/01/75
CH MATSU KAZE'S KURO TENNO	(m)	5/01/75
CH KIN HOZAN'S SHOKIN	(f)	5/01/76
CH MATSU-KAZE'S DEACON OF CHEREED	(m)	2/01/76

CH KITA MARU *sired:*

CH REMWOOD'S KOYIKO NO NAN CHAO	(f)	12/01/74
CH TANO KITA MARU TU NO REMWOOD	(m)	12/01/74
CH REMWOOD'S OSOROSHII KUMA	(m)	1/01/75
CH REMWOOD'S MIKADO JO	(m)	12/01/75
CH TANO SUZU	(f)	5/01/76
CH REMWOOD'S KIRA KIRA NIKKO	(f)	11/01/76
CH TANO DAISHERO SAN	(m)	11/01/76
CH REMWOOD'S KIEKO MARO	(m)	9/01/77

CH SAKURA'S BUSHI, CD *sired:*

CH KURO PANZU MARU NO ASAGAO, ROM	(f)	9/01/73
CH KRUG'S ICHIBAN AKEMI-GO	(f)	9/01/73
CH KRUG'S KOKO	(f)	12/01/73
CH SAKURA'S ENSHO, CD	(f)	6/01/74
CH ASAGAO'S MAGOKORO	(m)	8/01/74
CH SAKURA'S FUTOKOROGATANA	(m)	1/01/75
CH SAKURA'S GENSEN	(f)	1/01/75
CH LACHLEA'S ANA JOGI	(f)	11/01/75

KRUG'S SANTO *sired:*

SAKURA'S CHUJITSU (EROM)	(f)	
KRUG'S TEKIHIME (EROM)	(f)	
KRUG'S SOTTO (EROM)	(m)	
CH SAKURA'S DONSU	(f)	3/01/74
CH SAKURA'S DANGAN, CDT	(m)	4/01/74
CH KRUG'S TOSHIKO	(f)	11/01/74
CH KRUG'S DAIYUSEI	(m)	6/01/75

KRUG'S SOTTO *sired:*

O'SHEA PRINCESS BARA GO, ROMP	(f)	
CH MER PRINCE SUNA GO	(m)	11/01/73
CH BRENRICK'S KURO KUMA	(f)	12/01/73
CH MER PRINCE TAKSAN GO	(m)	12/01/73
CH O'SHEA PRINCESS HANA GO	(f)	9/01/74

ROWDY SAN *sired:*

CH GAYLEE'S O'KAMINAGA, ROM	(m)	1/01/75
CH BIFU NATSU HIME	(f)	7/01/75
CH BIFU NIKKEI TAIKO	(m)	11/01/75
CH SHOGUN'S KEMURI KUMA	(m)	1/01/76
CH GAYLEE'S SAKANITUYA	(f)	2/01/78
CH ARIGATO MIKO'S BRANDY	(f)	1/01/79
CH BIFU'S ICHIBAN	(m)	7/01/80

AKA GOMA JOO GO *produced:*

CH O'SHEA ISSEI MISAO HIME GO	(f)	7/01/75
CH O'SHEA ISSEI SHOZO GO	(m)	11/01/74
CH O'SHEA ISSEI YOSHIME GO	(f)	10/01/75

AKIJIKAN NO BOSHOKU KIN JO TEI *produced:*

CH GOLDEN SUN'S KUROMAKU	(m)	11/01/77
CH GOLDEN SUN'S RISING STAR	(f)	4/01/75
CH GOLDEN SUN'S HACKI MITSU KUMA	(f)	2/01/76
CH GOLDEN SUN'S KIKU HIME	(f)	7/01/75

KUMA'S AKAI-KOSHO GO *produced:*

CH MITSU KUMA'S SATOHIME-GO	(f)	7/01/74
CH MITSU KUMA'S TORA-OJI-GO	(m	7/01/73
CH MITSU KUMA'S O-KASHIHIME-GO	(f)	11/01/73

SAKURA'S CHEI, CD *produced:*

CH SAKURA'S ENSHO, CD	(f)	6/01/74
CH SAKURA'S FUTOKOROGATANA	(m)	1/01/75
CH SAKURA'S GENSEN	(f)	1/01/75

Ch. Okii Yubi's Sachmo of Makoto, ROMXP (Mikado No Kin Hozan, ROMP x Juho Mariko No Kin Hozan, ROMP) is the #2 Sire of all Working Breeds with 101 AKC Champion get from a lifetime total of forty-nine litters. He was owned by Bill and Barbara Andrews.

ACA AT LAST

Due to family and business pressures, I discontinued the *Akita Handbooks* but kept the data base current until giving the records to Sue Oswald. She carefully validated and continued the ROM except for tabulating ROM progeny which was admittedly, an arduous task.

Many years later, as the ROM Committee Chair, Sue wrote the REGISTER OF MERIT HISTORY. "When we moved to Florida, and I became a member of the Akita Club of Tampa Bay, the idea of an official ROM was born anew. I knew BJ Andrews had begun an ROM project during the early years of AKC recognition. This project was not picked up by the ACA which was basically non-functional at the time. Being breeder-oriented, I thought this was an excellent project and that something should be done to bring it back and make it an official title. When I discovered others in our small Tampa club were equally enthusiastic, we applied to the Akita Club Of America for member club status and when that was granted, we submitted our Registry Of Merit proposal and in August of 1980, the Registry of Merit became an official title.

"A great deal of thought went into setting the requirements. We wanted the ROM title to be an 'exclusive' achievement, yet be within reach of the small infrequent breeder also. We feel this goal has been achieved by the present requirements.

"Another project of our club's original proposal to the ACA was item #6: Any dog or bitch earning an ROM title several years ago will, of course, retain that title, but we will not include their name on the new list unless they meet the new requirements." These are the Akitas who earned their ROM through BJ's system in the early years.

"The first official ROM list contained the names of 13 stud dogs and 27 brood bitches. From there, the list has grown and will continue to grow with the names of great producers owned by breeders who knew their craft.

"In closing, I would like to say I am very proud to be involved in the ROM project. These beautiful animals are the backbone of our breed. Congratulations and continued success to all of you who are blessed with one or more of these extraordinary producers!"

The persistence of Sue Oswald and the Tampa Bay Akita Club finally paid off. After *ten years* the Akita Club Of America officially adopted my original Register Of Merit system with the exception that credit was no longer given to those dogs who produced ROM-titled offspring. Calculations reverted simply to counting Champions, casting aside the significance of genetic prowess. This was sad, especially for those early breeders who recognized the importance of building on prepotent lines. They were left on their own to laboriously piece together the fabric of genetic dominance and few had the time or patience to burn midnight oil in order to illuminate the pathways to success.

Further complicating serious research, outrageous claims once again became common, as will happen when there is no standardized reference. That breeders were confused was evidenced by the wide variations in type and quality which flooded rings of the early '80s. Several ACA officers lobbied for order instead of chaos, but they were overruled. The huge influx of new breeders drifted across a turbulent sea which offered no guide to safe ports. As Bill

Haiiru Kitsune, Shoyo-Go's aunt, owned by Liz Harrell.

Ch. O'BJ Nikki No Nikki, ROMP (Ch. Okii Yubi Sachmo of Makoto, ROMXP x Dragon House Nikki No Kenicia) considered one of the greatest bitches in the breed, Nikki is the dam of All Time Top Producer, Ch. The Mad Hatter O'BJ, ROMXP.

Andrews cryptically remarked, many of them set sail without a boat much less a compass....

Popularity skyrocketed and genetic problems multiplied out of all proportion. The ACA newsletter (*Akita Dog*) was irregularly published and rarely contained the ROM list. (Although *Akita Dog* is currently published on a timely basis, it seldom contains ROM information.)

Requests for reprints of the *Akita Handbooks* escalated as serious breeders demanded records and genetic information. Feeling that a reprint of the *Akita Handbook* would be inadequate but recognizing the need for an update of some sort, in 1984 I began the task of reconstructing and computerizing my old card file system. Thus was born *Akita Reference*. My daughter had long since married and was unable to help but Bill offered both moral support and practical assistance - He became an inventive cook, played with puppies, and watched TV alone while that Apple and I got acquainted!

Ch. Noji's The Count Crown Royal, ROMX (by Ch. Mike Truax Royal Tikara Pal, ROM x Ch. Daijobus Vampirella O'BJ, ROMX) at eight months and at four years of age. "Bo Hunk" is currently the sire of ten Canadian and ten American champions. He's owned by Ingrid Linerud and Marcia Erwin, bred by Marcia Erwin and BJ Andrews.

I called on fanciers whose opinions I respected, looked at other breed club projects, wondered if I could manage what was beginning to take shape in my mind and if it really was needed .... and then got on with the EXPANDED ROM SYSTEM.

Akita Reference also documented the first ten years of AKC recognition but it was primarily a breeder's tool meant to identify and honor the outstanding dogs and people who together had elevated the Akita from a "trash breed" into a respectable "pure breed."

The Expanded formula was simple enough but a nightmare to implement. It is still a monumental task which invites error but the risk of complaint is outweighed by the value of the system.

Sires and dams which achieved *double* the required numbers of Champion progeny were awarded an "X" after the ROM letters. No small feat considering how few dogs ever produce more than one or two Champion offspring. Register Of Merit Akitas with ROM progeny received the letter "P" designating them as Producers of dominant progeny. In the eyes of some, this was an even more significant title. Certificates were sent to as many owners as could be tracked down.

The ROM list had by then become somewhat cumbersome, making it ever more difficult to trace a pattern, especially when the list was so seldom published. With the Expanded titles, the size of the list no longer obscured the accomplishments of the most powerful producers. The tedious work of tracing dominance had for the most part been done on behalf of everyone interested in the genotype of a particular dog or bloodline. *Akita Reference* was enthusiastically welcomed by the fancy and many pedigrees today proudly include "X" and "P" titles.

In 1986, as Past President of ACA, I introduced a motion to establish an Awards Committee to validate the XP system. The motion passed but was immediately thrown out by the succeeding board. If you share the same amazement as was felt by most Akita owners, I can only tell you that few of the board members had anything which

Ch. The Dame's on Target O'BJ, ROMPX (Ch. The Real McCoy O'BJ x Ch. The Same Dame O'BJ, ROMP) litter sister to Ch. Widow-Maker, bred and owned by BJ Andrews. Bred to Ch. Ransom, she produced many multi-Group winners, including multi-Best In Show Winner, Ch. Goshen's Chariots of Fire. Snapshot taken at seven and a half years.

would have qualified for an Expanded title.

The grumbling grew louder and ACA eventually responded to the extent that a responsible and respected individual was appointed as the ROM Committee Chair. The highly successful mother-daughter team of Megan and Cathe Harvey are well known to the fancy. Megan has won many top awards as a Junior Handler and Cathe manages the dogs, her household, a successful breeding program, and somehow still can devote precious time to ROM research and tabulation.

The fancy owes a big thank you to Cathe Harvey and Sue Oswald for officially and accurately preserving valuable breed records which were of little importance to the club. Without Cathe's assistance in cross checking and correcting (hopefully all of) my mistakes, this chapter might never have been included. Cathe also agreed to give us a current look at the official ACA Register Of Merit system.

Ch. The Same Dame O'BJ, ROMP (Am./Can. Ch. Kakwa's Orca, ROMPX x Ch. O'BJ Dame of the Game, ROMP) whelped one litter (by Ch. The Real McCoy O'BJ) in the States before being sent to Meg Purnell-Carpenter, Overhill Kennels, Pensford, England. She is shown here in Meg's garden at age 7 years, 11 months.

REGISTRY OF MERIT SYSTEM

By Cathe Harvey

"The RegistryOf Merit system was developed in 1973 in conjunction with the *Akita Handbook*. This system, developed by Mrs. Barbara J. Andrews of Akitas O'BJ, was designed to recognize individual Akitas who had contributed to the quality of the breed by producing champion get. During the late 1970s, Mrs. Andrews turned over the system to Mrs. Susan Oswald who continued keeping the records in the same manner. The Akita Club of America, Inc., the breed's national parent club, dropped the EROM (Early Registry Of Merit) dogs from Mrs. Andrews's system and continued the system criteria that is still in force today. This system requires a sire to produce ten champions and a dam to produce five of the same to be eligible for the ROM title.

No longer are dogs recognized for having produced ROM-titled get who themselves do not carry an AKC title of champion. This is an unfortunate omission, one that makes the connection between dogs who are quality and those who produce quality.

There are over 250 Registry Of Merit titleholders as of this writing. Many of these have produced well over the required number of champions. The original and correct ROM system did recognize these Akitas, noted by the addition of the letter "X" following their ROM title. There are many dogs who also have been the producer of an Akita who also is a ROM title-holder. These dogs are awarded the letter "P" in the original system which designates them as Producer, not only of quality, but a genetically strong reproducer. The parent club chose to leave out both additions in their current system thereby denying breeders an easy, informative method of identifying those dogs.

Recognition of quality is an important tool by which newcomers to the breed can familiarize themselves with dogs who are no longer living but have left their imprint on the Akita today. Not just a pat on the back as some may feel, the ROM system shines a light down upon a breeder's path to success, which will help them guide their breeding programs in the right direction. Most breeders recognize this, as evidenced by reading the advertisements in our breed publications. The dogs listed in the pedigrees advertised seem to carry Mrs. Andrews's ROMX and ROMP titles despite the Akita Club of America's feeling that the additional titles are not necessary. One would assume that in choosing to use the X and the P titles, breeders are proud of the accomplishments that the ancestors in their pedigrees have attained, and rightfully so. As the old saying goes, "Anyone can finish a champion," but it takes years of dedication to learn how to guide a breeding program to *produce* a producer of champions!

As more and more breeders use Expanded titles in their Akita's pedigrees, I hope the trend will become obvious to the parent club. Until such a time we will continue to only list those dogs who have obtained the required number of champion get."

Cathe Harvey is the ACA Register Of Merit Committee Chairperson

Ironically, a growing awareness of the repressed information and its value to the serious breeder may be all that's necessary for the membership to once again prevail. There are more Akita fanciers now. They are more sophisticated. And they recognize the three basic concepts which will enable the Akita to begin the next century as a strong, healthy, handsome dog of quality.

First, genetic strength is the most valuable virtue a dog can contribute to the welfare of its breed. Two, acknowledgment of prepotency is the highest honor that can be bestowed upon a breeding animal. And finally, official recognition is required in order to affirm the significance of the first two conditions.

Achievement awards are bestowed by most parent clubs, by the canine press, and by almost all other organizations, including the two largest cat registries in the world. I'm confident that the ACA will soon acknowledge its responsibility to Akita breeders. In the meantime, T.F.H. Publications allows me to fill the void by presenting the Hall Of Fame.

HALL OF FAME

The following Akitas are in every sense, the cream of the crop. We used the basis of ten and 20 champions as HOF criteria but stretched it to include a combined total of champion or ROM progeny. To do otherwise would have resulted in the exclusion of several prominent dogs such as Nikki No Nikki, Bara Go, Ashibaya Kuma, High N Mighty, and Tom Cat, breed greats remembered for their positive influence rather than for how many champions they produced. To omit them from the Hall Of Fame would have diminished the purpose of this work.

With an emphasis on genetic strength, when a tie in the number of Champion get occurred, rank is decided by the number of ROM titled progeny.

The Honor Roll lists sires and dams which could soon move into the Hall Of Fame as well as dogs that have proven their dominance by the quality of their progeny This chapter is about significant achievement.

Mistakes are not only possible, they are assured when such a vast amount of cross-tabulation is required. We have attempted to correct *Gazette* spelling errors by comparing various issues of the AKC *Awards* magazines. I risk the wrath of disgruntled owners who may feel their dog was overlooked in order to bring you a smogasborg of delectable information available no where else! Enjoy.

Ch. Golden Sun Seawood Wa Wa' L'Wilac was the first bitch to be included in both the American and Canadian ROM systems. "Micha" is among the first, if not the first Akita, of either sex, to qualify for both ROM titles from one litter. Her pups (sired by Ch. Akita Tani's Daimyo, ROM) finished with multiple Best of Breeds in both countries, two also had Group Placements. Breeder, Merry and Frank Atkinson; Owner, Kelle Clinton, Seawood Akitas.

HALL OF FAME SIRES*

	Ch Get	ROM Get
CH OKII YUBI'S SACHMO OF MAKOTO, ROMXP	101	16
CH THE WIDOW-MAKER O'BJ, ROMXP	65	3
CH O'BJ BIGSON OF SACHMO, ROMPX	49	3
CH JAKURA'S PHARFOSSA MICHAEL, ROMXP	39	3
CH AKITA TANI'S DAIMYO, ROMXP	35	5
CH HOT'S MO'S BARNABY JONES, ROMX	35	
CH KIN HOZAN'S TOKLAT, CD, ROMXP	31	3
CH NOJI'S THE COUNT CROWN ROYAL, ROMX	31	
CH TOBE'S ADAM OF GENESIS, ROMPX	28	3
CH RAIDEN OF JO-UBA, ROMXP	28	1
CH GOSHEN'S CHARIOTS O'FIRE, ROMX	27	
CH O'BJ KING'S RANSOM, ROMXP	26	2
CH FU-KI'S HIDEKI TOJO, ROMPX	24	1
CH KAKWA'S ORCA, ROMPX	23	1
CH KENJIKO ROYAL TENJI, ROMXP	21	5
CH O'BJ HIGH N MIGHTY NO GOSHEN, ROMP	19	3
CH SAKUSAKU'S TOM CAT GO, ROMP	19	1
CH FUKUMOTO'S ASHIBAYA KUMA, ROMP	18	3

HONOR ROLL SIRES

	Ch Get	ROM Get
CH YUKO'S HAPPY GRIZZLY, ROM	18	
CH TOBE'S ABRAKADABRA, ROMP	17	1
AKITA TANI'S KURO CHIKARA, ROM	17	
CH CROWN ROYAL AMERICAN DREAM BOY, ROM	17	
CH TOBE'S RETURN OF THE JEDAI, ROM	17	
CH KOMA-INU BRONZE BRUIN, ROM	16	
CH SHO-GO'S JOBOY TUFF N STUFF, ROM	16	
CH TAMARLANE'S WILLOWDEEN AIKON, ROM	16	
CH TRIPLE K TOMO GO, ROMP	15	4
CH KIM-SAI'S ROYAL JIKARA KUMA, ROMXP	15	3
CH HOT'S VAN SCOTEN JONES, ROMP	15	1
YUKAN NO OKII YUBI, ROMP	14	2

* as of 12/94.

	Ch Get	ROM Get
CH KRUG'S YOSHINORI, ROMP	14	1
CH TOYO NO CHARLIE BROWN, ROMP	14	1
CH HOT'S I HAVE ARRIVED, ROM	14	
CH FRAKARI'S DATE TENSHA DIBOTSU, ROMP	13	2
CH MIKE TRUAX'S ROYAL TIKARA PAL, ROMP	13	2

HALL OF FAME DAMS*

	Ch Get	ROM Get
CH THE MAD HATTER O'BJ, ROMXP	16	2
CH FREROSE'S SARAH LEI, ROMXP	15	2
CH OKII YUBI'S DRAGON HOUSE KO-GO, ROMPX	15	1
WINDOM ALL THAT JAZZ, ROMPX	14	1
CH DAIJOBU'S VAMPIRELLA O'BJ, ROMPX	12	2
CH DON-D'S DIETKA OF THE H.O.T., ROMPX	12	1
CH MATSU-KAZE'S KEY-TOO KINOUK, ROMXP	12	1
CH O'BJ GEORGIA PEACH, ROMXP	12	1
CH DATE TENSHA'S POT LUCK, ROMX	12	
CH FREROSE'S DARK MOON OF SHO-GO, ROMX	12	
KOFUKU-NO'S SHOGA HIME, ROMPX	11	2
CH CROWN ROYAL'S AKAI O-KASHI, ROMXP	11	1
CH MASUMI'S NINJO KARA SUTEKI, ROMPX	11	1
CH MS MATSU KAZE LOVES COMPANY, ROMXP	11	1
CH THE DAME'S ON TARGET O'BJ, ROMPX	11	1
CH GOSHEN'S JUNGLE JENNY OF NOJI, ROMX	10	1
CH O'BJ KOTAUSHA-MO OF WESTWIND, ROMPX	10	1
CH ECHOL'S ICHI-BAN TAMIKO, ROMX	10	
CH KUROI KAO DALLAS ALICE, ROMX	10	
CH MATSU-KAZE'S CHEREED NOTAKALI, ROMX	10	
CH JAG'S KAMI, ROMP	9	1
CH MAXWELL'S KURO BAN KUMA, ROMP	9	1
CH O'BJ NIKKI NO NIKKI, ROMP	9	1
KAMOTI'S SU ZEE BO MAR, ROMP	9	1
O'SHEA PRINCESS BARA GO, ROMP	9	1

* as of 12/94.

HONOR ROLL DAMS

CH CROWN ROYALS TOKER TOO, ROM	9	
CH KITA HOSHI KUMA OF WINDRIFT, ROM	9	
CH KUMA YAMA'S GOLDEN STAR, ROM\	9	
CH N BAR J'S AKARRI SU OF KAJO, ROM	9	
FREROSE'S AUBRIE, ROM	9	
CH KINOUK'S TABITHA OF SALT BUSH, ROMP	8	1
CH LIJO'S SPIRIT OF TOBE, ROMP	8	1
CH MASUMI'S LADY SUNSHINE, ROMP	8	1
CH TO-ZU'S MISTY MORNING, ROMP	8	1
HANA HIME, ROMP	8	1
JUHO MARIKO NO KIN HOZAN, ROMP	8	1
KARIZMAS ANOTHER KINDA CANE, ROMP	8	1
CH BEASTIE OF TOSHIRO, ROM	8	
CH GOSHEN SHADOWDANCER HAIKARA, ROM	8	
CH KINOUK'S CHICK-A-BOOM, ROM	8	
CH MAGIC LADY JACKALYN, ROM	8	
FREROSE'S BETTY JO, ROM	8	
CH KINOUK'S KOR-I, ROMP	7	2
CH GOSHEN'S KUROI KAO TAR BABY, ROMP	7	1
CH OKAMI'S KORI OF KRUG, ROMP	7	1
SHIMI KUMA, ROMP	7	1
CH BUTTERWORTH BOG SUMI MENDO, ROM	7	
CH KARASU OKA NO SHIMANAWA, ROM	7	
CH KIN SUE'S B-B, ROM	7	
CH TORA'S MICHIKO O RYAN, ROM	7	
CH TRIPLE K CHO CHO, ROM	7	
DRAGONFIRE CRESSIDA, ROM	7	
KIMONA KURO SIWO NO PEARL, ROM	7	
LENMAR'S SACHIKO, ROM	7	
FREROSE'S HONEY BEAR, ROMP	6	3
CH JADE KO SAMURAI, ROMP	6	2
CH FREROSE'S ANNIE TILL, ROMP	6	1
CH MATSU-KAZE'S KURO KITSUNE, ROMP	6	1
CH O'BJ DAME OF THE GAME, ROMP	6	1
CH SAKUSAKU'S PERFECT PEARL, ROMP	6	1
CH TAMARLANE'S MI-MAGIC, ROMP	6	1
YUKO'S RED RED ROBIN DEALICIA, ROMP	6	1
CH THE SAME DAME O'BJ, ROMP	5	3

BIS Ch. The Widow-Maker O'BJ, ROMXP (Ch. The Real McCoy O'BJ x Ch. The Same Dame O'BJ, ROMP), the #2 Sire of All Time, is the only Akita to have produced a Best in Show winner that sired a Best in Show winner. Even more notable, Widow-Maker is the sixth of seven unbroken generations of ROMP-titled sires.

The above lists represent generations of "trendy" knowledge which wise breeders use but are usually not sorted out until many mistakes and several decades have passed. That's unfortunate. If the statistical information contained in this chapter helps astute breeders to avoid some of those mistakes, then my time has been well spent.

There are for example, salient points which one would be foolish to overlook. Only a negligable fraction of the dogs sold as show-quality ever earn their Ch. title. *AKC Awards* records reveal that less than 10% of the dogs that do become Champions ever win a Best Of Breed and only a third ever *produce* a Champion. For example, of all the male champions, only 597 went on to sire a Champion. But those 597 Champion sires produced 2,664 of the total 3,351 Champions recorded, an astounding 79%!

By the same token, only 593 female Champions produced Champion progeny. But, and this is another biggie, those few great bitches produced 1,642 Champions, nearly *half* of the Akita Champions of record.

Even a cursory analysis reveals relevant patterns. Sachmo is the grandsire and great grandsire of HOF littermates, Widow-Maker, Target, and High N Mighty. The odds against littermates sharing the Hall Of Fame are astronomically high except through genetic "luck" But it gets better.

Sachmo is BigSon's sire. In addition to being the youngest male to earn an ROM title, when bred to a Sachmo granddaughter, BigSon produced an all-Champion litter of five.

Sachmo is Hatter's grandsire and great grandsire. Hatter earned her #1 ranking by being bred to Widow-Maker, tight linebreeding on Sachmo. Those breedings produced HOF sire Ch. Ransom, a dog who also ranks among the breed's Top Five All-Time show dogs in spite of an untimely death the weekend of his sixth Best In Show, ending plans for his first campaign year as a mature adult.

National Specialty winner Vampirella is one of seven Champions from HOF dam Kuro Ban Kuma's BigSon litters. Kuro Ban is a full sister to HOF sire and top show winner Michael. Vampirella produced a National Specialty winner by Ransom but most of her champions were by Tikara Pal (another multi-BIS dog), which doubled up on Michael. As would be expected, both Michael and his HOF son Hideki Tojo produced well with Sachmo bitches but were extremely successful when backcrossed through Michael's grandsire, HOF Royal Tenji.

All of the Champions by the Royal Tenji daughter HOF dam Ch. Sarah Lei were sired by the Akita Tani Dynamo, HOF Daimyo. And why not? Royal Tenji is an Ashibaya Kuma

Top Producers, father and daughter. Ch. O'BJ Kotausha-Mo of Westwind, ROMPX (Top Five Dam All Time) meets her sire, Ch. Okii Yubi's Sachmo of Makoto, ROMXP, #1 Sire All Time.

grandson through a double up on Kuma's sire, Kinsei Suna.

Jag's Kami is the granddaughter of HOF Tom Cat Go. Weaving the fabric tighter, old pedigree study shows that Tom Cat's sire Teddy Bear is also Royal Tenji's grandsire and that relationship, the golden thread of HOF sire Ashibaya Kuma, is repeatedly woven through the pedigrees of most of the dogs in the Hall Of Fame.

HOF Georgia Peach is an outcrossed Sachmo daughter that produced exceptionally well with her half-brother BigSon and with top winner Ch. Orca, a half-brother to Sachmo through Mikado. Outcrossed on his dam's side, Orca earned his HOF title almost exclusively through being bred to

Sachmo bitches and daughters of HOF dam Ch. Ko-Go, who was also a granddaughter of both Ashibaya Kuma and Mikado.

Ko-Go's dam was a half-sister to Sachmo through her sire, an Ashibaya Kuma son. Partially outcrossed, Ko-Go earned her place in the Hall Of Fame through her Sachmo litters and one litter by a Sachmo son.

HOF Kotausha-Mo is Ko-Go's daughter by Sachmo, and she too produced extremely well when doubled back to her half-brother BigSon. Like her mother, she was sparingly bred and yet she passed on the ROM genes.

Kara Suteki is an outcrossed Sachmo daughter that excelled when bred to HOF

Ch. The Mad Hatter O'BJ, ROMPX (Ch. Daijobu's Joto x Ch. O'BJ Nikki No Nikki, ROMP) pictured at 8 years of age. Although pregnant and happily wagging, Hatter exemplifies the classic coat, bone, cat feet, and overall structure which passed generously to her progeny, thus earning her the title of #1 Dam All Time.

Raiden, a Sachmo son. Incidentally, Raiden is the litter brother of HOF Nikki No Nikki. Ashibaya Kuma appears repeatedly on both sides of Nikki and Raiden's pedigree. Doubling on Sachmo proved very successful for Sachmo daughter HOF bitch Ninjo Kara. She produced six Champions by Raiden.

HOF dams Jungle Jenny and National Specialty winner Dallas Alice are Sachmo granddaughters by Ura Gin. Jungle Jenny produced four Champions by Budweiser (Pal x Vampirella) and two by Raiden. Proving herself with different sires, Dallas Alice earned her HOF title when mated to Sachmo grandsons, O'BJ Zack The Spotted Bear, Koma Inu Bronze Bruin, HOF High N Mighty and double great grandson, King's Ransom.

HOF Key-Too racked up four champions by Sachmo, three by a Sachmo son, and six by an Ashibaya Kuma son! Her lovely litter sister HOF Ms. Loves Company had three Champions by Sachmo and six by an Ashibaya Kuma grandson, proving that good combinations work. Both are by Kin Ko out of the great HOF dam Shoga Hime.

Nikki No Nikki, four times Ashibaya Kuma, proved the genetic pedigree by being successfully bred back to her sire, Sachmo. In addition, Nikki No produced the top winning bitch Cotton Ginny O'BJ when bred to Mikado grandson, HOF Kakwa's Orca.

Top winner and HOF sire Barnaby Jones is a Sachmo grandson who sired six of HOF Pot Luck's champions and other multi-champlion litters although no ROM progeny has emerged. Three more of Pot Luck's champions were by Raiko-Go and three were sired by all time top winner Return Of The Jedai.

HOF The Count Crown Royal is a Pal son out of Vampirella. Proving his dominance, he has produced very well

Ch. O'BJ Nikki No Nikki, ROMP (Ch. Okii Yubi Sachmo of Makoto, ROMXP x Dragon House Nikki No Kenicia) pictured at two years, owner handled by Bill Andrews.

with several rather outcrossed bitches, including the lovely National Specialty winner, HOF Akai O-Kashi.

Top winner Chariots of Fire is not only third generation HOF on the sire's side, his dam is Widow-Maker's HOF litter sister Ch. Target! His paternal grandam is Top Dam, The Mad Hatter.

HOF and top winner Toklat carries both Ashibaya Kuma and Hayai Taka, Ashibaya Kuma's grandsire. The champions by HOF All That Jazz, (Ch. Krug's Red Kadillac x Lijo's Jasmine of Windom) were all sired by Toklat.

Adam's most notable male ancestor is Abrakadabra, a Sachmo grandson. Adam is a grandson and great grandson of Ch. Yamakuma Itazura Sama through the repeat breedings of Itazura and Sachmo daughter, Leia Organa. HOF Adam consistently produced multi-champion litters with bitches of different lines, stamping his get with his own great virtues.

If there's anything to be learned from this chapter, it's that genetic strength begets dominant progeny. There may be an occasional name in the Hall Of Fame which seems to have come from nowhere but when one studies the pedigrees and compares them to those of other HOF dogs, the same linking ancestors are easily identified.

Ch. Okii Yubi's Dragon House Ko-Go, ROMXP, former #1 Dam of All Time. By Yukan No Okii Yubi (an Ashibaya Kuma son) out of Ko-Tori of Okii Yubi (a Mikado daughter) breeder Robert Campbell. Ko-Go is pictured at 8 years, "just tagging along" to shows with owner, Barbara Andrews.

BREEDER HALL OF FAME

Genetics is a simple science compared to the complexities that determine successful breeding decisions. Some people have the knack of combining that intangible "eye for a dog" with a big dose of common sense, determination, and ethics. Anyone who hopes to enjoy a decade or more of ring success must consider a lot more than love for a dog, show records, friendships, and financial rewards when deciding which two dogs are "right" for each other. Some would say it's easier to plan a wedding!

Akita Reference brought overdue recognition to the people who played such a positive role in the development of the breed. The Breeder's HOF was welcomed by everyone except those who had perhaps stretched the truth a bit and of course by those who had missed the list by only a dog or two. *Akita Reference* issued framable Hall Of Fame certificates to the following:

Bill and BJ Andrews, 53 Chs. 2 ROM; Robert Campbell, 38 Chs. and 1 each ROM, ROMX, ROMP and ROMPX. Gus Bell, 30 Chs. 2 ROMP, 1 ROMX, 1 ROMPX; Stephanie Rubenfeld Olsen, 30 Chs., 2 ROM, 1 ROMP; Bettye and Francis Krug, 28 Chs. 2 ROM, 2 ROMP; Fred Duane, 26 Chs, 2 ROM, 1 ROMX, 2 ROMP; Mary Echols, 26 Chs, 1 ROM, 1 ROMX; and Joan Harper Young, 24 Chs., 2 ROM, and 1 ROMP.

The following bred over 15 Champions and/or ROM dogs and thus received Distinguished Breeder Awards. Liz Harrell, 19

Ch. Alii's Storm Warning, ROM (Ch To No Koichi x Alii's Two Minute Warning) bred by Phil Gray, owned by Linn Greene. "Stormy" was bred to Ch. Koma-Inu's Nukum and Ch. O'BJ Bigson of Sachmo, from which she produced several multi-Group Placers and BB winners, as well as exceeding the basic requirement of five champion get.

Chs., 1 ROM, 2 ROMP, 1 ROMX; Mona Rubenfeld, 18 Chs. 2 ROM; Bea Wright Hunt, 17 Chs. 1 ROM, 1 ROMP, 1 ROMPX; Alice Mazzola, 17 Chs.; Dr. Sophia Kaluzniacki, 16 Chs; Tom and Beverly Bonadonna, 15 Chs.; Gloria Kerr, 15 Chs.; Ceil and Jerry Hoskins, 14 Chs, and 1 ROM.

It was ever so much simpler in those days! As more owners expanded into full scale or long-range breeding programs, the practice of co-owning became common. Co-owners, leases, and financial backers afforded bigger campaigns through a sharing of expenses and advertising. Co-owner-ships also allowed those who had been restricted by time, space, or zoning regu-lations to produce many more litters. Keeping a choice female pup on a co-ownership meant a litter or pick pup back from her at a later date thus enabling serious breeders to keep fewer dogs but still plan with an eye toward the future.

Admittedly, for others, it was just a clever way to become a "puppy mill" without having the evidence on one's property! Some people create vast numbers of dogs through co-ownerships or satellite breeding establishments scattered around the country. Champions are inevitable and "problems" are sold into the commercial pet market or conveniently buried. It's unfortunate that such practices cast a shadow over reputable breeders who

Ch. O'BJ BigSon of Sachmo, ROMXP (Ch. Okii Yubi's Sachmo of Makoto, ROMXP x Vi-Brook Tonya) winning out of retirement under long-time Akita authority Mrs. Eleanor Evers, breeder-owner-handler Barbara Andrews.

co-own for altruistic reasons.

It is left up to the reader to determine which breeders have influenced the genetic pool in a positive manner and which might have co-bred their way onto a list by the weight of sheer numbers.

Although bitch co-ownership allowed

rapid expansion of a once rare breed, it unmercifully complicated tabulation! At one point my editor tactfully suggested I forget the whole idea. With arthritic joints screaming, his words were as welcome as a winning lottery ticket. Had he been more demanding, I might have given up at that point.

But the genetic information contained in the *Handbooks* and *Akita Reference* was well received. Convinced that knowledge makes better decisions resulting in proportionately more healthy, handsome breed representatives, I gave the antiquated data base a 486 kick in the motherboard and went back to work.

After about a month, innumerable ice packs, and a ton of NSAIDS , Bill switched off the TV and asked that all-too-familiar question, "How much longer?" I shrugged. He leaned forward, "Honey, does anyone really give a damn?" I thought about my own quest over 20 years ago, the inquisitive phone calls from new breeders, and the often desperate calls from old hands trying to deal with an unexpected problem. "Some do."

A long minute passed and I knew he was trying to see it objectively instead of counting missed shows and a cabinet full of

Ch. Matsu-Kaze's Key-Too Kinouk, ROMX (Ch. Kin Ko x Kofuku No's Shoga Hime) bred by Gus Bell. A Top Dam of the Seventies, "Horrible Hanna" produced 12 Champions for her owner Joan Harper Young.

Campbells. Then he sighed, "OK kiddo, take six aspirin and call me in a year."

So thank Bufferin, Bill Andrews, and my editor for this chapter. And please, don't nitpick. The intricacies of the Breeder section are beyond description. First, there's the problem of AKC not listing breeders prior to October 1975. Rather than not credit breeders such as Liz, Gus, Bea, and Bettye, I made a few guesses based on kennel names or in some cases, first hand knowledge of who bred what. I've probably missed a few from those early days but most have been tabulated.

Secondly, there's the question of who gets credit when a parent "gives" a litter to a child or a couple divorces and both continue to breed. The parent is still credited with the litter as is the spouse who most often appeared as "Breeder." If several litters are co-bred by parent(s) and child, they are listed as a family, an example being Frank, Sylvia, and son Aric Thomas. When a youngster has bred several litters on his own but didn't make the list, credit has not been shifted to the parent as in Kara Harper. When both husband and wife are known to share equal involvement in a breeding program, they have been jointly listed as in Francis and Bettye Krug. When a couple separates, the one who remains active retains credit for the champions bred or co-bred, even if he or she remarries. Thus you will see Frank and Merry (Wicker) Atkinson, Art Wicker being inactive and new spouse Frank having become an active participant. Talk about complicated! When only one partner was routinely listed as breeder and the couple splits and then *both* continued to breed independently, I went by AKC listings rather than give credit to someone who may or may not have actually had an active involvement in breeding decisions prior to separation. A case in point would be Fran Wassermann and Ira Winkleman, both well known figures in the sport but neither independently having enough champions to make the Hall Of Fame. When possible, I called breeders to verify maiden or previous names but finally realized that sort of meticulous detail wasn't worth the effort as it rarely affected who made the HOF.

The bottom line rapidly became more clearly defined. Outstanding breeders are just that. — O u t s t a n d i n g . Regardless of co-owners or the temporal nature of friendships and marriage, the people who have devoted themselves to the art of breeding great dogs stand out. They may be quiet, unassuming, in the background. They may be flashy, outspoken, even obnoxious. But they stand out! And they deserve not only our

respect but our thanks. They are what made the Akita breed a force to contend with at the Group and Best In Show level. They are what keeps the breed strong and beautiful. They are what created that magnificent, loyal friend laying by your chair. Tip your hat to the following people:

Am/Can. Ch. Kakwa's Orca, ROMPX (Am/Can. Ch. Shuso Saki Tumi of Okii Yubi x Am/Can Ch. Langan's Amaretsu O-Mi-Kami) winning under one of dogdom's greatest "All-rounders", Mr. Phil Marsh. Purchased from Canadian breeder Andy Russell, Orca was owner-handled by Barbara Andrews to his American Ch., achieved his ROM title, and became #1 Akita Dog before being sold to Shibumi.

HALL OF FAME BREEDERS

	Total	CHS	ROM	Co-bred
ANDREWS, BILL & BJ	188	168	20	87
KALUZNIACKI, SOPHIA DVM	69	61	8	42
OLSEN, MELVIN & STEPHANIE (RUBENFELD)	60	55	5	14
HOEHN, LEWIS & JULIE	58	53	5	38
DUANE, FRED	52	42	10	8
LINERUD, JERRY, INGRID, & JUSTIN	52	48	4	20
BONADONNA, BEV	48	44	4	16
CAMPBELL, BOB	47	42	5	10
DUNN, JUDY	45	43	2	23
YOUNG, JOAN (HARPER)	42	35	7	24
DOOMS, VICKY	41	39	2	21
HENSON, LINDA	38	35	3	18
ISRAEL, ED & ADRIENNE	36	34	2	5
KRUG, FRANCIS & BETTYE	34	31	3	8
BELL, GUS	32	28	4	9
ECHOLS, MARY	32	30	2	7
GRAVES, PHYLLIS	31	29	2	22
HERRMANN, DEAN & BONNIE	31	30	1	13

HONOR ROLL BREEDERS

	TOTAL	CHS	ROM	Co-bred
MAZZOLA, JOHN, ALICE, & VIVIAN	29	27	2	19
KEFFER, REED & CHER	29	29	0	11
HARRELL, LIZ	27	22	5	5
BESSETTE, JUDY	27	25	2	5
FONTANO, NADENE	27	26	1	14
WYNN, BILL & JUNE	27	26	1	15
ELLIOTT, BETH	26	26	0	15
MUCHER, PAT	25	20	5	15
MUSISCA, RICK	25	22	3	8
KLETTER, SARA & LILLIAN	24	21	3	
BELL, CHARLES & CATHERINE	24	23	1	1
SHIELDS, WARREN & DEBBIE	23	22	1	5
ERWIN, BILL & MARCIA	22	20	2	14
ATKINSON, FRANK & MERRY (WICKER)	21	19	2	11
NISBET, MARK	21	20	1	5
THOMAS, FRANK, SYLVIA, & ARIC	21	20	1	11
KERR, GLORIA	20	18	2	20
WEATHERMAN, CHRIS & AUDRY	20	19	1	11
LANGAN, SHERYL	20	20	0	1
WRIGHT, BEA (HUNT)	19	17	2	1
McKULSKI, GEORGE & CAROL	19	18	1	6
MILLER, ROBERT	19	18	1	17
GERSBACH, SARA	19	19	0	12
LINDERMAN, JOAN	18	14	4	3
SCHWARZ, KARL & PAT	17	15	2	8
HOSKINS, JERRY & CEIL	17	16	1	2
PRATT, BETSY	16	14	2	6
WEST, DEBBIE	16	14	2	9
KETCHER, GLORIA	16	16	0	12
HAMPTON, BARBARA	15	14	1	5
LAGUS, PETE	15	15		
WALLIS, SHERRY	15	15	0	15

These top 50 breeders account for 1,286 AKC Champion Akitas. That is almost 40% of all the Akitas that ever finished! While we can and will extrapolate the significance of the data, it would be grossly incorrect to state that those numbers represent an average of 26 champions per breeder.

The discrepancy arises because, with but two exceptions, over half of the 1,286 Champions were co-bred. For those of you who calculate faster than a cobra strikes, co-breeding, as is defined for this work, means two or more people other than immediate family, thus several people may receive credit for a single Champion. The Champions column totals 1,476 but remember that HOF and HR breeders co-bred with others who are not on the lists so no need to wear out the calculator trying to balance columns.

In fact, 40% of the HOF and HR breeders co-bred more than 50% of their Champion and ROM dogs. Topping the list of most litters co-bred are Gloria Kerr and Sherry Wallis at 100%, followed by Robert Miller and Phyllis Graves. Robert co-bred with several people, none of whom qualified independently. Phyllis, Gloria, and Sherry all co-bred very successfully with each other and with Sophia Kaluzniacki, therefore they each qualify individually.

To date, the more than three thousand AKC Champions represent the work of 1,341 breeders, many of whom produced multiple-champion litters. On the other hand, the number of titled dogs is small compared to nearly 12,000 a year registered just since 1990. By also factoring in a significant number of purebred but unregistered Akitas, it becomes clear that only a tiny fraction of the thousands of people who put male and female Akita together can be termed "breeders" (no less "Breeders")

Of an estimated hundred thousand Akitas in this country, few will ever be shown. Most spend their time at home, enriching the lives of their owners. That's as it should be and is in itself, a distinct credit to the Akita breed.

Still, a thoughtful breeder would not ignore the disappointing ratio of Champions compared to the thousands sold as show or

Ch. The Same Dame O'BJ, ROMP (Am./Can. Ch. Kakwa's Orca, ROMPX x Ch. O'BJ Dame of the Game, ROMP) is the dam of three Top Producers, Widow-Maker, Target, and Uriah. Dame displays the size, substance, and elegance which is the hallmark of her breeding and which she passed generously to her offspring.

Greatness Never Dies. Ch. O'BJ BigSon of Sachmo, #3 Sire All Time, pictured at eleven years of age. At private stud only, he sired over forty eight AKC Champions and dozens of Group and Specialty winners, as well as numerous ROM titled get.

breeding quality each year. Based on AKC statistics, advertising, and owner surveys, we can safely say that fewer than 20% of "show-quality" Akitas ever win so much as a single point. Understanding how few show-quality Akitas actually earn a Championship puts the accomplishments of HOF breeders into perspective. We must also confront the rather uncomfortable fact revealed by *AKC Awards* records that less than ten percent of the dogs that do become Champions ever win a Best Of Breed and only about a third ever produce a Champion!

How important are these statistics? Depends on whether or not you plan to breed and if so, will you breed for all of the virtues which are tested in the show ring. If so, and if you are trying to figure out who to breed your new Champion bitch to, then you need to consider that 18% of the Champion sires themselves produced over 75% of all Champion Akitas.

If by chance you are about to breed your bitch but she isn't finished, yet you hope to produce champions from her, then you should know that 18% of Champion dams account for 49% of Ch. titles.

In pouring over pedigrees, talking about and looking at potential breeding partners - the most important factors often escape us. . . such as the reason for competition, why livestock exhibitions occur, and why the first dog show was taken so seriously that people today spend hundreds of thousands of dollars proving the value of their bloodlines.

Whether performance or bench, shows are about breeding worth. Nowhere is that

The legend continues: out of Ch. The Widow-Maker O'BJ x Ch. The Mad Hatter O'BJ, this is Ch. O'BJ Nikki Oh Nikki handled to BOB by James P. Taylor over many specials. Owners, BJ Andrews and James P. Taylor.

purpose better defined than in purebred dogs. We don't care about breakaway speed, early weight gain, or milk production. Companion animals are judged on health, beauty, and soundness but also on intangibles such as personality, intelligence, and breed character. So "if it isn't a champion, it isn't breeder quality" is not just a saying, it's the key to excelling in the sport!

The statistical data I've provided to you reveal why that's a sensible rule for the aspiring breeder. Rule number two should

probably be "if a dog wins but fails to produce outstanding quality by the second litter, spay or neuter and don't look back."

This chapter has introduced you to the best breeding lines in America. You will be able to meet many of the Hall Of Fame dogs and their equally famous breeders and owners elsewhere in this book. I'm sure each of these distinguished breeders join me in welcoming you to the fascinating study of an art as old as that first litter of semi-wild canines whelped by human hands.

Timely Tips

The best advice is always based on common sense and personal experience. So is this chapter. I am not a veterinarian. I have no degrees because there's no college that comes close to teaching what 30 years of practical application is worth. Through both personal and consulting experience, workable ideas come together. Feedback from other breeders has pretty well sorted out what works and what doesn't.

This book is breed-specific so if any of these condensed subjects interest you, there's sure to be another book or trade magazine which goes into more detail.

NUTRITION

Eavesdrop on any conversation between breeders and sooner or later the subject of nutrition comes up. Thumb through any magazine and note the number of advertisements for food and supplements, all of which are guaranteed to make you healthier, or enable your dog to be better than the competition. There is truth in advertising after all! Top-quality food and supplements will build a better, stronger, healthier, more competitive dog.

Premium foods are more likely to enhance health and forestall disease. Dog-food manufacturers allocate much more money towards marketing/advertising than to research. The wise breeder's challenge is to separate science from hoopla. It's a dog-eat-dog world when it comes to the food industry—figuratively, we hope.

Table Scraps

A lot of myths are manufactured right along with the artsy packaging and sugar-laden foodstuffs. One of them has to do with table scraps. No doubt you've been warned, "Never change your dog's diet." We're told any variation will surely upset the canine digestive system and cause dire consequences. Excuse me, but my dogs never get upset over a fast-food burger "all the way" ...except when they see the last bite disappear.

It's only natural for manufacturers to worry about the millions of pounds of table scraps with which we surreptitiously supplement the canine diet. Many vets are well programmed (and supplemented) by major pet-food companies. Expect a recent graduate to carefully arrange a concerned expression as he offers what is obviously pre-packaged advice. Unfortunately, many highly trained people know as little about a dog's digestive system as they do about its preferences!

Now I ask you, if Fido was getting total nutrition from a bag, why would he want your filet of haddock? Is there some inherent code in his genes which causes him to turn up his nose at all that red dye and ethoxyquin and instead follow the delicious scent of aged meat straight to the nearest garbage can?

Why in the world would he turn down leftover meatloaf when he could be eating a can of chicken feet and beet pulp? Convince me he would rather have by-products than real meat, eggs, and fresh veggies.

Most premium pet foods are better balanced than what you or I could cook, even if we had the time. But "complete"? No way. One simple question for you and then, having convinced you of the irrationality of so much of what you've been told elsewhere, we'll move on. You watch TV. Would you raise your child on only a single-brand breakfast cereal and nothing else? It's "total" nutrition, if we're to believe the commercials.

Well, we don't give our dogs much choice. They can't trot down to the grocery store and select that which their bodies so desperately need. Thanks to slick promotion, about the only place dogs are able to obtain a little freshness nowadays is from your yard.

Eating Grass

Does *your* dog become deaf when he finds a delectable patch of green vegetation? Mine do. Every spring I think they've undergone some sort of metamorphosis. No longer carnivores, they become fanged herbivores! Like a herd of cows (or a gaggle of geese?), they graze here, nibble there, upchuck on the patio, and then eat some more. With the most intense concentration, they pluck tender green sprouts, snuffle up seeds, sneeze them out again, and then determinedly gobble up rough, saw-tooth grasses to cleanse that delicate digestive system everyone is so worried about!

Eyes glazed with happiness, they amble past me with that "gimme a break" look which so eloquently conveys that strawberry ice cream doesn't compare to the backyard buffet. Having satisfied their baser instincts, they are the epitome of the blue-blooded canine as I serve their "complete and balanced diet" in their shiny stainless steel bowls.

They sniff and walk away!

Kenneled and apartment-dwelling dogs often literally are starved for green vegetation. Fasting also stimulates the desire to browse on grasses.

All dogs should have access to a yard free of pesticides. If you live close to a heavy traffic area where exhaust emissions settle on the grass, purchase a mixed seed preparation for cats and plant a little grass-garden on a sheltered patio or even by a sunny window. Large white gravel on top of the soil is attractive and will prevent him from dropping so much dirt on the floor. Housecats crave the tender grasses and, trust me, so do dogs.

Don't be alarmed when he regurgitates. It doesn't mean he thinks less of your thoughtfulness in providing him savory grasses. It's perfectly normal, it cleans the system, and that's probably why he ate it to begin with!

Too Thin

One of the more common dietary concerns is a lack of appetite. If it's a yearling pup which just gradually cuts back to "barely eating," it is quite likely he needs to be wormed. If there's a sudden loss of appetite which persists more than 24 hours, collect a stool sample and call your vet.

Pay attention to his bowel movements. Are they well formed? Loose, sloppy stools indicate a digestive or parasite problem. Copious diarrhea which persists for more

Carrots are a healthy chew toy for your Akita! This is Am. Ch. The Target Rose O'BJ owned by Maurizio Moretto, Chile, South America.

than two movements and is unresponsive to home remedy will require veterinary attention. Bloody diarrhea should have you calling your vet the first day.

If the dog seems to feel OK otherwise, but just has no appetite, take a moment and go through this basic checklist before you panic: (1) Extremely hot weather? (2) Intimidation by another pet or family member? (3) Abrupt change of food? (4) Severe emotional stress such as a neighborhood romance (for the dog) or a change in residence? (5) Loose or infected teeth? (6) Side effect of appetite-depressant medication? (7) Have you switched brands at least once in case there was a change in the quality or formula of the regular rations?

There are development stages which affect appetite. The metabolism slows down when a dog blows coat and the appearance of being thinner is more than an illusion. Just as birds go "off" when molting, dogs also go off form during the shedding period.

Another appetite suppressant is the natural hormone activity which takes place during puberty. Often described as the "flakey stage" because the dog's behavior can seem a bit erratic, it may coincide with disinterest in food. As long as he is otherwise healthy as evidenced by a happy attitude, shiny coat, clear skin, good stool, and the vet can find no glandular or infectious problems, quit worrying. Consider it Nature's way of preventing excessive physical strain on developing framework! He will probably regain a hearty appetite as he nears two years of age, at which time the bone and joint structure has been set.

Spoiling the Dog

One other logical conclusion you must consider is that you have simply been creating an issue out of what should be a normal everyday occurrence. In either case, the remedy is the same. Quit trying to tempt the dog with exotic concoctions. Instead, consider the natural feeding patterns of the canine.

Dogs like company when they eat. Being not so far removed from the wolf pack which feeds together following the kill, dogs thrive on competition. Kennel (pack) dogs exhibit natural behavior as they gobble down every morsel, sharing nothing.

On the other hand, the family dog has no competition so, having passed the naturally ravenous puppyhood state, the young adult begins to get a little lackadaisical about

The Akita family of Drs. Jon and Cindy Strohmeyer welcome their infant daughter Savannah. Gri Gri and CoCo will have no jealousy or resentment over the most important new family member because Jon and Cindy have prepared them for Savannah's arrival.

food. Why not? He knows if he doesn't eat it right then, it's going to be there later or the kids are going to share potato chips and cookies.

The spoiled dog controls the doting owner who handfeeds, puts gravies over the regular food, experiments with this brand and that, until pretty soon all the dog will eat is a hot fudge sundae! (which you should know is very dangerous; significant amounts of chocolate can be deadly to dogs and cats).

The only way to help the spoiled dog is to quit spoiling him. Give him a good wholesome dog food, mixed with fresh food such as cooked meat, eggs, or fish. And do this:

When the family sits down for the main meal, place his food in an adjoining area, or in the dining room, if you're comfortable with that. Now I would bet that the dog has been hanging around checking out the action in the kitchen and no doubt takes a healthy interest in what the family has for dinner. Akitas are smart. I probably mentioned that already, right? So he thinks he's going to get a sample of that sumptuous meal, either directly from the table, or as an enticement added to his (refused) rations later. This time he's wrong. He'll continue to be wrong as long as he turns his nose up at dog food!

Serve him as you sit down so that he can eat with the family if he so chooses. You now have created the "community feed." The dog may ignore his instincts or at best stroll over to snort on his bowl, plainly letting you know he expects better. Before serving the last course, pick up the dog's bowl. Let him see you. If you don't mind looking somewhat silly, you might even pretend to find its contents tempting. If he's watching you, the game is halfway won—in your favor. If he remains asleep in the den, call it a draw! In any case, don't let him see you dump his food. Do that later when you're putting your own food away and cleaning up the kitchen.

Persevere for as long as it takes, even though it may seem that he's going to starve to death. You have already established the dog is healthy, and healthy dogs will not starve. Believe me, it's never happened. This is like playing poker. The dog is bluffing, but when he runs out of chips, he'll fold.

Akitas are smart, remember? Your dog will soon begin to take part in the community feed. He's going to learn that when feeding time is over, it's over. The food is gone. No leftovers. No ice cream later. Not a morsel until the next feeding time. Within three or four days, he should be avidly "wolfing" his food as you sit down to dinner.

Too Fat

Ironically, a more common and often a more serious health problem than "too thin," obesity leads to disease in animals just as it does in humans. It's the kiss of death to a breeding career. Fatty deposits around the reproductive organs dramatically reduce odds of a bitch conceiving. An active stud dog will rarely be too fat, but the mating will be difficult for a soft, heavy, out-of-condition male.

The solution is obvious though not necessarily simple. A strict reducing diet also reduces the intake of certain vital nutrients. Owners must be especially careful to ensure that the dog is still receiving adequate vitamin, mineral, and enzyme combinations when using a special reducing diet.

The dog will be hungry: Cooked rice and low-calorie roughage should be added to the diet along with minced fresh carrots, greens such as broccoli, spinach, turnips, etc. Oatmeal and bran are other high-quality, low-calorie foods which may be added in small amounts, preferably cooked. Many Akitas relish fresh fruit, although if your dog wasn't introduced to such delicacies during puppyhood, he may need some enticing. Try white seedless grapes, bits of banana, or citrus. Teething pups will usually accept chilled apple slices or carrot sticks to gnaw on.

Fasting

Somehow, in all the nutritional hype, one of the most basic management practices got lost. I strongly recommend fasting your healthy dog once a week. Mother Nature designed the carnivore's system to go relatively empty for days at a time. When hunting is poor, the animal will take in fruits, berries, roots, insects, and vegetation, all of which serve to cleanse and rest the intestinal tract.

On fast day, give nothing other than a piece of fruit or perhaps some leftover (uh oh, that word again) spinach or greens. The fast day is a perfect time to introduce fruit, a raw carrot, or other experimental treat.

Do not skip prescribed medications. If it should be administered with food, then by all means, give the dog a small amount. Check with your vet regarding any special health problems that would endanger the dog during the fast day.

Puppies too? The answer is, "sort of, depending on the age." Babies up to four months or so require the higher levels of blood sugar and calories afforded by twice a day feeding. So, to answer your question, yes, if pups are over 12 weeks, we feed one light meal on a fast day. If they're over six months, we fast them completely. Always have plenty of fresh, clean water available.

One other benefit. A day of fasting is a day of relaxation. The dogs will readily trade a routine day of feeding for one spent grooming, bathing, and spending extra time with the family.

Bloat, How Often to Feed and What to Feed?

The three questions I'm most often asked have to do with these three areas. Dogs over a year old do quite well on one meal a day. We usually feed everyone twice because of old dogs on medication and growing puppies. It seems somehow unfair to feed some and not the others, but for many people, once-a-day feeding is much more convenient and fits the canine physiology quite well.

Most experts believe that smaller amounts fed twice a day are less likely to cause bloat than is one large meal per day. Dogs should never be exercised after a meal (or vice-versa) but my personal belief is that avoidance of bloat depends more on the type of food than how often it's fed.

We use a good-quality dry kibble, not the "expanded" food. Our dogs are occasionally fed "dry" and they always eat every crumb. Remember the communal feed?

Most days the dry food is supplemented with one or more of the following items discussed. Cooked white or brown rice is excellent. We purchase 20-pound bags at wholesale outlets, very inexpensive. We use cooked, canned (restaurant-size tins), or minced raw vegetables. Use raw beef from a reliable source. Loose stools suggest salmonella or giardia, whereas if coats and overall condition goes "off," suspect hormones, antibiotics, or other contamination of the meat supply. In either case, return the rest of the buy. If a replacement order doesn't return the dogs to normal function, demand a refund and find another source for beef.

Watch for chicken or turkey legs on sale. We forewarn the store and buy several hundred pounds when the price is right. Ditto for canned mackerel or whatever fish is on sale.

For special treats, boil beef or pork liver along with several cloves of fresh garlic. Cut into cubes and freeze part of your batch for ring treats. Mix the broth in with the dry food. Don't use too much at a time and don't feed too often or digestive upsets will occur.

Boil eggs and crush them in the food, shells and all. Do not feed raw. Raw egg white is counterproductive and there is now the danger of salmonella. One of these days, I'll successfully use a yogurt maker. Mostly, we settle for cottage cheese and buttermilk. There's nothing better than goat's milk for weak babies,

Awake or asleep, Akita puppies are huggable. This 8 week old Coal Miner son is owned by Fran Cox, bred by Myra Addington.

diarrhea, or a boost after illness, but the canned variety is expensive. Try to locate a safe source for fresh goat's milk. Your dog will love it. For everyday "dairy" calcium, use powdered cow's milk.

Alternate the natural foods and your dog will not only be well nourished, he'll never be indifferent to food. Wild canines have a varied diet. For families with only one or two dogs, go ahead and cook a big batch or mince large quantities while you're at it. Freeze the excess in daily portion-packs.

Bear in mind that just because five million dogs or cats don't die from a certain food or product is no guarantee that your dog will survive or maintain optimum health on that product. It's not unlike smoking. Look how long the tobacco industry managed to suppress the facts about smoking. At least we might have been allowed to make an informed decision but no, our government went along with the powerful (and rich) tobacco lobby. So just because something "is," doesn't mean it should be!

For example, millions of cats died from dilated-cardiomyopathy as a result of insufficient taurine in the commercial foods. Rodents are also a major staple in the diet of the wolf and other canines *closely* related to your dog. I wonder how many believed-to-be-hereditary heart problems could be avoided by a change in diet? A whole mouse, yes, that means fur, feet, bones—all the good stuff a wild animal considers a meal—contains about two thousand times (!) more taurine than the average prepared food.

Does your dog ever get any "roughage" other than beet pulp?! A wild-caught feline or canine will sicken and likely die if fed only commercial dog food. Experienced breeders often wonder why, the "better" we feed our dogs, the more health problems they develop.

Choose your dry food carefully and pay attention to results. If your dog goes "off" or develops a chronic health problem, change the food. Manufacturers often change formulas and by-product sources. One must also consider chemical pollution of food. Alar and apples got a lot of press, but there are other chemicals which you won't hear much about.

We are cautioned more than ever to wash our fruits and veggies before cooking but who washes the ingredients used in pet foods? Grains can be contaminated by direct spraying or through absorption of treated soils. There's not enough inspection of meat and poultry marked for human consumption and no inspection at all of fish. Meat, particularly the fatty portions, often contain even more harmful substances than vegetables. If you've seen any TV specials on the FDA inspection failures, you are more than aware of my warnings. Manufacturers of animal feeds are exempt from even the minimum standards imposed on slaughterhouses which process for your table.

You should also be aware that growth hormones are used to speed animals to market weight, and antibiotics are still added to animal feeds, thereby entering the human foodchain. Humans have developed drug immunities or allergic reactions because of prolonged low-level consumption in table meats. Quoting current news data is one thing, but let me give you a very real example.

A packing house from which we purchased our dog meat also raised mink. They told us of a very large northern ranch which "went out of the mink business" because the animals quit producing. By the time the veterinary university had pinpointed the problem, the ranchers were bankrupt. Chicken necks are standard fare at mink farms. It turned out that the rancher had changed to a cheaper supplier who used chickens which had growth hormone pellets injected into the necks in order to circumvent USDA regulations which prohibit addition of such substances to the feed within a certain period prior to slaughter.

Chicken farmers had found a way to avoid detection, but the hormone pellets still contaminated the flesh, which caused reproductive problems in the mink and that was the end of that business. It makes you wonder why you rarely see chicken necks in the meat case nowadays...

If you pooh-pooh the danger, assuming that the government protects us from "bad things," think again. The USDA only inspects a fraction of the beef, fish, and poultry approved for human consumption. If a conscientious inspector refuses a cow considered DDD (dead, diseased, or dying), it's diverted to the pet-food industry. The Food and Drug Administration doesn't even bother testing for most of the toxic and carcinogenic substances known to be a part of the human foodchain. That's the human-risk factor. Now, double the danger for your pets! Should you become paranoid? YES.

For example: A March 1990 release by a conscientious pet food manufacturer deals openly and honestly with a contamination problem. To quote: "At this point we are still trying to establish how the contaminant, monesin (a poultry feed additive) got into the product....We sincerely regret any problems this situation has caused within the dog breeding community. Our President is personally meeting with those people who lost dogs as a result of these unfortunate circumstances."

In 1994, USDA approved the use of recombinant bovine growth hormone (rBGH) in dairy cattle. It increases milk production by 20 percent, which is an inexplicable rationale for possible contamination of a primary food source since we have had an oversupply of milk for more than a decade! Nearly 90 percent of dairy farmers are initially refusing to inject their cows. Why? Most cite the fact that their children and those of their neighbors depend on the milk. They also say it causes mammary tumors. It does. In people too....

The hormone rBGH is not approved in Canada, Japan, Australia, New Zealand, or Europe. The inadequately tested substance is estimated to earn $500 million annually for Monsanto. It is not destroyed by pasteurization, it survives the digestive tract and is carried through the blood. In other words, into both the milk and meat. Meat fed to your dog.

Senior Diets

Older dogs have special dietary needs. Even in young dogs, hip dysplasia may actually be linked with premature arthritis. According to published medical reports, nearly 75 percent of humans with rheumatoid arthritis show evidence of malnutrition. There are specific nutrition therapies which may prevent or alleviate advancing canine arthritis.

Human studies have shown that saturated fats, sugar, and processed foods should be kept to a minimum and the diet should be rich in fresh vegetables, whole grains, and fish—not just any fish, though. Cold-water fish such as salmon, cod, mackerel, sardines, and herring are rich in Omega-3 oils and fatty acids which reduce joint inflammation and aid the immune system. They also contain natural pain killers called prostaglandins.

Plasma zinc levels are lower in human arthritics and since zinc is a companion mineral to other important anti-oxidants, such as vitamin E, selenium, and manganese, proper vitamin and mineral supplementation may help reduce tissue damage and joint pain while improving mobility. Even though non-steroidal, anti-inflammatory drugs (NSAIDS) have gained favor in human medicine, the risk of ulcers, upper gastrointestinal bleeding, and kidney disease has raised red flags in many veterinary circles. Furthermore, NSAIDS may disrupt normal intestinal function and actually contribute to the permeation of food antigens into the blood thus actually promoting food allergies. Toxins and allergens have been shown to precipitate development of arthritis.

There is now ample evidence in human medicine which supports therapeutic use of supplements, regular exercise, food allergy evaluation, and dietary manipulation. Those studies offer a promising outlook in the management of canine arthritis and other orthopedic problems.

In closing this discussion on nutrition, I'd like to remind you that many of the live foods I've mentioned are cheaper by the pound than what comes out of the premium dog food bag! There is no reason to skimp on the quality of foodstuffs we give our dogs. Cutting corners on nutrition will inevitably result in more expense in the form of vet bills!

TOTAL HEALTH

Allergies

It's a statement of our times that more and more people and their pets are suffering from allergies. As more is learned about the canine immune system, proper management becomes even more important. Too often, we fail to associate allergy symptoms with something the dog has always been exposed to. We think, "He's always played on the grass" or "I've always dipped my dogs." An allergy is a prime indicator that something new has been added. Your dog seldom reacts to any one thing in his environment but after prolonged exposure

Sam, a handsome red fawn owned by Liz.

to a single substance or simultaneous contact with multiple allergens, his system can become overwhelmed and react in a very predictable way.

A dog may be allergic to something which bothers none of the littermates. Exposure allergies have nothing to do with the dog's genetic makeup. People develop allergies to a particular sub-stance, for in-stance, a bee sting. That does-n't mean they inherited an allergy to a bee sting! The trick is identifying and separating con-tact allergies from symptoms which may in fact be hereditary.

If the dog develops a prob-lem which defies diagnosis, and diseases such as Lyme and Erlichiosis (both transmitted by ticks but often relegated to the end of many di-agnostic checklists) have been ruled out, then you need to become a detective. You are the only one who really knows what's going on in your particular environment. Put your thinking cap on and consider everything your dog may have been exposed to.

Some medications (such as heartworm preventative) bring on "allergy" symptoms from chronic to severe, particularly when combined with other irritants such as lawn spray, fertilizer, new carpet, carpet sham-poo, remodeling with fiberboard insulation or particle board (which releases formal-

Ch. Windsong's Oriental Express (Sachmo x Nikki No Kenicia) is a full litter brother to Ch. O'BJ Nikki No Nikki. Bred by Brooks Smith and BJ Andrews, twice sold as irrevocably sterile, he later sired several litters but failed to realize his genetic potential or his ROM title.

dehyde), and any number of other easily overlooked environmental conditions. When two or more such exposures are combined, the challenge can overwhelm even the healthiest dog's defense system.

Please consider the facts. Pets are much closer to the ground than you and I. Children and small animals inhale more air per body weight than adults. Most pollutants are heavier than air, thus are even more concen-trated at a pup-py's height. Now you understand why your child or pet can be af-fected by chem-icals in, for in-stance, carpet cleaners. At five or six feet tall, you never inhale such vapors, and you also don't fall asleep on the carpet, in the front yard, or by the air-conditioner return vent.

There is one simple method of controlling inhalation of and direct contact with known toxins and allergens. Don't use them. Don't take your puppy for a walk in the park or across the golf course after the grounds have been treated. Par-ticularly when the grass and shrubbery is wet! While a good rain will help to dissolve residue, a heavy dew will make most chemicals more readily absorbable through the foot pads and nose leather.

Let me give you a current example of an extreme "allergic" reaction.

Chemicals and Environmental Toxins

In 1993, the Burke family of St. James, NY filed suit against Dow Chemical Company and Core Marketing, which produces Rid-A-Bug™. Their suit charges that chemicals in the spray crossed the placental barrier and caused severe damage to two of their unborn children. Their first child was born with congenital cataracts, static encephalopathy (brain damage), hydrocephalus ("water on the brain"), and cerebral palsy, a medical term which covers a wide number of muscular and motor disorders. The wife was pregnant again before they began to suspect the magnitude of the problem or its possible source.

The Burkes' dog Dino came and went as he pleased. Concerned about tick-related disease, they regularly used Rid-A-Bug™ on the carpets. The flea and tick killer contains xylene (a solvent) and chlorpyifos, tradename Dursban, which is a neurotoxin.

Not satisfied with do-it-yourself treatments, the Burkes happened to call in an exterminator who told them they would have to leave during the treatment. He warned them that the pesticide could harm youngsters and that Mrs. Burke, being pregnant, could also be at risk. This was the tipoff and raised horrible doubts for the Burke family. The second child was born with cataracts, severe brain damage, and cerebral palsy. There are many more details to this tragic

Kobun's Zoie-Go (Shinto x Kobun's Shoko-Go-No-Shukan) at four months old, bred by Ben and Melanie Herrera, owned by Rodney Harriel and Ben Herrera.

story. The point is that we still don't know enough about short-term exposure to certain chemicals (Agent Orange is a good example of scientific blundering), much less the long-term effects on human health. And who is looking out for your pets?

Regarding carpet, according to a report published in *Home Mechanix:* Carpets not only attract and hold dirt, dust, micro-organisms, toxic pesticides, and even lead but they retain many of these contaminants in spite of thorough vacuuming. In addition, wall-to-wall carpet must be cleaned with strong chemicals which may harm your children or pets. A safer solution would be area carpeting which can be removed and cleaned with safer products.

The development of highly toxic substances has enabled the United States to lead the world in agricultural production, but not without health costs. According to Jeffrey Brent, M.D. of the Rocky Mountain Poison Control Center in Denver, common pesticides such as Diazinon and Malathion can be particularly hazardous. Dr. Brent says that organophosphates "are more harmful to pets than fungicides or herbicides such as Chlorothalonil or Dicamba. Most herbicides are fairly harmless to most pets."

Relying on product labels can be foolhardy. Many ingredients may not have been tested for that use or approved by the appropriate agencies. If an ingredient is not specifically on the forbidden list, it may be used even though known to be toxic!

Fleas and Ticks

Flea- and tick-control methods can be dangerous to all concerned. In 1993, it was disclosed that certain pesticides are proven to cause breast cancer and, goodness knows, the spiraling rate needs to be explained in some way. There is now a new legal specialty field, environmental law!

We already know that frequent dipping presents serious risks to groomers. One such victim suffered for over a year and with no diagnosis in sight, ran out of insurance while his health steadily deteriorated. He had lost his home and was living in his boarding facility, when the doctors finally told him it was a rare form of cancer.

He is alive today due to the intervention of a boarding client, a medical doctor who also practiced alternative medicine. He suggested certain diagnostic tests which satisfied a suspicion that the hours spent dipping dogs with a certain solution was killing the patient. Chelation and homeopathic treatments were successful, and, although my friend remains chemically sensitized, he's otherwise recuperated from the mysterious "cancer."

The problem is one of confusion. Most symptoms of chronic toxicity are very similar to those of other diseases. Human or animal, the victim may experience one or more of the following: difficult breathing, excessive salivation, drooling, vomiting, runny eyes, itching, dermatitis, diarrhea, seizure, hallucination, memory loss, inability to concentrate, and coma. Obvious symptoms which occur immediately after use of vaporous chemicals are easily recognized. More insidious is the chronic poisoning which produces less dramatic but often more deadly symptoms.

You would think flea collars might be safer and to some extent they are because the entire skin surface is not compromised. Even on double-coated dogs, the collar releases a vapor which penetrates through the undercoat and eventually reaches the skin, where it can cause problems. The skin may erupt in tiny itchy blisters, resulting in even more irritation as the dog scratches. Once this cycle begins, removing the collar will not effect an immediate cure because the protein compound which has formed in the skin will remain there for some time, and secondary infection is likely to be present. The healing process can take weeks.

Other reasons to avoid flea collars are the unsightly ring around the neck and the risk to toddlers and other dogs. Children breathe in as they hug pets around the neck. Dogs mouth each other about the neck when play-fighting. When the flea collar becomes wet, it's twice as toxic to the dog wearing it and to the one mouthing it!

A little Pennyroyal Oil from the health food store, added to the rinse water (or a dilution sprayed on after a bath) will smell good to you but is repellent to fleas. It's safe and nontoxic. Check your health food store for other all-natural flea and insect repellent herbs such as rosemary, rue, wormwood, eucalyptus, and citronella. The citrus-based products are not the most effective but you can experiment until you find one that works.

Diatomaceous earth is made up of fossilized diatoms, a mineral-like powdery nontoxic substance which is 90 percent silica, sort of like quartz or white sand in powder form. It clogs the breathing and pores of fleas, clinging to their waxy shells and dehydrating them. While not a "knock-down" treatment, it will considerably reduce the flea population and prevent new generations of fleas from living long enough to jump on your dog.

The two best methods for flea control and other skin problems are pretty simple. One is brewer's yeast and the other is a genetically strong immune system which is not compromised by chemicals! A healthy dog will tolerate the tiny amount of poison the flea injects when feeding but that same dog may eventually succumb to chemical and pesticide assault.

The simple truth is that animals were meant to have fleas! Mother Nature would never make a host allergic to the parasite she designed for it. It just doesn't happen. None of us would care to go back to caveman days with the "natural" wolf dog, but neither should we ignore the obvious. What is unnatural about our wonderfully evolved domestic canines is that Nature never intended them to be inundated with *un*natural substances. Trust me, if you breed them right, and raise them right, Nature will take care of the rest.

Okay, you're becoming a well-informed owner. Should your dog develop strange symptoms that defy diagnosis, you'll be able to help unravel the clues. Your veterinarian doesn't know when you've exterminated or that you take early morning strolls across the ninth green with the dog. He doesn't know that you live between two fields which were just crop-dusted or next to a freeway interchange or that you just installed new carpeting and paneling in the rec room. Not unless you remember to give him the information. Oh, and you who would disregard my words, please remember, there were no warnings on lead-based paint,

cigarette packages, Agent Orange, asbestos products, etc., etc.

Contact Dermatitis

In part due to the protection of their dense, heavy coats, Akitas are not prone to contact dermatitis. Even so, we can compromise them in other ways.

In discussing airborne allergies, we should mention that while people sneeze, sniffle, and experience congestion, dogs are more likely to itch. Your vet can explain why, but it does make it harder to distinguish between rashes caused by direct contact or a systemic irritant.

A condition called pemphigus may cause a loss of nose pigment and often appears as contact dermatitis on the muzzle and around the eyes. A similar condition which may result from the use of soft plastic or rubber food bowls should not be confused with the serious immune-system disease.

Dermatitis can be caused by pine-oil disinfectant. As the warm, often moist un-

Ch. E Oka's Nihon No Akai, bred by Lina Henson, owned by Rebecca Field.

derbody comes in contact with the freshly scrubbed floor, the pine tar residue is absorbed into the skin. Intense itching and tiny pimples in the groin area are a good clue.

And then there's "grass rash," which appears on the underbelly and inner thighs of puppies and is due to that early morning potty trip across dew-laden grass, which brushes the underbelly with the residue of many various airborne pollutants. It drives owners and vets crazy and doesn't do much for the puppy's happy attitude either. For goodness sake, don't get caught up in the merry-go-round of ointments, steroids, and expensive treatments. Until his short legs grow enough to raise his tummy and sparsely coated inner thighs above the taller grass, just keep him out of it! If need be, rinse the exposed areas and dry carefully. A little old-fashioned talc will soothe the irritation and time will take care of that common (and usually expensive) "puppy rash."

Soap in the coat will set up a chronic irritation. It's particularly important to rinse the genitals and surrounding skin thoroughly. Those areas retain heat and moisture which, combined with soap residue, are almost sure to lead to a moist eczema and the beginnings of a serious infection.

As we learn more about the effects of toxins, chemicals, and air pollution upon our environment, concepts which we've held to be true are falling like worn-out leaves.

Realizing that the use of disinfectants was once considered as radical as bathing, dog owners are beginning to question other previously common procedures. Just because something *is* does not necessarily mean it should continue to be.

Along with other journalists willing to risk life, limb, and reputation, I have warned about the dangers of repeated x-rays. And repeated is the name of the game, beginning with "prelims" and followed by "studies" and in some cases, interspersed with medically necessary x-rays.

In particular, I've stressed the routine shielding of humans as compared to the total lack of concern for animals. When the dentist x-rays your tooth, your lap is shielded.

There's a good reason for this. When the vet x-rays your dog's hips, the reproductive organs and genitals receive the full radiation blast.....

The result? Finally in 1992 there was one small phrase which caught my eye—one discreet paragraph contained in a press release by OFA entitled "Role of the Orthopedic Foundation for Animals in the Control of Canine Hip Dysplasia" by E. A. Corley, DVM, PhD:

"Proper collimation and protection of attendants is the responsibility of the veterinarian. Gonadal shielding is recommended for male dogs. Radiography of pregnant or estrous bitches should be avoided."

Period. No elaboration on the subject but thankfully, at least that paragraph was there. Let's hope your vet will have a lead shield handy when he x-rays your dog, male *or* female.

Thyroid

Thyroid imbalance is linked to all of the above. Compromise of the immune system can affect the thyroid gland. Immune-system breakdown can also bring on disease of the liver, heart, pancreas, and the largest "gland" of all, the skin.

Pointing a finger at diet, Drs. Mark E. Peterson and Duncan C. Ferguson authored a comprehensive chapter on thyroid diseases in *The Textbook of Veterinary Internal Medicine,* third edition, 1984. Dr. Ferguson described the canine thyroid as relatively inefficient in retention of iodine. The canine gland requires a large quantity of iodine but secretes only one-third of it as hormonal iodine. This supports my personal theory that Akitas, like many other Arctic breeds which evolved on a high iodine (fish) diet, are more sensitive to today's diets.

Lymphocytic thyroiditis and idiopathic atrophy are the two most common forms of hypothyroidism in the adult dog. Lymphocytic thyroiditis is thought to be an immune-mediated disease caused by a build-up of antibodies that attack the dog's own tissues or glands. Idiopathic is defined as "an independent disease neither relating to nor dependent on any other existing condition." In other words, not related to any other existing disease and in the veterinary sense, originating from an unknown cause. Congenital (at birth) and secondary hypothyroidism (caused by tumors or other abnormalities) comprise but a tiny percentage of thyroid problems.

Hypothyroidism has not been established as genetic, although I do agree with Jean Dodds, DVM. There can be a genetic predisposition and depending on external factors, some animals (and humans) become symptomatic while others do not. Thyroid imbalance *has* been proven to be initiated by stress, diet, environment, radiation, chemicals, antibiotics, and toxins. Dr. Dodds and some other researchers believe the incidence of thyroid and/or immune-system problems to be higher in some family groups. Still, that doesn't eliminate the obvious. The incidence may be higher (or lower) in a given *kennel* of related dogs due to environmental factors.

There is plenty of room to debate whether or not thyroid imbalance is due to a genetically weak immune system or if it's the other way around. Thyroid hormone actually acts as an immune system stimulant by causing the pituitary to release growth hormone. Thyroid hormone may stimulate the immune system by another route as well. The hypothalamus in the brain measures the amount of thyroid hormone in the blood. When levels are too low, the hypothalamus sends a hormone message of TRF (thyrotropin releasing factor) to the pituitary, which in turn releases TSH (thyroid stimulating hormone), which then causes the thyroid gland to release thyroid hormone. There is no question about the link between the immune system, thyroid gland, and the pituitary (master) gland. Thus the question, "which came first?"

Quoting from the package insert on a major brand of thyroid replacing hormone, "Canine hypothyroidism is usually primary, i.e., due to atrophy of the thyroid gland. In the majority of cases, the atrophy is associated with lymphocytic thyroiditis, and in the remainder, it is non-inflammatory and, as of yet, *unknown* etiology." (Emphasis mine.)

According to R.W. Nelson, DVM and S.L. Ihle, DVM, Purdue University School of Veterinary Medicine, "Hypothyroidism is a common endocrinopathy facing today's small animal clinician." Secondary hypothyroidism may be caused by "congenital malformation of the pituitary gland, pituitary destruction and pituitary suppression from concurrent illnesses, drugs or glucocorticoids."

That one sentence sums up the subject factually and concisely. It is *common*. It can be hereditary in the sense that it can be a congenital defect. It can be caused by external influence to a totally normal dog. Statements of simple fact are usually followed by examples so....

You may remember that in 1991 President Bush was diagnosed with thyroid imbalance. I'm unclear as to whether or not Mrs. Bush was also treated, but the big news story was that both she and her Springer Spaniel had complete thyroid panels run! Are we to believe that the best medical brains in the United States thought that President Bush, his wife, and their dog all inherited the same genetic code? Indeed not. Several reports specifically implicated the water supply.

When a kennel begins to produce unusual genetic defects, it's easy to say, "it must be something in the water." While such statements are seldom realistic, we can't overlook water contamination as dramatized by the Love Canal and other well documented tragedies.

There has been a measurable rise in the incidence of thyroid malfunction in humans. There are as many theories among doctors as there are among veterinarians. Many professionals attribute almost all failures of the immune system to the immediate environment, specific medications, disease-induced stress, or direct chemical toxicity. To name but a few of the drugs which are known to trigger thyroid problems: antibiotics such as Tribrissen, Septra, Bactrim, and Diatrim. Other drugs such as the Nitrofurans, Butazolidin, Phenobarbital, and heartworm preventatives have been established as culprits.

Diagnosis

It is not always simple. Reading test results is largely a matter of interpretation based on the frequency with which the lab runs the tests, the norm for that particular breed, and taking into consideration the clinical signs in the dog.

Many vets unfamiliar with the Akita (or hypothyroidism) will look at a dog in good hair coat, with no visible skin lesions and say, "Looks okay to me." Should you protest that your dog is gaining weight even though she is on a strict diet or that he or she has missed several breedings, your vet will again note a dog in visible good health and reassure you that he's fine and does not have a thyroid problem.

You may have to insist on a blood test, in which case, my advice is to get a second opinion on the readings. You know your dog better than anyone. If you suspect a problem, do not be put off by your vet's reluctance to perform testing which will require him to become conversant on a subject in which he may have no knowledge—or interest.

To add to the diagnostic complexities, thyroid levels can fluctuate depending on something as seemingly unrelated as a fence fight, show stress, or estrus. If test results are normal but borderline, a recheck in two weeks could result in a completely different reading. Also, a dog with seemingly normal blood levels may still have a hormone deficiency if the thyroid receptors are low, insensitive, defective, or blocked. Lab tests may also disagree with symptoms because a quantity of thyroid hormone is measured rather than its biological effectiveness for that animal. A conscientious vet will take test results, symptoms, and clinical condition of the dog into consideration before making a diagnosis.

I've gone into a bit more detail than is normally called for in a breed book because owners should know that difficult-to-diagnose health disorders could be due to thyroid imbalance. Complacency following a normal screening could be very detrimental to the overall health or breeding career of a beloved dog. Thyroid levels can slide downward without our knowledge, and, according to researchers, health can be compromised even before clinical signs become apparent.

We have always had each of our dogs thoroughly vet-checked once a year and for the last few years, thyroid tests have been added to our checklist. My vet thinks I'm paranoid, perhaps because we have never ever had a dog with immune-system disease or any other debilitating health problem.

I say this not to be self-serving but to emphasize that my dogs are *not* genetically clear for autoimmune or thyroid disease or hip dysplasia. I wish we could make that claim! I know that the notably lower than average rate of HD and thyroid and the total absence of immune problems in dogs owned or bred by us are due to awareness and good management.

Until we moved to Candler, NC, thyroid imbalance was unheard of in our kennel. My otherwise conservative and very traditional vet of 13 years agrees that something suddenly affected the overall health of our dogs. He was the first to point out that living downwind from a paper plant, which made environmental headlines, could be affecting our dogs because they were outside, breathing unfiltered air, and even under roofed kennels, their bodies were in constant contact with pollution-laden air. He also speculated that dogs don't wear shoes and are running around on ground covered with acid rain!

Bill pointed out that our property was at a major truckstop exit on Interstate 40 and that led to an unpleasant realization of what was causing that bluish film on Widow-Maker's previously glossy black back! At that time, we had three dogs on thyroid supplementation, and Bill was having new and mysterious health problems.

The point was really brought home when we learned of a breeding facility which had experienced repeated episodes of inexplicable diarrhea. Located in an agricultural area, the kennels had no roof and after three years, the owners realized that the bouts with diarrhea were concurrent with planting season. The owners began to rinse water buckets after each rain shower and immediately after spraying and crop dusting. Mystery solved. The digestive upsets ended when "acid" rain and airborne substances were prevented from collecting in the unprotected water buckets. They erected a kennel building that winter but I heard that eventually they sold out, fearing for the health of their children.

you now have a new awareness.

Several things have happened since we moved. Two of our former neighbors passed away and another is very ill. A PBS special documented previously suppressed news showing thousands upon thousands of acres of national forest that have been decimated by acid rain. Aerial footage of Mt. Mitchell and Grandfather Mountain dramatically revealed the damage that hikers and forest rangers had been trying to make public. We're not completely "out of the woods,"

Ch. Cinder's Minimeadow Yogi Bear, T.T. owned and trained by Cindy Fahey.

It took a while but we finally found land in a pristine area of the famous Tryon Steeplechase hunt country and F.E.N.C.E. horse farms. We were lucky. We had an above-average awareness of airborne toxins due to the publicity surrounding the paper plant. We had a vet who over the years had begun to pay attention in his own practice, and most of all, we had the ability to make a total change in our environment. Not everyone who reads this will be so lucky but at least

but our dogs are returning to the vibrant good health which had begun to slip away little by little. And so are we!

It was a hard lesson but one which brought about an interest in new subjects. We've learned to question, and not always to be satisfied with the first answer. I hope that relating our own experience will enable you to more effectively safeguard your dog's health—and your own.

One other tip about thyroid. Do not rely

on one test and then believe your dog to be (or advertise) "certified clear." Such beliefs or claims are declarations of ignorance unless the dog is certified in the normal to high-normal range at least once a year. Additionally, an interim recheck is indicated if the dog goes "off condition" following a change in diet, medication, or environment.

By now, you already have several answers to the common question, What can I do to prevent hypothyroidism?

In 1984, parvovirus was linked to rheumatoid arthritis. Parvovirus was also discovered in healthy humans. Regarding the disease of the immune system, Dr. Jean Dodd's well-researched facts resulted in a statement that

With the proper full, standoff coat, even an out-of-coat Akita is capable of winning. This is Ch. The Cat In The Hat O'BJ, so perfectly groomed by her handler Carol Laubscher that it's difficult to tell that she has just blown her puppy coat, including of course, her undercoat.

the "increased prevalence of these types of problems appears also to be linked to the frequent or recent use of modified live virus vaccines for parvovirus, distemper, or rabies, either alone or in conjunction."

All across the country, breeders and vets are waking up and there is a strong move back to killed vaccines. The documentation is practically overwhelming. Cat breeders have long known of the dangers, even as the pharmaceutical companies keep introducing more and more modified live vaccines to the market. This is not the place (or the book) to go into the subject in detail. I hope you are prompted to do your own research.

One of the most interesting studies on the effects of toxins is Michael H. Brown's book *The Toxic Cloud.* While it's primarily a dissertation on the dangers of dioxin and other toxins such as Agent Orange, he makes repeated references to the high incidence of thyroid problems in areas known to be blanketed with dioxin fallout.

The U.S. Department of Health and Human Services lists many common metallic contaminants such as arsenic, beryllium, chromium, and cadmium as carcinogens, all of which can cause thyroid problems. The release of radioactive iodine, such as occurred in 1986 at the Hanford Nuclear Reservation in Washington, spread hundreds, if not thousands of times more radioactive iodine than was released at the infamous Three Mile Island incident. The probable effect on the immune systems of both humans and animals is frightening.

So there is no simple answer to the above question. You can become paranoid, you can become a student of nutrition and environmental effects, you can ignore the threat, or, you can use common sense and remember what you have read in the previous pages. If problems arise, you have a new way of thinking which may enable you to provide better overall care for your best friend. You will be more informed when making decisions about food products, supplements, and routine medications, and there may come a time when you will ask your vet's advice on an alternative treatment.

HERBAL AIDS AND VITAMINS

You can be sure, there's good reason for the unprecedented popularity of alternative health programs. If it interests you, by all means, explore naturopathy, herbology, homeopathic remedy, holistic, and all the other exciting options available in today's health-care field. It isn't necessary to do an in-depth study of complimentary medicines, but every breeder should become familiar with certain herbal aids and vitamins.

I'll mention just a few of the more popular herbs and their common uses. Herbology is a field unto itself but one doesn't have to become an expert to reap the benefits. Those we have chosen to list have no harmful side effects if used in moderation and with common sense. There's that word again. You find it throughout this book!

FDA regulations prohibit claims for any substance which has not been proven effective through lengthy, costly, controlled clinical studies. Although many herbal remedies have been used successfully for centuries, few have been certified to meet FDA requirements. Frankly, there is little motivation. Herbs are natural, they can't be patented, so what drug company would want to spend millions of dollars in clinical trials? On the other hand, white willow bark is standardized into one of the most common OTC medicines in this country, acetylsalicylic acid, otherwise known as "aspirin"!

This section is included only to ignite your curiosity and provide you with a few basics which we have found personally successful in caring for our Akitas.

One of the most popular herbs in human-folk medicine is the red raspberry leaf. It is used for routine prenatal care, female disorders such as morning sickness, hot flashes, and menstrual cramps. Red raspberry tea leaves strengthen the uterine wall and decrease menstrual bleeding. For the pregnant and lactating bitch, a daily pinch of the dried leaves on the food will aid in smooth, speedy delivery of the whelps, and reduces the pungent odor, amount, and duration of post-delivery discharge.

Any nutrition- or health-conscious person can tell you of the health benefits of ginseng. It is most often used to promote sexual performance but is also known to stimulate the immune system and strengthen the adrenal gland, thus aiding in the treatment of stress.

We rely on Echinacea root for colds and flu just as did my American Indian grandmother. Here we are a hundred years later "discovering" its benefits! Because it has antibiotic, antiviral, and anti-inflammatory properties, it's considered an immune- and lymphatic-system stimulant. It can be helpful for dogs suffering any form of viral ailment or respiratory congestion.

Echinacea's companion is Goldenseal root. It has most of the same properties, plus a cleansing action on the mucous membranes and other organs. It is not advised for long-term use as it may weaken intestinal flora.

This brings us to the multitude of shelf products which are designed to replace the good intestinal bacteria that are killed or depleted by prolonged antibiotic therapies. Lactobacillus products are indicated any time your dog is on antibiotics. Ask your vet if the particular antibiotic can be given with dairy products (some are rendered ineffective by dairy products), and if there is no contraindication, you might wish to begin giving cultured buttermilk or yogurt. Both contain healthy forms of lactobacillus and will prevent digestive upset. Lactobacillus in tablet form is especially useful after or during severe diarrhea if there is no vomiting. You can rely on the tried and true "rice and buttermilk" therapy. It works.

Long used in Russia, bee propolis is finally being seriously studied in America. Health-care practitioners in the States are learning the many applications of a substance long referred to as "Russian penicillin."

Propolis is the resinous substance bees collect from tree buds and then combine with beeswax to construct, seal, disinfect, and protect the hive. Russian scientists believe it stimulates phagocytosis, which helps the white blood cells to fight bacteria. Research in many countries such as Germany, Cuba, China, and Romania has shown that propolis has strong antibacterial, antifungal, antiviral, antiamoebic, anti-inflammatory, and antipyretic properties.

My father kept bees and worked as a silk spotter in a small dry-cleaning business. Beeswax was used regularly in our household. We chewed it for toothache or any inflammation in the mouth; we sucked on it for sore throats; and we rubbed softened wax on serious cuts or bruises, after cleaning it with Clorox. I was prone to ear infections and my father heated large beeswax "bricks" to hold against my ear, insisting that the "vapors" would cure the infection. My mother attributed the definite beneficial effects to the soothing warmth but now medical science is validating that which my father knew from his father who learned it from his full-blood wife.

Curiously, we are about to see new toothpastes with propolis due to recent Japanese studies which concluded that propolis can prevent cavities and the build-up of plaque. I have never quite felt the need to brush my dog's teeth (we do give bones), but I can foresee "propolis-coated chew toys," can't you?

Since I mentioned Clorox, I'll give you a few tips about that. I'm not a chemist and I don't claim to remember everything my father tried to teach me, but no household should be without it! We keep spray bottles filled with diluted (30:1) Clorox under the sinks. We clean the kennels with a pressure washer and Clorox solution. Ever since I can remember, immediate first aid for burns was Clorox full strength, then a cold water dilution soak followed by cold water flush. My father said it was "liquid oxygen" and helped stop tissue destruction and begin the regeneration process. I can tell you that we rarely ever blistered due to a burn which occurred within reach of the Clorox bottle.

As a disinfectant, Clorox has no equal although it doesn't penetrate a thick buildup of grease or dirt. Sprayed over a pre-cleaned surface, it kills tough stuff like parvovirus and fungus. My father used to fill a big washtub with water and a cup of Clorox, and then proceed to dip the dogs! No flea or skin problems in our dogs. Ever. It should not be mixed with certain detergents due to chemical reactions and the fumes should not be inhaled.

Back to the bees. Bee pollen is rich in B-complex and vitamin C, amino and fatty acids, and many other excellent nutrients. It is said to be an excellent source of quick energy, as is honey. We add it to the vitamin mix I prepare for our dogs and I believe it may also have a systemic effect which aids in repelling fleas.

Speaking of which, fleas just hate brewer's yeast, a single-celled organism that multiplies at a rapid rate. It's rich in many important nutrients and is a common additive to commercially prepared dog supplements. Brewer's yeast should not be confused with live baker's yeast, as the latter is known to deplete the body of B vitamins. Brewer's yeast is used for eczema, nervousness, and prevention of fatigue. Beneficial factors are enhanced when it's combined with garlic.

Garlic predates Biblical times and its praise has been sung in literature of the ancient Hebrews, Greeks, Babylonians, Romans, and Egyptians. It is said that the builders of the pyramids ate garlic every day to increase their stamina and strength. It's a potent immune stimulant and current research on this common little veggie may well lead to its documentation as a treatment for cancer. It was used during World War I to treat battlefield wounds and infections and to prevent the onset of gangrene. It's an effective antifungal agent and reports from Brigham Young University indicate that garlic extract will destroy certain viruses such as those associated with fever blisters, genital herpes, the common cold, and other respiratory viruses. It's good for the heart and colon and has been used in the treatment of arthritis, candidiasis, and circulatory problems. Its usefulness in animal husbandry has been less well documented, but its safety makes it well worth adding to your regular feeding program. It's available in tablet, capsule, and oil-extract form.

Kelp may be especially beneficial to Arctic breeds, which have evolved on a high iodine/fish diet. It can be purchased in dried or powdered form and is a rich source of vitamins, minerals, and many trace elements. It has been used in the treatment of thyroid problems in both humans and animals due to the high iodine content. It should be used in moderation although most experts believe it doesn't accumulate in the system.

Vitamin C is highest on our personal list of vitamins. Very few food or supplement manufacturers use "C" for anything other than its preservative qualities and, therefore, we add from 500 to 1500 mg daily to the food, depending on age, size, and indications of stress. There's a common belief that dogs synthesize their own "C" and do not require supplementation. I disagree. If today's canine still had free access to fresh vegetation and the intestinal contents of its prey, perhaps it wouldn't need supplements of any sort. Actually, if our dogs were still in the wild, they wouldn't need us to provide that which instinct would direct them to seek out and consume in the form of roots, wild herbs, and mineral-rich soil.

Animal nutritionists and breeders figured out long ago that "C" aids in the formation of collagen and healthy soft tissue; it also may help to prevent the development of hip dysplasia. Collagen may be familiar as a cosmetics ingredient, but for dog people, its importance is as the substance which cushions and lubricates joints.

Recognized as a powerful anti-oxidant in human nutrition, the significant benefits attributed to vitamin C and its companion, vitamin E, are equally applicable to animals. Most good brands of dog food contain satisfactory levels of "E" used as a preservative, although there is concern about the vitality of vitamins that are subjected to extremes of heat during processing. When combined with 15 to 30 mg of zinc, "E" and "C" seems to help the hocky, soft feet, weak pastern stage which many bigger pups go through.

TRAINING

The first question is, "When do we start training?" The answer is, "The first day." Like children, puppies begin to build their vocabulary at a very young age. They tune in to the dynamics of human conversation, the tone and inflections of your voice. The first word puppies learn is usually "No." You know why. But you really shouldn't have to repeat that command more than once or twice about the same situation.

Owner-breeder-trainer John Seaborn emphasizes the importance of setting a foundation with toys in early puppyhood. He says it pays big dividends in later training and also gives the dog something which is uniquely "his". A teddy-bear such as John is using seems somehow fitting for your young "Teddy Bear."

They may pretend not to understand "No!" but with food reward, babies learn "come here" in about 30 seconds. The problem is, by the third day, they've figured out you don't always mean it and that if they ignore the command, you'll come to where they are. "Shut up" or "quiet" will be harder to teach because Akita pups won't hear that command very often!

formal obedience training, I wouldn't recommend you begin before six months of age anymore than I would advise you send your six-year-old to college. Let puppies be puppies and children be children.

Puppies should learn respect for the leash within a week. By 16 weeks, he'll be heavy enough to pull you around but his little legs don't need the strain of doing it!

Checan's Ko-Goma, owned by John Seaborn, is getting used to being up on tables. Make a point of introducing your puppy to different places, footing surfaces, steps, heights, sounds, and people! Let him explore under bushes, wade through puddles, and dig a hole - in the empty lot of course! Puppies should not be deprived of a normal "childhood" just because we love them and keep them in our homes.

Don't expect complete obedience in a three-month-old baby. He's your little friend, not your robot. If you wanted a dependable machine, you should have bought a TV and spent the rest of the month figuring out how to program the remote controller! This little guy is easy to program, and you'll have a ton of fun doing it if you start out right.

Baby training can set the stage for formal training to come. Use his name first (to get his attention) and then immediately follow it with the command. I say immediately because a puppy's attention span is short. Real short. If you haven't told him what you want him to do when he first looks up, he'll forget you called his name and go back to chewing your slipper.

We don't recommend kindergarten classes before the 16th week. That's when he's had the last booster shot and is ready to go out and face the world. As for

Obedience Training

I know, someone told you never to do obedience work with a conformation pup. Why? If he can learn to stand for examination in the obedience ring, why can't he do it in the breed ring? If properly done, it not only allows a dog to develop as an individual, it encourages alertness and responsiveness. It will not dampen pride or break a dog's spirit. Don't worry about him "hitting the lead" in the Group ring. He will. The female will still smile at the judge and perhaps pinch a goodie from someone at ringside, all the while wagging her tail and thoroughly enjoying being centerstage. A breed dog doesn't have to stand like a stone statue. He or she will be "showy" but well mannered and easily handled. In other words, obedient.

The Akita does not respond well to nagging. No dog does although most other breeds will be more tolerant of the repetitive leash jerking and oft-repeated commands some methods employ. Like a precocious child, the Akita learns, and then becomes bored with the repetition required to earn high scores in obedience competition.

Formal obedience begins with the "Heel" exercise and, in the minds of many trainers, a preconceived notion that Akitas are "stubborn." That ignorant opinion doesn't say a whole lot for the expertise of the trainer so you'll need a few grains of salt throughout the schooling. The fact is, Akitas learn quickly but then, having gotten the basic idea, are apt to ask, "Why? Why do you want me to walk exactly by your left knee? We're not really going anywhere. I've quickly caught onto that. And why do you keep stopping for no reason? Why do you want me to sit down every time *you* get tired? And then, why, as soon as I sit down, do you want me to get up and go in circles again? Can't you figure out where we're going? May I suggest that tree over there?"

After a session of seemingly aimless wandering and being jerked or worse yet, strangled, the novice Akita will likely say to his novice trainer, "Okay, that's it. I'm gonna sit right here and let you go 'round in circles, and when you're ready to go somewhere, come back and get me. My neck is tired..."

Go ahead, laugh. Experienced trainers will be nodding their heads because they recognize superior intelligence and doggy reasoning, not Akita "stubbornness." Sometimes one wonders who is training whom...

We're attracted to the breed's dominant nature. The very trait makes him want to be in front of the handler, in the leadership position with the human in a subordinate position. The handler loses face even more if the dog is allowed to pull at will. It's not amusing when that 30-pound puppy becomes a hundred-pound package of bone and muscle, capable of pulling a two-hundred-pound human off-balance. Therefore, early contests of will, subtle and often subconscious in a puppy, must be recognized for what they are. Appropriate training methods will ensure that the dog retains its pride but understands its place in the pecking order. There will be times when you will allow your youngster to be a bit headstrong, but, when it comes to basic manners, you must maintain control and you must be the dominant member of the team.

Collars

The nylon choke collar is usually sufficient for all forms of training regardless of the dog's size and weight. Some people prefer a chain collar, which is sometimes useful, but a prong collar is totally unacceptable and indicates a lazy or incompetent

A beautiful healthy puppy produced by Warren and Debbie Shields, Sho-Go Akitas. Note the bone size, the thick healthy coat, and the lovely head shape.

handler. It also results in a resentful dog, expressed by growly disagreement or tail and ears hanging; in other words, a hangdog performance.

Buy a good obedience book or enroll in class for complete training help. I'll pass along just a couple more basics. Buy a cotton-web leash, not a pretty nylon one which causes friction burns. Chain or leather leads are too heavy for early training. Position the collar high on the dog's neck so that it rests at the base of the skull, goes right under base of the ears and snugly up under the jawline. In the correct position, it works like a halter. Allowed to slide down the neck, it's about as effective as trying to control a fractious horse with only a lasso on the lower neck.

Will obedience training give an owner total control over the dog in any situation? My answer is a simple and unequivocal *No.* The most well-behaved child can have a flare of temper and react in a way that he later regrets.

Should we expect an Akita to tolerate challenge from another dog without some sort of response? Often, insults from other dogs go unnoticed by the owner. Suppose the neighbor's cat that has routinely teased the family Akita (cats do that, you know) is suddenly encountered while you and your well-trained dog are out for a stroll. This time there's no fence to protect the cat, and it realizes the danger. After a momentary stand-off, it spits and runs. Should your Akita calmly shrug his well-schooled shoulders and ignore the instincts embedded in his nature for a thousand years before he felt your hand on his head? I think not. If you think otherwise, please, buy another breed.

CONFORMATION SHOWS

If you plan to show in conformation, begin getting the puppy accustomed to "examination" by running your hands over his entire body. Handle the legs, pick up the feet, tickle under the belly, touch the testicles or vulva (judges will), look in the mouth, and when he's panting, teach him to allow his mouth to be closed so that judges can see the "bite."

After he knows what "stay" means, bait him with cooked liver or a special treat. When you're cooking and he begs for a

Ch. The Silver Spoon O'BJ (Ch. Sea Breeze Grand Wizard x Ch. Goshen's Silver Lining O'BJ) was handled to BB wins and Group placements by Shirley Merritt for breeder-owner Barbara Andrews.

handout, go ahead, tease (bait) him with the food. You want him to follow the movement of your hands, ears forward, eyes sparkling. Do not allow him to jump up, paw at you, or bounce around like a jackrabbit.

Begin to use the same commands which you will use later in the ring. "Stay" is best reserved for obedience. Try "steady" or private words such as "pretty boy" as you pose him.

Two of the most common mistakes are over-handling and over-training. Dead give-aways are a lack of interest, swinging the rear out, sagging topline, refusal to stand, or a general "hangdog" demeanor. A dog which performs well in class and then blows it in the ring is reacting to the handler's nervousness and constant handling and posing of the dog.

While a person cannot spend too much time with their dog, there's that old

Ch. Kuroi Kao Mariko To-Zu (Ch. Akita Tani's Daimyo, ROMX x Ch. Me-Tu of To-Zu, ROM) is bred by Priscilla McCune. Larry Simmons is the owner of this outstanding female.

saying about quality... When it comes to training, it is definitely the quality of time spent more so than the amount of time. Better to devote 15 minutes of quality training, three times a week, than a half-hour of regimented routine every day.

Make sure you're in a good mood before you begin school. If you're in a bad mood, the puppy will assume you're mad or displeased with him, and it will defeat your whole purpose. A few relaxing minutes with your dog before training begins can often wash away the tensions of a bad day. If it doesn't, just give him a hug and put off the training session. Maybe a car ride or a walk will do you both more good.

Concentrate on understanding him as you teach him to understand you. Learn to read his signals. Dogs have "bad days" too. A tummy ache, a tooth coming through—heck, dogs probably get headaches! If he feels bad, you won't have his attention. If he feels really bad, he may even associate posing, gaiting, and baiting with feeling bad! That's the last thing you want.

How often do we see handler and judge struggling to examine teeth and testicles? Be assured, the judge won't be impressed with a dog that can't be examined. How do you avoid the wrestling match which your dog will probably win? First, avoid setting up a problem to begin with. I hear that word again. "How?"

Don't cover his eyes as you grasp the muzzle to open the mouth. Before you risk anyone else doing a clumsy mouth exam,

379

Ch. Kinouk's A Piece of Work, by Ch. Kinouk's Showdown x Ch. Kinouk's Flower Child. "Work" is a double Sachmo grandson bred and owned by Joan Harper Young.

to having his belly, stifle, buttocks, and testicles handled.

Whether show or obedience training, if you have multiple dogs to work, put one in a crate so that he can benefit from watching you work the others. Dogs learn from watching. More trainers should use it to advantage. Scientists are beginning to explore the ways in which animals learn. Dumb pigeons placed so that they can watch smart pigeons lift the lid on a cache of seed quickly learn how to deftly grasp the tiny handle and lift the lid to expose the food. Your Akita is smarter than a pigeon! He'll learn from watching an experienced dog go through its paces. And he won't miss the fact that the other dog is getting a lot of your attention!

make sure he's totally familiar with the process and steady on the stand. The blood of fighting dogs is still in your Akita's veins. He probably doesn't know it except at times when his security or dominance is challenged. After he understands that certain people have a weird greeting which involves opening his mouth, and that it isn't some sort of new challenge, (after all, he's still learning about human body and vocal language), he'll forgive a judge who inadvertently obscures his vision.

Don't give him bait just before the mouth exam! Wait until the judge has finished the head, and then you can step in front and bait him as the judge completes the exam. The last part of the exam (testicles) probably won't even be noticed by a dog intent on the bait. Especially if you have accustomed him

THE NEW BABY

One of the most common questions is "Will my Akita accept the new baby?" If the dog is not a spoiled child himself, he will not only accept but become fiercely protective of the new arrival. Conversely, if the dog runs the household and is himself treated like an only child, sibling rivalry can be expected.

The worst thing new parents do is isolate the dog from the baby. The dog wants to check out the new guest and, if prevented from doing so, he may feel threatened or insecure with the possible result being animosity towards the infant.

Don't wait until baby comes home from the hospital to prepare the dog. Doesn't matter that he's "well behaved." Since you cannot control every moment of a growing child's behavior, it's important that you control the dog. Now more than ever, the dog must learn his place within the pack and respect the leader—you. If there is any doubt about rank, settle the issue before baby comes home.

If your Akita will no longer be allowed to sleep in your room because of the baby, get him used to sleeping elsewhere now so that he doesn't relate the infant's arrival with being banished from the bedroom. Expose him to children, particularly small infants. If you're preparing a room for the baby, invite the dog to help you, and praise him as you arrange the room.

Buy a life-size doll and accustom the dog to seeing you care for it. If you have time to really get into this, play a recording of a baby crying and your response to that sound. The dog will begin to react as hearing dogs do—he'll proudly (and always) alert you when the child needs help.

Have a family member take the receiving blanket home from the hospital. Let the dog become accustomed to the new family member's scent before baby comes home. While these measures may seem silly, they can be fun and will alleviate any concern about how the dog will react to being "bumped" by the arrival of a much more important family member.

BOARDING

Akitas become extremely bonded to their owners and consequently do not take well to being kenneled. There will be times when your dog(s) will have to be cared for by strangers, so take a little time now to prepare for the inevitable. It's better to accustom him to the boarding kennel of your choice prior to having an emergency and find yourself with a dog that refuses to eat, or becomes aggressive, hyper, or fearful due to separation stress.

Select a good facility, go talk to the people, take the dog and let him meet the permanent help, and vice-versa. Then schedule a day when you can leave him for a few hours. Some kennels will work out a package deal for day-stays designed to familiarize the dog with his home away from home. If you're sure the groomer will make it fun, perhaps you'll want to have him bathed while he's there. If you think it will be too stressful, skip that part the first trip. Don't make a big fuss when you go to collect him. Just pick him up as though nothing unusual has occurred. When he understands that you are not punishing or abandoning him, leave him at least once overnight.

This works for any breed, any dog. The dog loves you so be considerate of the separation anxiety he feels when you're forced to leave him. Some owners are successful in having a close friend come by to feed and water the family dog, but many guarding-breed owners have discovered that the easygoing friendly dog suddenly discovers his heritage when the family departs, leaving him *in charge!* The dog-sitter may not be allowed to enter and you may have to rush home.

In the unfortunate situation when the dog must be left in the overnight care of a veterinarian, his experiences at the boarding kennel will be of immense help. Being left in a place which is filled with fear sounds and smells is very traumatic to any dog, adding to separation anxiety.

One more word about vet facilities. Do not board your dog there. Ever. That's a place for sick dogs. Your dog will be much more stressed in such a clinically sad environment, his resistance will be lowered, and he'll be more likely to contract a virus or some other disease while staying there. Your vet may be much more qualified and conscientious than a regular boarding kennel but that doesn't make his facility the best choice for a healthy dog. Reputable boarding kennels do not accept dogs with contagious disease, and all good kennels have a good vet on call for any medical problem.

It's "the good life" for these two Akitas owned by Katie Asling, Hoka-Hey Akitas. They are, left, Ch. The Tawnee-Ko O'BJ (Ch. O'BJ BigSon of Sachmo, ROMPX x Ch. O'BJ Ko-tausha Mo of Westwind, ROMPX). Tawnee finished with BW majors and is a Group placer. Right, Ch. O'BJ The Maker's Rebel Yell (Ch. The Widow-Maker O'BJ, ROMPX x Ch. O'BJ Ko-Tausha Tuc, ROM) who also finished easily, owner handled by Katie.

SUMMER STRESS

Whoops, did I say stress? You bet. Animals instinctively "cool it" during the hot part of the day and, for that matter, all summer. Your Akita lazes around appearing quite relaxed, but his thermostat is working double time to regulate temperature and keep vital organs functioning. Haven't you ever just wilted on a really hot muggy day? Now you know why you feel tired and listless. Take your dog's advice, slow down and let your body get on with the job of keeping cool. That takes energy! Do you get grouchy when it's oppressively hot? Just a little bit peevish? So does your dog. You may be sainted, but he isn't. The truth is, he's less likely to be short-tempered with those he loves than you are after a "bad day" and a long hot drive home from work. Even so, give him some emotional space on "dog days."

Don't freak out if he digs a cool damp bed in your manicured lawn. The double coat acts as an insulator against heat as well as cold, but you should remember that a dark coat will absorb the sun's rays. No Akita likes direct summer sun and too much will burn that gorgeous coat, turning it rusty. Buy sunscreen. Build a roof. Provide access to the garage or utility room, if necessary, install a window air conditioner but do not lock him in! If the power goes out, your dog will die. Better yet, install a doggy door which allows him access to your cool kitchen floor and the central air. Akitas are only animals and, yes, they can stand more pain with less complaining than we humans, but they shouldn't have to!

Add a little ice to his fresh water; he may love it just as much as you look forward to that cool drink. If he hasn't been wormed since fall, now's the time to make sure both internal and external parasites are under control. Shedding? No doubt. A good bath, regular brushing, and flea control will make his summer a lot easier and avoid vet bills for "skin problems" and summer doldrums.

Do not wet him down to cool him off. It's a good emergency measure for a dog which is actually having a heatstroke. Total body wetting with cold water and ice packs will help him make it to the vet. But otherwise, don't hose him on a hot day. He'll love it, but unless he stays out in the sun long enough to dry completely (and no Akita would ever do that), the dampness trapped next to the skin is likely to erupt into moist eczema otherwise known as a "hot spot."

Do not ever, ever, ever do a mating in the heat of the day. And never give him a "nice, big cool drink" immediately following any sort of vigorous exercise or a heavy meal, even on a cool day. Give ice cubes to satisfy his thirst and cool him down.

Change his diet. Don't you naturally cut back on heavy gravies, sauces, fats, even sweets, during the hot months? Sure you do. Your dog would too if he could select his own food. It's a shame dog food companies haven't come up with a summer diet, but until they do, shift him to one of the lower protein mixes made for older or overweight dogs. Not a cheaper grocery food, but a lower fat formula. Add a bit more rice and veggies and less meat and dairy product. With puppies, it doesn't matter so much because they are going to burn off the fat and protein, just like small children do.

OUTSIDE SHOWS

If you insist on participating in outside shows during the summer, for goodness sake, have pity on him. Take a big ice chest. Not for your beverages. For the dog. If you want ice for your drinks, take a smaller one for yourself. Pack an old bath towel. Keep it in the ice chest. Now you know why I suggested

you take another ice chest for yourself. When he comes out of the crate, (which in a really bad situation you can line underneath with ice packs or cold towels) wring out the towel and drape it over him for that long wait at ringside. Take a spray bottle of plain cold water and an ice bucket. Treat him better than you would your child in severely hot weather because he can't tolerate heat and humidity as well as your child can. Better yet stay home.

Never leave him unattended. Surely you would rather mercifully shoot him than torture him to a horrid death in a car which, though

The dog should move freely in a straight line with no twisting to look up at (or interfere with) the handler. Bill Andrews and yearling Ch. O'BJ BigSon of Sachmo at the 1982 National Specialty. Note the pup gaiting well away from his handler as they round the corner.

parked in the shade, becomes exposed to the sun. And don't ever leave him in the van or motor home with the air conditioner running. If the engine becomes overheated and shuts off, your dog can die in less than 20 minutes. Only a "few minutes" of ringside goodbyes or a "quick trip" back for something you forgot can kill your best friend. Despite all the warnings and the presence of professional dog people, one or more show dogs die from heat prostration every summer. Don't let it be yours.

KENNEL PLANS

We of course know the importance of shade and fresh water. If you plan to pour concrete, remember to rough the slab and then seal it completely. We've found a colored concrete stain and sealer works very well. A silicone caulking compound where wall meets floor will help keep "things" from growing in the block or in hard-to-clean corners.

Sunlight

Sunlight is all important. Include large windows and/or skylights. Dogs suffer from SAD too! It's called Seasonal Affective Disorder because depression occurs more during the winter months, when the sun's rays are weakest and we're inside out of the cold! Your dogs will spend a lot of time inside during the hot summer (assuming you air-conditioned) and fluorescent lighting is the worst but most common choice. Medical science has proven that failure to obtain adequate exposure to full-spectrum lighting causes physical and mental problems in humans. Light must enter the eyes in order to stimulate the hypothalamus, pineal gland, and the pituitary gland, which is the body's master hormone-secreting factory.

Studies are revealing the hazards of the 20th-century ban on sunlight. We now use tinted glass windows, "sheers" have given way to wooden or plastic blinds, and all modern buildings (including schools) are equipped with fluorescent tubes or incandescent bulbs that emit electromagnetic energy and unnatural light rays. People are being damaged in ways which may one day be compared to the asbestos revelation.

Even children are "cool," growing up in sunglasses which assure that the pineal gland receives inadequate amounts of light. Light is necessary for the production of serotonin, the "feel good" substance contained in some anti-depressant medications. Not only are most people deprived of sunlight in the workplace, the great rush to the suburbs often decrees a long pre-dawn trip to the city with an after-dark return, even further depriving a large percentage of the population of those precious hours of sunlight. Since this is about dogs, I won't bore you with a list of symptoms associated with light deprivation. Suffice to say that a whole generation of the populace is under treatment for (or should be)

A simple solution to an "uphill" problem. The Thompsons of San Diego have a magnificent canyon view, but a very steep back yard, impractical to fence. So they turned the large second story deck into a "run" for their two Akitas. From this securely fenced vantage point, their dogs have fresh air, sunshine, and can observe all the goings on in and across the canyon. A sliding glass door and huge picture window means the dogs are also in the house - when they are outside in the run! They are hand walked and exercised three times a day and so they never soil their run.

clinical depression. Society suffers, counselors profit, and not much is changing in the workplace. We can do better for our animals!

There's another drawback to artificial lighting. If you aren't interested in your own health, keep reading for the sake of your house pets. The increasing use of artificial lighting, especially at night, interferes with the production of melatonin. You know about circadian rhythm, the day/night cycle which is disrupted by wonderful technologies such as jet travel. Many scientists also believe circadian rhythm is linked to your biological aging clock. In any case, interruption of the balance between light and dark causes stress, continued disruption causes disease. As we turn on the lights earlier and earlier during winter, we're interfering with our pet's production of melatonin too! If your dog is a "house dog" and you pull the shades during the day, well, just think about that for a moment. While you're thinking, keep reading....

There is an inseparable relationship between the neuroendocrine and immune systems, especially between the pituitary and the thymus glands, which actually regulate the immune system. Melatonin works in the hypothalamus region of the brain, during darkness. It stimulates tissue regeneration and along with serotonin, it influences neurotransmitters, helps to stabilize homeostasis, and maintain those all-important connective tissues, muscles, and bones! Pretty important, wouldn't you say?

Through the production of melatonin, the pineal gland plays a master role in the immune system's ability to respond to virological or environmental challenge. There is also mounting evidence that melatonin suppresses the development of tumors and may actually reconstitute bone-marrow integrity. It has also markedly increased the life span and the reproductive ability of mice. Remarkable stuff, this natural substance which we insist on depriving ourselves and our pets of. If you have house dogs, turn off the bright lights! There may be a reason he keeps trying to get you to go to bed early...

An example of a small but comfy outdoor security area for the one or two dog owner. Note the sun screen which provides shade but allows for good ventilation. Courtesy Carolyn Burrell.

Outside Kennels

Outside kennels are healthier. Drawback: you have to go out in rain or snow. Prepare a quick path with sure-footing and allow for at least a four-foot-wide roofed walkway in front of the runs. Use a shed-type roof high enough to allow air circulation but low enough to provide shade throughout the day. Your dog doesn't have to bake in the sun in order to get sufficient amounts of light for good health. Too much summer sun will destroy that glossy coat.

Water Systems

Water systems are pretty straightforward. Buckets versus automatic waterers to ensure clean cool water supply. Automatic waterers are great but they drip. Messy. If your dogs are on concrete, you'll need a drainage trough underneath. Same can be said of buckets, and they need regular scrubbing.

If you use buckets, for goodness sake, spend the extra money and buy stainless steel! The cheap galvanized buckets rust, wear out, dent easier, and are just plain ugly and hard to keep clean. But most important, they leach iron and lead into the water! Would you drink from lead pipes or dirty pots? Neither should your dog. If you want healthy dogs, buy stainless steel. If you use automatic waterers, be sure the plumber uses lead-free solder or PVC plastic and have any old feeder lines tested.

If I had my druthers, I would build a shallow stainless steel "bowl" in each dog's run. I'd connect it to a pipe through which carbon-filtered water would recirculate. Sort of a self-cleaning "stream" for dogs. Then instead of wrestling water buckets off the fence and scrubbing the awkward things every day, I'd just wipe the bowl clean and spend the extra time playing with the dog....I know it wouldn't work in freezing weather, but then frozen buckets of ice aren't convenient either!

Best Surface

This is the $64,000 question, with just as many answers and opinions. Dirt is the cheapest and easiest on the feet and pasterns. Drawback: "dirty" dogs and an unkept look to your kennel. Fungus lives there, along with fleas, worm eggs, and other icky things.

Patio block, field stone, or brick laid over limestone provides the best drainage and, like slab concrete, can be steam cleaned and sanitized. Drawback: kennel dogs relieve boredom by digging up the blocks.

Gravel is a suitable compromise between dirt and patio block and some believe it's better on the feet. Pea gravel (smoothly rounded river gravel) doesn't do much for feet except spread toes. Smaller, flatter stone will help tighten feet and provide a good non-slippery, well-drained surface. Drawback: digging; keeping it *in* the kennel! Reinforcing, non-rusting wire laid down before the gravel is spread can help prevent the degree of "rearranging" which occurs as dogs dig or wear a path along the fence line. It's difficult to clean, especially after a bout of parvo or moldy food. A pressure washer filled with salt solution or Clorox will help.

Poured slab is the easiest to maintain and looks the best. Drawback: hard on growing bones and joints. In order to be rough enough to prevent slipping and spreading of feet, it will be hard on elbows and hocks. Even barring actual injury during a spill on concrete, feet and pasterns will suffer from constant contact with smooth concrete. We're not sure how much damage results from constant jolting on the hard surface and possible leaching of minerals from the bones.

Rubber mats help protect bones, feet, and elbows. Drawback: the dogs hate them except as sparring partners. They like to drag them around by the scruff of the edge.... Seriously, they seldom lay on them and you'll be as disgusted as we were with wasting so much money just to provide difficult-to-clean playmates for your dogs. Amazing that puppies can move them but it's a struggle for me to lift them for cleaning underneath. And clean underneath you will. Feces and other stuff tends to collect, incredibly, on both sides of the mat! In other words, forget matting to solve your surface problems—unless you'd like to buy our old ones.

The most perfect surface I ever saw was a Greyhound kennel in Florida. Rolled, hard-packed, limestone-sandy stuff. Firmly packed non-dusty surface, not so hard as concrete, whitish so it looked good, and perfect drainage. Sun-baked clean and dry, and for some reason, the Greyhounds didn't dig in it. I don't know if something similar would work for other breeds or not. If anyone perfects this surface, let me know.

In the meantime, we've settled for concrete slabs, with an 8-inch-high divider between runs. That keeps washdown going in the right direction towards a 6-inch PVC half-pipe open drain which feeds into a trapped and screened septic system. We have pickup service for bagged feces but an oversized, covered clean-out stack can be installed at the septic tank so that the pickup bucket can be directly dumped.

The Bathroom

Did I tell you to put the bathroom in the back of the run? New Akita owners sometimes don't realize how clean our dogs would be if we just help them. Most of their time is spent eating, playing, and sleeping. That's done at the front of the run where we hope you've affixed the water supply. They won't potty where they eat. If you put the dining room and bedroom in the toilet, you're going to frustrate or possibly corrupt your instinctively clean dog.

Many kennel plans have the house or resting bench at the back of the run, and, for convenience, the water and food at the front. Think again. You're giving that dog a difficult decision and probably making cleanup tedious. If he decides the front room is the bathroom, you know what you'll encounter as you try to enter the gate. As he rears up to greet you, well, let's just say, put the bathroom at the back.....

Houses

You can buy or build. We use commercially manufactured polyurethane houses, practically indestructible, lightweight, correctly shaped (round, not rectangular), raised bottoms with drain trough and hole for easy hosing out. Dogs are not supposed to be able to get on the pyramid shaped top. Akitas do but ten years later, the houses are still together. There are many brands that are good, and, trust me, it's cheaper to buy one of the plastic deals than to try to build a wooden one. Males will urinate on them, puppies will chew on them, and, if not peaked or plastic-slick, Akitas will sit on top of them. You better be a good carpenter when your hundred-pound monarch assumes his or her throne fifty times a day.

Fencing

Most kennels employ chain-link fencing. Save yourself some trouble and get 2-inch heavy gauge, or as your numbers grow (and they will), you'll be out there putting up double fencing. Climb-proof diamond-shaped horse fencing is nice, strong, and slightly cheaper than chain link. Two-by-two welded wire is small enough but get very heavy gauge. Any of the regular wire is not as institutional looking as chain link and lends itself to use with 4 x 4 treated posts which can be fenced on the other side if need be. We prefer the look but it depends on your particular landscaping and taste.

Gate locks should be flip type with snaps to keep them from being nosed open by smart dogs. There are automatic closures and, of course, dead bolt types. Whatever your choice, don't skimp because the security of that lock can mean life or death for your dog.

Another tip we learned the hard way: gate stops. A welded bar which prevents the gate from being slammed into your face. All gates should open inward only to prevent escape, but gate stops protect you against possible injury should a dog jump on the gate just as you unlock it.

Hot wires can be useful to deter climbers and fence fighters. Solar-powered chargers can secure even the largest exercise fields. They only "hurt" the dog once or twice (Akitas are quick learners!) and may prevent serious injury.

Crates

Most male dogs won't lie down when they're traveling. On a long journey to a show, this can be worrisome for the owner and tiresome for the dog that's expected to show his best upon arrival. Tranquilizers are a deplorable practice. A more practical solution is any rubberized product designed to cushion elbows and pressure points. Any sort of perforated rubber mat which eases the vibration will do quite nicely. We use the bar and restaurant mats carried by one big wholesale chain. Such products also keep the dog cooler as it allows air to circulate. Watch him at first to be sure he doesn't decide to chew up his new crate pad. Give him a great new treat and pray he'll be more interested in chewing that than sampling the rubber matting.

When a dog is just the least bit too warm, the first instinct is to dig down to cooler earth. Your dog isn't being unappreciative when he rips up those lovely, cushy, pillow things you put in his crate. They are unbearably hot, he hates them and has no ability to throw them out of his crate. Put him on a cool lining and distract him long enough so that he realizes it feels good, and he'll love it.

Another advantage of the perforated matting is that sand and debris drop right through the little holes. White leggings will stay white longer, and, even when a dog is panting heavily, the saliva will not turn his crate pan into a mud bath.

You will occasionally see a vehicle with a little chain dragging the pavement under the back bumper. This is said to disperse static electricity. I can't say it works, only that you might try it. No one knows for sure

Taffy Shields and Frerose's Dark Moon of Sho-Go. "Moonie" is about three months old.

why males don't like to lie down when riding. Static electricity, jolting of the testicles, constant vibration: any number of sensations can annoy the unseasoned traveler.

My best guess is he's just reluctant to relinquish his perceived masculine control of the vehicle. Unwilling to ask directions and afraid he'll doze off and miss a signpost, he sits up trying to watch the road. Ladies, it's your turn to smile.

Mating and Whelping

Let me remind you that a visiting bitch is a stranger in a strange territory. What does that mean?

That her body may instinctively decide that your house or kennel, already owned by strange dogs, is not a suitable place to bear and raise her young! Of course, animals don't reason and think ahead, but their instincts are infallible and when they aren't secure in an environment or if a good food supply seems doubtful (competing in a new "pack" with dominant bitches), they will not conceive.

She may cancel the reproductive cycle entirely or just postpone ovulation until she's satisfied that she can establish herself in the new place. There's no way you can explain to her that she will go home if she'll just cooperate!

Supplies

This is a short list. Most people overbuy when anticipating that first puppy. In fact, even long-time owners buy all sorts of junk that really isn't needed. Ask me, I know. You should do as I say here, not as I do...

All of these items are available through pet shops or mail-order pet supply houses. Buy 3-quart, flat bottom, stackable, stainless steel food bowls, as many as you have dogs and extras for traveling. Can't be beat for easy clean up and they last forever.

Order a good-quality, heavy-duty wire show crate. Don't buy the plastic airlines type if you plan to use it very much. Akitas hate those and they're too hot for summer shows. You'll need one adult-sized crate per dog, 42" deep x 24" wide x 28" high will

Pacifiers from Nylabone® come in all shapes and sizes. This young puppy is greeting his first Tug Toy. Photograph by Isabelle Francais.

accommodate the largest male Akita. If you have a female, a 36"-deep crate will do. Be sure the lock is secure and fastens top and bottom. Then fasten it again with a large bolt snap, just to be sure.

Get a heavy crock-type bowl for inside water. Put it in the kitchen or bathroom; puppies drip when they drink. You might want to set it on a pretty bathmat or rug. Keep it clean and cool and that just might keep puppy from standing on tippy-toe to drink out of the big bowl that all dogs love.

Buy Nylabone® bones, balls and toys. Do not buy smaller than the hard 4-inch size. *Never* give squeaky toys, latex, or regular rubber toys. They are very dangerous to large breeds. Nylabones® are safe, clean, and last forever. If you order rawhide chews (some puppies may confuse them with your "rawhide" shoes), be sure to get *American* rawhide. "Sterilized" bones and cow's hooves may chip but we occasionally use them in the house or motor home where we would be aware of any problems. Puppies love hard rubber toys that bounce and the "almost" indestructible polyethylene balls made by Gumabone®.

For goodness sake, get an undercoat rake. Looks just like a miniature garden rake with a short handle. You're going to need it. It will pull the dead undercoat without damage to the topcoat. Get a good-quality pin brush. Choose the rectangular shape that looks like a wig brush with metal bristles set in a wooden back. Get a good-quality one with smooth-ended bristles. Do not get rubber-tipped bristles, they won't penetrate the coat down to the skin.

Buy a good-quality large greyhound comb, a plated metal, smooth-toothed implement for coated breeds. I use one for my own hair; they don't make a better comb!

Buy several nylon chokes in graduated sizes. Forget the leather lead until he's big enough to carry it! Get a cotton-web six-foot training lead.

Decide on a

Two puppies engaged in "Nyla-fun"—Nylabone® products are the safest and longest lasting for dogs. The Nylafloss® is made of nylon, not cotton, and therefore is neither destructible nor degradable. Top breeders recommend Nylabone® products for puppies and adults alike. Photograph by Isabelle Francais.

good multi-vitamin supplement with vitamin C. Have the same puppy food on hand that he was raised on.

Buy yourself some cheap help with bathing. Paid by the hour, nothing is more cost-effective than one of the powerful forced-air dryers which literally blows the water out of the coat. It'll cut drying time in half. Finish off with a hand-held regular hot-air hair dryer.

Use a good-quality doggy shampoo. Dogs have a different pH than people. A tearless product is preferred for obvious reasons. Wait until you know what you're really going to need before experimenting with shampoos. They cost the earth and the temptation is to buy them all! Forget flea shampoos and conditioners. You don't need them. The first contains chemicals your dog can do without and the second will make his coat too soft. Coat condition comes from proper diet and good health!

Well, these things will help get you started with your new puppy, and even if you're a seasoned owner, perhaps you've added something of value to what you already know.

I hope so. Not long ago an old friend was forced to sit thumbing through magazines while I spent considerable time on the phone with someone who owned a young dog of another bloodline. When I finally hung up, she asked me why I "gave away all our secrets." I hesitated not a microsecond. "Because she needed help" was my response. My friend reminded me that the same person had been publicly critical of my line on more than one occasion. I bristled at the memory of what I'd heard and then told my friend what I say to you.

I don't care whether you like my dogs. If just one thing I've shared will make your dog healthier or happier, then I've made a tiny little payback on a huge debt owed for all the help we've had over the years.

If you want to return the favor, just share a helpful tip with some other dog owner.

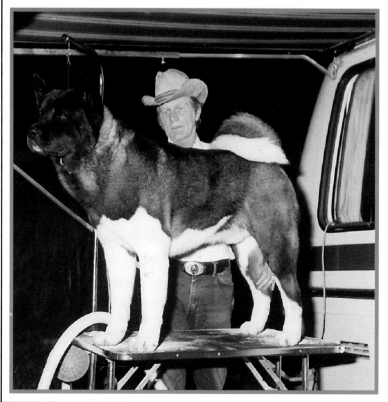

Bill Andrews readies The Widow-Maker for Group judging. One doesn't need a lot of grooming tools and equipment, just a strong arm, a good coat, and a little time!

Ch. O'BJ The Maker's Rebel Yell, pen and ink head study by owner Katie Asling, Hoka-Hey Akitas.

Future Perfect

PAST TENSE

In the summer of 1991, my good friend Joan Harper Young, Shiba Club Registrar, said, "BJ, the Shiba will be the wedge that opens the door for acceptance of JKC Akitas. Mark my words." I did.

Sure enough, Joan called me on Easter Sunday morning with the unofficial news. Without preparing the breed clubs which would be so dramatically affected, the AKC agreed to recognize the Japanese Kennel Club. Akita breeders were left gasping as

The Gold Digger O'BJ (Sea Breeze Gold Miner O'BJ x Ch. O'BJ A-Lotta Pizzazz) at ten weeks, owner Barbara Andrews, co-bred by Sally Jo Allen and BJ Andrews.

the Shiba officially entered Miscellaneous Class in April of 1992!

Everyone assumed that the Akita Club Of America had been too busy with internal problems to be aware of the impending changes. Ignorance might serve as an excuse but compounding the controversy, the ACA Board provided no notice or verification of the historic pronouncement until several months had elapsed—and certain breeders had already succeeded in bringing the first imports into the country. Oh well, business is business and insider trading is not confined to Wall Street.

In the ensuing excitement, caution went to the winds as some breeders hastened to catch up with the competition. Others were simply intrigued by the opportunity to acquire the heretofore unacquirable. The inevitable occurred for most early importers because no matter which foot the shoe is on, dog sellers of all breeds export mostly second-rate stock to foreign buyers. Americans have sent great numbers of pets abroad and then turned around and converted their newly acquired dollars into pounds, rubles, and marks, buying foreign cast offs. Dollars sent to Japan were just as frequently exchanged for similar rejects.

Meanwhile, glowing from their successful pact with AKC and accurately predicting American response, the JKC pulled off yet another coup. The Japanese leaders cleverly manipulated the largest show organization in the world (the Federation Cynologic International) into an almost total ban on American type!

The FCI recognizes the country of origin's breed standards. While that sounds only fair, most European breeding programs were based on English and American bloodlines. When the JKC Standard suddenly banned black masks and other so-called American features of type, owners found themselves with unshowable (and unbreedable) Akitas

The Akita is loved everywhere! Uno and Spike were imported to South America by Maurizio Moretto who has founded a top winning kennel in Chile.

Our Oriental friends have long memories. They are patient, talented business-men with great cultural pride. Therefore, they wisely left a way to save face if a total coup failed. As 1994 drew to a close, concessions had been made and it was gener-ally accepted that AKC type would not disqualify but was to be tacitly rejected in FCI shows.

THE PRESENT

Unless Akita fanciers overcome their apathy and

due to something as definitive and inar-guable as color. Awards were no longer decided by a judge's evaluation of overall type, soundness, condition, show-manship, and breed character.

In one fell swoop, the new JKC standard eliminated pintos, most silvers and fawns, and blacks. A black- masked Akita was arbitrarily deemed unshowable. Only self-masked brindles, whites, and white-faced reds would do. With preference given to the white-faced reds, the American Akita was effectively eliminated from international rings. Just as significantly, we were kicked out of the international marketplace. It was a bold move, one which could have locked most Akita fanciers into buying only from Japan. The brilliant plan was risky, but the perceived rewards must have justified the gamble. To some, it also read as a not-so-subtle victory over the allied countries which brought about the surrender of Japan.

disorganization, hundreds, perhaps thousands, of healthy Akitas will be destroyed as "no longer useful" to breeding programs outside North America. The solution is simple: The type and bloodlines that in fact evolved in North America must be designated by the AKC as the American Akita, thus FCI will recognize the United States as the country of origin and the AKC standard will apply to all dogs registered or descended from the AKC stud book prior to 1992.

Discussion on splitting the breed (e.g., the English and American Cocker Spaniels) continues, and the Americas and England favor two separate breeds. A small but vocal minority still contend that the current Japanese type is the only correct Akita. Others point out that Japan has repeatedly changed its direction as regards the Akita and that one country's preferences and fads should not be forced upon the breeding programs of other countries.

Dog fanciers are characterized as "kennel blind" but most Americans can also be short-sighted. With only a handful of breeders actively exporting, JKC and FCI politics are of little concern to the majority of Akita fanciers. Turning a blind eye toward the international scene may be a costly mistake for those breeders who steadfastly avow loyalty to the American type. The table continues to turn in favor of the JKC as more Americans seek to capitalize on the attraction of "something different."

In the long run, however, the opportunity to import may prove to be more gold-plated than golden. Looks great on the surface but could soon wear thin. There's nothing wrong with adding a little glitter to a solid steel breeding program, so long as we don't forget what made the American Akita the most sought-after "type" in the world. The exotic look of some imports can be wisely used to highlight the strong framework Westerners have built upon over the past two decades, but it should not replace it!

Unless AKC, CKC, and The Kennel Club decides in favor of two separate breeds, the Akita of the '80s will disappear. My prediction is that there will be no split in North America.

Change is inevitable. While shifts may be subtle, they are recognizable if one is attuned to phraseology. The term "old-type Akita" is being heard more often. I predict it will become as commonly understood as the term "west coast type" was during the '70s.

Strangely, only 20 years ago a breed purist was one who held steadfastly to Japanese type as it existed at that time. They now have only faded photos to remember because the breed has so radically changed in Japan. Now it is those who remember and treasure the "old style (aka American) Akita" who are destined to become known as breed purists. It's a tricky world out there. Personally, I hope that the old-style Akita will always be there for those who loved a dog like Sachmo.

Whether the breed is split or not, our concepts have been jolted. Many Japanese imports quite literally are another breed. Importers have no kennel club records from which to verify claims of parentage or quality. It is impossible to determine if there are genetic health or temperament problems which might occur with more frequency in one line or kennel than another. A wise

Winners from the World Show, 1991, Dortmund, Germany.

person recognizes that Japanese exporters may not insist on total accuracy in their rush to supply dogs to eager Americans.

To further complicate an already confusing situation, there's the inevitability of domestic breeders trying to make a fast buck from the interest in Japanese type. Dogs with not a drop of import blood in a six-generation pedigree are passed off as "import type." The sad truth is they are often only fine boned, weedy, skimpy headed non-show types, which were previously difficult to sell, even to the pet buyer. It's a chuckle that the Japanese Kennel Club has unwittingly created a market in which Americans are buying pet-quality stock from fellow Americans thinking its "import" type.

Is any of this important? How does it affect you as a present or future owner or as a judge? Barring the remote possibility that AKC, CKC, or The Kennel Club will officially separate the Akita into two breeds, I predict that several things will occur:

The aforementioned non-show or commercially bred examples will continue to be sold as show/breeding stock even though they don't fit into *any* breed standard. Both sub-quality domestic stock and imported dogs will be bred to American stock because that's what most often wins. And so

Japanese import, Tetsumine of Takeshita Kensha, known as Tora. By Daitokai of Tatsumi x Kurokocho of Takeshita Kensha, the handsome silver brindle is bred by Susumu Kurokawa and owned by Ben Herrera and Frank Sakayeda.

little by little, what we have come to expect in Canada, the Americas, and England will begin to blur. The breed, which both Americans and Japanese would like to claim as pure, will become completely bastardized.

I don't suppose it's all that bad. There have always been show dogs that stretch the AKC standard thinner than taffy shared by twins. Many rings are so filled with mediocre dogs that a truly great Akita appears so different as to be considered "untypical" by judges and spectators, at least for that show. If rings become more often filled with mediocrity, there is the real danger that the definition of quality will become obtuse.

1994 and 1995 passed with no plan or proposal emanating from the ACA. One British source believes that ultimately there will be an international standard which everyone can live with. It is rumored that not everyone at the JKC is in total agreement with what has transpired. I believe this to be true, if for no other reason than that I have been approached by Japanese buyers. Is it possible that the JKC (this has nothing to do with Nippo) would like to add just enough of the American virtues to strengthen health or size of the current Japanese dogs? Who knows? The question will resolve before the end of the century.

As chairperson of the new Judges Education Committee, I am charged with defining a dog under the breed standard of the American Kennel Club. Fortunately, my committee is comprised of experienced fanciers representing a broad spectrum of the fancy and a wide appreciation of type. The committee will fulfill its duty but it will be complicated as more and more American show rings include dogs which do not show like, move like, or look like what judges have been told is the correct Akita.

We trust that the parent club's growing awareness of its obligation to Akita owners will be honored. Printed materials furnished by the club is sadly outdated. My committee will revise with an eye to including previously rare features of type such as white masks, and to improve accuracy.

For example, the otherwise excellent foldout entitled "The Akita, A Dog For All Seasons," states that "Akitas have been trained successfully as sled dogs." While a few dogs have been recreationaly used for that purpose, the text neglects to mention that the trainers were exceptionally adept. The implication that the Akita dog is suited for or was historically used for sledding is misleading. In explaining that many Akitas have been trained to hunt, the pamphlet states "...heavy coats and heavy bone handicap them in long-distance swimming." This makes little sense considering that the proper coat should be buoyant and air filled and isn't nearly as abundant as that of the Poodle or Portuguese Water Dog. The Akita is much lighter in bone than one of the most famous water dogs, the Newfoundland. I do, however concede that no self-respecting Akita would engage in lon,g distance swimming.

The pamphlet deals objectively and accurately with the Akita's relationship with children

The Silver Spoon O'BJ (Ch. Sea Breeze Grand Wizard x Ch. Goshen's The Silver Lining O'BJ, ROM) is a multi-Group winner and winner of the distinguished Champion of Champions competition! Her titles include Am., Mex, Gua, Hon, C.R., Central America, International, and Ch. of Champions. Bred by BJ Andrews, she's owned by Luis Cincunequi, Cinsilu Akitas, of Guatemala City.

and other pets, but I predict someone will want to delete the cautionary statements.

How realistically do we want to portray the pureness of the Akita as a breed? Whether in North, Central, or South America, in Europe or in Japan, the Akita is a developing breed. It does not have the authenticity of the Greyhound. To deny this is, in my opinion, to take away one of the breed's most valuable assets!

It's funny really. Many features which we pedigree records were mongrels descended from Akitas brought back by servicemen who had no other Akitas with which to breed their Japanese dogs. And of course most of these pet owners did not share the dog fancier's concern about keeping the breed "pure." The raw truth is that until the late '70s, the Akita was still a mutt trying to become a breed! Now, having finally struggled almost to the summit of Genetics Peak and casting an eager eye at Mt. Consistency, we are about

Shinto of Shimoda Fuji and Kobun's Sanko. The lovely white Sanko is by Sanmark Akihito-Go x Kobun Nanzen's Tamiko-Go, and is bred by Ben and Melanie Herrera.

strive to enhance or, at the least, hang on to are those which were diluted by mongrel breedings in post-war Japan and even in the States during the '60s. As in all modern-day breeds, these distinguishing features are elusive due to the leveling effect of mongrelization.

Many of the dogs entered into the AKC stud book under blanket acceptance of ACA to experience an avalanche of diversity and differing genetic combinations. While hybrid vigor has definite value, its place has seldom been found in American show rings—and it drives pedigree researchers mad!

So here we are, valiantly emerging from the same difficulty in defining type which got the Japanese all in a tizzy in the '50s. The educated eye can sit ringside at any large

Elegance and style have always existed in American bloodlines. The challenge is to know how to produce it - and how to hold it. This is Ch. O'BJ Canduit Tuya, already showing "The Look" which sets a great dog above an average dog.

entry and still see subtle examples of interbreed matings. The German Shepherd influence is obvious. So are the genes of Japan's smaller breeds as evidenced by the absence of bone, stop, backskull, and guarding instinct. The distinctive Rottweiler black and tan pattern is rarely seen nowadays but Dalmatian/Pointer spots are still common. Blotching instead of brindling, Keeshond spectacles, Elkhound greys, and Mastiff colors are so common that some of the newer judges don't even recognize them as faults, much less as indicative of "foreign" type. The molosser influence (Tosa) has re-emerged as a result of our obsession with size and bone. Luxating patellas are just one problem which accompanies the looser ligaments, which seem necessary in order to accommodate such rapid growth. Soundness and agility are almost always sacrificed when the frame becomes that of a giant breed.

And what of temperament? Well, everyone has his own ideas about what the Akita should be. Most fanciers still love the strongly protective instincts, no doubt attributable to the more recent influence of the Mastiff and in the distant past, to the Chow Chow. Perhaps a Shiba-like personality is better suited to today's litigatious society, but many believe there will always be a demand for dogs with inherent guarding instinct and the physical ability to stop an intruder.

Although the imports lack

Ch. O'BJ Mighty Maverick, owned by Terry and Nancy Calloway, is shown winning Best of Breed from the puppy class. He's by Ch. The Widow-Maker O'BJ, ROMPX x Overhills Pacer, a half Japanese bitch imported by the Andrews in the mid-eighties.

protection proclivity, they still retain much of the dog-dominance traits for which the breed is famous. My guess is that Japanese society didn't have the same need for home security which concerns the average American. But the question remains, are North Americans and Brits willing to give up that which attracted them to the Akita in the first place? Time will tell.

There are other factors which those who love the import type are trying to either preserve or blend with American lines. Loren Egland, Northland Akitas, is a popular breeder of long standing. I asked him about his goals and would like to share Loren's response with you.

WHAT ARE SOME OF THE REASONS FOR OBTAINING AN AKITA IMPORTED FROM JAPAN?

The reasoning was to seek excellence beyond what is typically found in the U.S. Though the Akitas in Japan will individually vary in appearance, the eyes of their dogs appear more exotic partly because the outside corner of the well-defined triangle slants slightly upward. Those eyes combined with an open face add immensely to the facial expression. The small ears, thrust into a broad flat skull at a very forward angle, have a wide base and are deeply cupped. The exceptionally thick ear leather is covered on the inside of

Tsubakihime of Kyushu Fukabori (Kita No unryu of Sasahara Kensha, CD x Yoshi No Hana of Kyushu Fukabori) and her proud owner handler, Loren Egland. "Japan" as she's called, is co-owned by Frank and Alice Sakayeda and was bred by Ukiyoshi Fukabori Kasugashi. The lovely two year old is a direct Japanese import, is OFA excellent for hips, and is pictured going Best Opposite Sex in Sweeps at the 1994 Region IV Specialty, June 1994. She was also Best In Match - Golden Gate Akita Club, Jan. of 1994.

the ear with a plush coat that is quite attractive. The thick high-set tail, majestically carried in a stylish curl, is exquisite. The colors are extraordinary with a choice of brilliant clear fire red, striking brindles, and clean whites. The colors of the bristling stand-off coat are naturally set off with the elegant urajiro markings. The eye rims, lips and skin are all very tight. It all blends into a beautiful distinctive look unique to the Akita.

WHY WOULD WE WANT TO BREED JAPANESE STOCK TO AMERICAN STOCK?

Some Akitas in America possess excellence beyond what is commonly seen in Japan. There are Akitas in the U.S. that are larger with more substance and heavier bone. When these features are combined with soundness, they result in a very impressive animal. Though the American and Japanese standards are nearly identical except for color, the Akitas in America tend to have a heavier muzzle and broader rear stance. It is hoped that by breeding the excellence of the Japanese stock to the excellence of American stock, some Akitas with overall standard excellence will eventually be the result.

Some felt the outcrossing will dilute the Oriental beauty of the imports and the imposing stature of the domestics. We hope

Ch. The Pacer-Pattern O'BJ, co-owned by Myra Addington and Barbara Andrews. Patty-Pacer is shown at one year, finishing with three 5 point majors, including BW at the Regional Specialty. She's by Ch. The Widow-Maker O'BJ, ROMXP x half-Japanese bitch, Overhill's Pacer, English Import. Patty-Pacer demonstrates the upstanding "import" appearance but with the bone and substance of her 3/4 American heritage.

Ch. Shinto of Shimoda Fuji (Togoku of Shimoda Kurofune x Shizu of Isehara Futami) is a Japanese import bred by Hajime Murakami and imported and owned by Kiyoshi Yamazaki. The brilliant red "Shinto" lives with Ben Herrera who says the 27" dog has produced well with his American Kobun females. Shinto took Best In Match at the Inland Empire Akita Club in 1993 at only 18 months. He has since won BB over Specials and completed his AKC title.

not, but it is a point well taken. The expected results may take some time. By choosing to breed animals that physically compensate each other, we feel that some percentage of the offspring will help accomplish the goal envisioned. Our first outcrossed litter was encouraging. Our red import was bred to our large white male, whose sire and dam were white faced reds. The resulting litter was interesting because all were orange-red with urajiro white markings. It has been a joy to watch the development of a large heavy- boned male we kept from the litter. There are no guarantees that other outcrosses will produce as expected, but the possibilities have us excited (and others curious) about what the future breedings will produce.

by Loren Egland

If we refrain from labeling features as Japanese or American, certain qualities are desirable to every Akita fancier. Most will agree that coat, ears, tail, cheeks, and expression define the Akita. We may differ on finer details such as the length of coat, ears, and tail. We all have color preferences but the standard says "any color" as long as it's clear and brilliant. Thanks to the ring success of so-called mismarks and hooded dogs, serious breeders are finally turning their attention to the much more serious problem of dull, dingy, ugly colors. We all like fat cheeks and small dark eyes and an intelligent expression. We love a big curled-up, proudly cranked tail which esthetically balances an equally large, proudly carried head.

This ideal is shared by some who would combine the "best of both worlds." Ben Herrera sums it up quite well in stating, "At Akitas No Kobun we have been trying to produce a nice mixture of Japanese type and color with American bone and head. With "Shinto of Shimoda Fuji," our import, I now believe that this is not only possible but probable. The breedings that have been done so far with Shinto and Japanese imports and American bitches have proved this. Shinto is the first male import to have taken the breed from the open dog class in the U.S."

Ben has three dual-registered males, two of which were imported from Japan and a third, co-owned with Mr. Yamazaki, is a Shinto x Lulu son. Ben believes that each dog has something to offer in their breeding program. Others would prefer to keep the two types separate and distinct.

Visiting with Ch. The Joker Is Wild O'BJ, bred by the author, this is television star Betty White, well known for her involvement in the dog fancy. Joker is posing with his handler Papoose in the purple and gold benching of the Westminster Kennel Club. Courtesy of Roger Kaplan.

Ch. Regalia's Snapdragon (Polar Ranger O'BJ x Regalia's Silver Scrimshaw) is a multi-BB winner, Group Placer, and #1 ranked bitch in 1992. A big bitch with exceptional side gait, bred and owned by Carol Laubscher, handled by Jack Patterson.

FUTURE PERFECT

In order to see the future, one must understand the present and view it realistically. The Akita is high on the list of most popular breeds. By the close of the century, it may well be in the top 20. Every breed that has hit that dangerous plateau has suffered accordingly.

It will happen to the noble Akita. Litter upon litter will be bred to meet the demand and, whether created in commercial breeding establishments or in the kitchen of a family struggling to make ends meet, thousands of Akitas will be created without regard to temperament, health, or the preservation of type. And when the madness is over, as always, a few dedicated breeders will laboriously pick up the pieces.

So what will the Akita be during the first decade or two of the 21st century? I should guess it will be comfortably on the downside of the popularity crest. Certainly, prices will have fallen and the lure of "big bucks" will be gone. One of the aftereffects of mass breeding may be an overall change in temperament brought about, not by public preference but by convenience. Since proper Akita temperament does not lend itself to housing a dozen females and a couple of males in communal breeding pens, the proud and dominant Akita we so admire will have become a rarity.

Unless we are very, very careful to preserve the elusive but distinguishing characteristics, the Akita could become "just another dog." Having generally lost its appeal as rare and with overall quality diminished, the Akita will give way to some other breed, no doubt another of the rare foreign breeds such as the Caucasian Ovtcharka or even the Chinese Foo Dog.

In the next century there will be other registries. Although that will tend to confuse the public, competition will serve a healthy purpose. Genetic screening and DNA testing will have become common. Health problems will have become a priority at AKC. The competing registries could, however, result in a wide divergence of type in many breeds. Some will put more emphasis on working titles, which means a dog will have to show it has brains as well as beauty. Some long-recognized AKC breeds have already split into

Ch. Shibusa Canadian Maid owned by Cindy Taylor and handled by James P. Taylor. "Cori" is one of the few Akita bitches ever to win a Best in Show at an independent specialty. Judge, Marcia Tucker.

Ch. Tequila Sunrise O'BJ (Ch. Sea Breeze Bounty Hunter x Ch. Goshen's Silver Lining O'BJ) at 10 months, breeder-owner-handled by Barbara Andrews. Tequila is a multi-BB winner and Group placer, owner-handled by Sally Jo Allen, St. Elmo Akitas.

Ch. Target Practice O'BJ (Ch. O'BJ King's Ransom, ROMXP x Ch. The Dame's On Target, ROMXP) breeder-owner-handled to BW over top males under judge Nial Koonts. Even as an out of coat teen-ager, Practice displays exceptional size, bone, and substance.

Silent screen and Ziegfield Follies Star, the legendary Miss Lina Basquett described him as "Sprinkled With Stardust." Miss Basquett achieved equal fame as a Great Dane breeder, top handler, AKC judge - and the last word on all Working Breeds. BIS Ch. The Widow-Maker O'BJ, ROMXP was one of her all time favorites.

bench, field, and obedience types. There will still be Schutzhund supporters and groups which seek to retain the protective instincts of the guarding breeds... so hopefully, lovers of the traditional Akita will still be able to find one that will protect as well as decorate his home.

The type controversies will calm down. The differences between the American and Japanese types will become less distinct due to the crossbreeding of the 1990s. Economic and political issues may be put aside in favor of common sense and the welfare of the dogs themselves. When all this happens, the kennel clubs of the Americas and Great Britain will correctly recognize the American Akita, thus allowing fanciers to continue to appreciate the uniqueness and distinctive beauty of both Japanese and American Akitas.

Evolution is certain. To speed the process by genetic intervention is okay if done for humanitarian reasons. We must remain first of all breeders, not scientists. As such, our duty is not to change the breed, not even under the tricky label of "improvement". Our duty is to preserve the Akita Dog as a uniquely handsome, naturally healthy, noble protector of family and hearth; a creature to be appreciated by future generations of dog

fanciers. Improve him? I don't think so!

He's bigger than life but has feet of clay. Love him for his commanding presence, intriguing sense of humor, his gentleness and his fierceness, and take pride in the way others perceive him. In your secret heart, love him for his shortcomings, accept his giant-size muddy pawprints on your living room carpet, the hairballs behind the sofa, and his inability to accept any other dog as his equal. If you can do that, then you are truly deserving of the loyalty and undying love the Akita is capable of bestowing upon his special person.

My hope is that by presenting the Akita as his glamorous, mystical, mysterious self while, at the same time, revealing him as the tame beast in your living room, we have helped you to better understand the essence of the *Ak-i-ta*.

Look at him. A luxuriously coated, powerful, 27-inch dog with no exaggerations. A noble, stand-up, upstanding animal of grand proportions. Sensitive, silent, protective. Wrapped in a limitless variety of rich colors and patterns.

That my friends, is an animal to thrill the heart of every dog lover. Today. Tomorrow. Forever.

Top of The Line O'BJ (Ch. O'BJ Mighty Maverick x Ch. The Cat In The Hat O'BJ) is a double Widow-Maker grandson and a World and FCI Champion owned by Luis Cincunequi of Guatemala City.

Index

Page numbers in **boldface** refer to illustrations.
For the reader's convenience, all titles (Ch., ROM, CD) have been omitted from the dogs' names.

THE WORLD OF THE AKITA

ROSEMARY GROUX

BELIEVE BOOKS
Stories That Inspire
WASHINGTON, DC

Believe Books is a registered trade name
of Believe Books, LLC of Washington, DC
www.BelieveBooks.com

Print ISBN: 978-1-940693-04-0

Cover design: Jack Kotowicz, VelocityDesignGroup.com
Layout design: Jen Anderson, www.boxen.consulting

First Edition
Printed in the United States of America